Student's Solutions Manual for

Beginning Algebra • 5th

Margaret L. Lial
American River College

Charles D. Miller
American River College

Prepared with the assistance of
Ken Grace
Anoka Ramsey Community College

HarperCollins*Publishers*

Cover: A detail from <u>Rhythm/Color: Morris Men</u>, copyright 1985 by Michael James, Somerset Village, Massachusetts. A quilt, pieced and quilted by machine in cottons, cotton satins, and silks, which first appeared in <u>The Art Quilt</u>, published by the Quilt Digest Press, San Francisco.

ISBN 0-673-18850-7

9 10 11 12 EBI 94 93 92 91

To the student:

This book is to be used with <u>Beginning Algebra</u>, Fifth Edition, by Margaret Lial and Charles Miller. The solutions to the following are given.

1. Section exercises numbered 1, 5, 9, ...

2. Chapter review exercises numbered 1, 5, 9, ...

3. All chapter test problems

This book should be used as an aid as you work to master your course work. Try to solve the exercises that your instructor assigns before you refer to the solutions in this book. Then, read these solutions to determine where you went wrong.

You may find that some solutions in each set are given in greater detail than others. Thus, if you cannot find an explanation for a difficulty that you met in one exercise, you may find the explanation in a similar solution elsewhere in the set.

When a solution instructs you to "see the answer graph in the textbook," please refer to the graph in the answer section in the back of your textbook.

TABLE OF CONTENTS

CHAPTER 9 QUADRATIC EQUATIONS

APPENDICES

CHAPTER 1   NUMBER SYSTEMS
Section 1.1   (page 6)

1. $30 = 2 \cdot 3 \cdot 5$

5. $65 = 5 \cdot 13$

9. 17 is a prime number.

In Exercises 13-21, to write a fraction in lowest terms, divide both the numerator and denominator by the greatest common factor.

13. $\dfrac{7}{14} = \dfrac{7}{2 \cdot 7} = \dfrac{1}{2}$

17. $\dfrac{16}{18} = \dfrac{2 \cdot 2 \cdot 2 \cdot 2}{2 \cdot 3 \cdot 3} = \dfrac{8}{9}$

21. $\dfrac{72}{108} = \dfrac{2 \cdot 2 \cdot 2 \cdot 3 \cdot 3}{2 \cdot 2 \cdot 3 \cdot 3 \cdot 3}$

25. $\dfrac{3}{4} \cdot \dfrac{3}{5} = \dfrac{3 \cdot 3}{4 \cdot 5} = \dfrac{9}{20}$

29. $\dfrac{9}{4} \cdot \dfrac{8}{15} = \dfrac{9 \cdot 8}{4 \cdot 15} = \dfrac{3 \cdot 3 \cdot 2 \cdot 2 \cdot 2}{2 \cdot 2 \cdot 5 \cdot 3} = \dfrac{6}{5}$

33. $\dfrac{5}{12} \div \dfrac{15}{4} = \dfrac{5}{12} \cdot \dfrac{4}{15}$ *Multiply by reciprocal*

$= \dfrac{5 \cdot 4}{3 \cdot 4 \cdot 5 \cdot 3}$

$= \dfrac{1}{9}$

37. $\dfrac{5}{9} \cdot \dfrac{7}{10} = \dfrac{5 \cdot 7}{9 \cdot 10} = \dfrac{5 \cdot 7}{9 \cdot 5 \cdot 2} = \dfrac{7}{18}$

41. $9\dfrac{1}{3} \div 1\dfrac{1}{6} = \dfrac{28}{3} \div \dfrac{7}{6}$

$= \dfrac{28}{3} \cdot \dfrac{6}{7}$

$= \dfrac{28 \cdot 6}{3 \cdot 7}$

$= \dfrac{2 \cdot 2 \cdot 7 \cdot 2 \cdot 3}{3 \cdot 7}$

$= \dfrac{8}{1} = 8$

45. $\dfrac{1}{12} + \dfrac{5}{12} = \dfrac{1 + 5}{12} = \dfrac{1 \cdot 6}{2 \cdot 6} = \dfrac{1}{2}$

49. $\dfrac{4}{9} + \dfrac{2}{3} = \dfrac{4}{9} + \dfrac{2 \cdot 3}{3 \cdot 3}$ *Use common denominator of 9*

$= \dfrac{4}{9} + \dfrac{6}{9}$

$= \dfrac{10}{9}$

53. $\dfrac{2}{3} - \dfrac{3}{5} = \dfrac{2 \cdot 5}{3 \cdot 5} - \dfrac{3 \cdot 3}{5 \cdot 3}$ *Write both 2/3 and 3/5 with denominator of 15*

$= \dfrac{10}{15} - \dfrac{9}{15}$

$= \dfrac{1}{15}$

57. $3\dfrac{1}{4} + \dfrac{1}{8} = \dfrac{13}{4} + \dfrac{1}{8}$

$= \dfrac{13 \cdot 2}{4 \cdot 2} + \dfrac{1}{8}$

$= \dfrac{26}{8} + \dfrac{1}{8}$

$= \dfrac{27}{8}$

61. $6\dfrac{2}{3} - 5\dfrac{1}{4} = \dfrac{20}{3} - \dfrac{21}{4}$

$= \dfrac{20 \cdot 4}{3 \cdot 4} - \dfrac{21 \cdot 3}{4 \cdot 3}$

$= \dfrac{80}{12} - \dfrac{63}{12}$

$= \dfrac{17}{12}$

65. $\dfrac{5}{14} + \dfrac{1}{6} - \dfrac{1}{9}$

$= \dfrac{5 \cdot 9}{14 \cdot 9} + \dfrac{1 \cdot 21}{6 \cdot 21} - \dfrac{1 \cdot 14}{9 \cdot 14}$

$= \dfrac{45}{126} + \dfrac{21}{126} - \dfrac{14}{126}$

$= \dfrac{45 + 21 - 14}{126} = \dfrac{52}{126}$

$= \dfrac{26}{63}$

69. $\dfrac{1}{8} + \dfrac{1}{3} + \dfrac{1}{4} = \dfrac{1 \cdot 3}{8 \cdot 3} + \dfrac{1 \cdot 8}{3 \cdot 8} + \dfrac{1 \cdot 6}{4 \cdot 6}$

$$= \dfrac{3}{24} + \dfrac{8}{24} + \dfrac{6}{24}$$

$$= \dfrac{3 + 8 + 6}{24}$$

$$= \dfrac{17}{24}$$

$\dfrac{17}{24}$ of the debt was paid.

73. The number of hours worked on Friday is week's total $-$ (Mon. + Tues. + Wed. + Thurs.) or

$$40 - (8\tfrac{1}{4} + 6\tfrac{3}{8} + 7\tfrac{2}{3} + 8\tfrac{3}{4})$$

$$= 40 - (\tfrac{33}{4} + \tfrac{51}{8} + \tfrac{23}{3} + \tfrac{35}{4})$$

$$= 40 - (\tfrac{33 \cdot 6}{4 \cdot 6} + \tfrac{51 \cdot 3}{8 \cdot 3} + \tfrac{23 \cdot 8}{3 \cdot 8} + \tfrac{35 \cdot 6}{4 \cdot 6})$$

$$= 40 - (\tfrac{198}{24} + \tfrac{153}{24} + \tfrac{184}{24} + \tfrac{210}{24})$$

$$= \dfrac{40 \cdot 24}{1 \cdot 24} - \dfrac{745}{24} = \dfrac{960 - 745}{24} = \dfrac{215}{24}$$

$$= \dfrac{215}{24} \quad \text{or} \quad 8\tfrac{23}{24}.$$

She worked $8\tfrac{23}{24}$ hours on Friday.

77. The number of chairs that can be upholstered is (the number of yards of fabric) ÷ (the number of yards or fabric needed for each chair) or

$$23\tfrac{2}{3} \div 2\tfrac{1}{4} = \dfrac{71}{3} \div \dfrac{9}{4}$$

$$= \dfrac{71}{3} \cdot \dfrac{4}{9}$$

$$= \dfrac{71 \cdot 4}{3 \cdot 9}$$

$$= \dfrac{284}{27}$$

$$= 10\tfrac{14}{27}.$$

There is enough fabric for 10 chairs.

Section 1.2   (page 9)

1. Since 6 is smaller than 9, insert < in the blank.

5. 25 is greater than 12, so insert >.

9. $\dfrac{3}{4}$ is less than 1, so insert < .

13. 12 is less than 17, so insert $\leq$.

17. 8 is less than 28, so insert $\leq$.

21. 6 is less than 9, so both < and $\leq$ may be used.

25. 5 equals 5, so $\leq$ and $\geq$ may be used.

29. 16 is greater then 10, so > and $\leq$ may be used.

33. Write .61 as .610 to see that .069 is less than .610. Both < and $\leq$ may be used.

37. 7 = 5 + 2

41. Use $\neq$ to get $12 \neq 5$.

45. Since 8 + 2 = 10, the statement is true.

49. 0 is less than 15, so the statement is true.

53. $\dfrac{25}{3} = \dfrac{50}{6}$ and $\dfrac{19}{2} = \dfrac{57}{6}$
$\dfrac{50}{6}$ is less than $\dfrac{57}{6}$, so the statement is false.

57. Since 6 = 5 + 1, the statement is false.

61. Since 8 is greater than 0, the statement is false.

65. $14 > 6$

69. $8 < 9$

73. $\dfrac{15}{7} \le \dfrac{18}{5}$

Section 1.3 (page 14)

1. $6^2 = 6 \cdot 6 = 36$

5. $17^2 = 17 \cdot 17 = 289$

9. $6^4 = 6 \cdot 6 \cdot 6 \cdot 6 = 1296$

13. $3^6 = 3 \cdot 3 \cdot 3 \cdot 3 \cdot 3 \cdot 3 = 729$

17. $(\frac{2}{5})^3 = \frac{2}{5} \cdot \frac{2}{5} \cdot \frac{2}{5} = \dfrac{8}{125}$

21. $(.83)^4 = (.83)(.83)(.83)(.83) = .475$

      This answer was rounded to the nearest thousandth.

25. $4 + 6 \cdot 2 = 4 + 12$ *Multiply first*

      $\qquad\qquad = 16$ *Add*

29. $3 \cdot 8 - 4 \cdot 6 = 24 - 24$ *Multiply first*

      $\qquad\qquad = 0$ *Subtract*

33. $5[8 + (2 + 3)]$

      $= 5[8 + (5)]$ *Add inside parentheses*

      $= 5[13]$ *Add inside brackets*

      $= 65$ *Multiply*

37. $\dfrac{2(5 + 3) + 2 \cdot 2}{2(4 - 1)}$

      $= \dfrac{2(8) + 2 \cdot 2}{2(3)}$ *Add or subtract inside parentheses*

      $= \dfrac{16 + 4}{6}$ *Multiply where indicated*

      $= \dfrac{20}{6}$ *Add*

      $= \dfrac{10}{3}$ *Lowest terms*

41. $9 \cdot 3 - 11 = 27 - 11$ *Multiply first*

      $\qquad\qquad = 16$ *Subtract*

      The inequality is now

      $\qquad 16 \le 16.$

      Since $16 = 16$, the inequality is true.

45. $12 \cdot 3 - 6 \cdot 6 = 36 - 36$ *Multiply first*

      $\qquad\qquad = 0$ *Subtract*

      The inequality is now

      $\qquad 0 \ge 0.$

      Since $0 = 0$, the inequality is true.

49. $[3 \cdot 4 + 5(2)] \cdot 3$

      $= [12 + 10] \cdot 3$ *Multiply inside brackets*

      $= [22] \cdot 3$ *Add inside brackets*

      $= 66$ *Multiply*

      The inequality is now

      $\qquad 66 > 72.$

      Since $66 < 72$, the inequality is false.

53. $$\frac{2(5 + 1) - 3(1 + 1)}{5(8 - 6) - 4 \cdot 2}$$

$$= \frac{2(6) - 3(2)}{5(2) - 4 \cdot 2} \quad \textit{Add or subtract in-}\\ \textit{side parentheses}$$

$$= \frac{12 - 6}{10 - 8} \quad \textit{Multiply where}\\ \textit{indicated}$$

$$= \frac{6}{2} \quad \textit{Subtract}$$

$$= 3 \quad \textit{Divide}$$

The inequality is now

$$3 \geq 3.$$

Since 3 = 3, the inequality is true.

57. $10 - 7 - 3 = 6$

$\quad 10 - (7 - 3) = 6 \quad \textit{Insert parentheses}$

$\quad\quad 10 - 4 = 6$

$\quad\quad\quad\quad 6 = 6 \quad \textit{True}$

61. $\quad 3 \cdot 5 - 4 = 3$

$\quad 3 \cdot (5 - 4) = 3 \quad \textit{Insert parentheses}$

$\quad\quad 3 \cdot (1) = 3$

$\quad\quad\quad\quad 3 = 3 \quad \textit{True}$

65. $\quad 3 \cdot 5 + 2 \cdot 4 = 68$

$\quad (3 \cdot 5 + 2) \cdot 4 = 68 \quad \textit{Insert parentheses}$

$\quad\quad (15 + 2) \cdot 4 = 68$

$\quad\quad\quad 17 \cdot 4 = 68$

$\quad\quad\quad\quad 68 = 68 \quad \textit{True}$

69. $4096 \div 256 \div 4 = 4$

$\quad\quad 16 \div 4 = 4 \quad \textit{Perform divi-}\\ \textit{sion from left}\\ \textit{to right}$

$\quad\quad\quad 4 = 4 \quad \textit{True}$

No parentheses are necessary.

73. $\quad 8 - 2^2 \cdot 2 = 8 \quad \textit{Insert parentheses}$

$\quad (8 - 2^2) \cdot 2 = 8$

$\quad\quad 4 \cdot 2 = 8$

$\quad\quad\quad 8 = 8 \quad \textit{True}$

77. There were 63 original passengers. Subtract 23 and add 17.

$$63 - 23 + 17$$

There are now 57 passengers.

Section 1.4 (page 19)

1. (a) $x + 9 = 3 + 9 \quad \textit{Let x = 3}$
$\quad\quad\quad = 12 \quad \textit{Add}$

   (b) $x + 9 = 15 + 9 \quad \textit{Let x = 15}$
$\quad\quad\quad = 24 \quad \textit{Add}$

5. (a) $2x + 8 = 2 \cdot 3 + 8 \quad \textit{Let x = 3}$
$\quad\quad\quad = 6 + 8 \quad \textit{Multiply first}$
$\quad\quad\quad = 14 \quad \textit{Add}$

   (b) $2x + 8 = 2 \cdot 15 + 8 \quad \textit{Let x = 15}$
$\quad\quad\quad = 30 + 8 \quad \textit{Multiply}$
$\quad\quad\quad = 38 \quad \textit{Add}$

9. (a) $\dfrac{3x - 5}{2x} = \dfrac{3 \cdot 3 - 5}{2 \cdot 3} \quad \textit{Let x = 3}$

$\quad\quad = \dfrac{9 - 5}{6} \quad \textit{Simplify nu-}\\ \textit{merator and}\\ \textit{denominator}$

$\quad\quad = \dfrac{4}{6}$

$\quad\quad = \dfrac{2}{3} \quad \textit{Lowest terms}$

   (b) $\dfrac{3x - 5}{2x} = \dfrac{3 \cdot 15 - 5}{2 \cdot 15} \quad \textit{Let x = 15}$

$\quad\quad = \dfrac{45 - 5}{30} \quad \textit{Multiply}$

$\quad\quad = \dfrac{40}{30} \quad \textit{Subtract}$

$\quad\quad = \dfrac{4}{3} \text{ or } 1\frac{1}{3} \quad \textit{Lowest terms}$

13. (a) $6.459x = 6.459 \cdot 3 \quad \textit{Let x = 3}$
$\quad\quad\quad = 19.377 \quad \textit{Multiply}$

   (b) $6.459x = 6.459 \cdot 15 \quad \textit{Let x = 15}$
$\quad\quad\quad = 96.885 \quad \textit{Multiply}$

17. (a) $3(x + 2y)$

   $= 3(4 + 2 \cdot 2)$ *Let $x = 4$ and $y = 2$*

   $= 3(4 + 4)$ *Multiply in parentheses*

   $= 3(8)$ *Add in parentheses*

   $= 24$ *Multiply*

   (b) $3(x + 2y)$

   $= 3(1 + 2 \cdot 5)$ *Let $x = 1$ and $y = 5$*

   $= 3(1 + 10)$ *Multiply in parentheses*

   $= 3(11)$ *Add in parentheses*

   $= 33$ *Multiply*

21. (a) $\dfrac{x}{3} + \dfrac{5}{y}$

   $= \dfrac{4}{3} + \dfrac{5}{2}$ *Let $x = 4$ and $y = 2$*

   $= \dfrac{8}{6} + \dfrac{15}{6}$ *Use common denominator of 6*

   $= \dfrac{23}{6}$ *Add numerators*

   (b) $\dfrac{x}{3} + \dfrac{5}{y}$

   $= \dfrac{1}{3} + \dfrac{5}{5}$ *Let $x = 1$ and $y = 5$*

   $= \dfrac{5}{15} + \dfrac{15}{15}$ *Use common denominator of 15*

   $= \dfrac{20}{15}$ *Add numerators*

   $= \dfrac{4}{3}$ *Lowest terms*

25. (a) $\dfrac{2x + 3y}{x + y + 1}$

   $= \dfrac{2 \cdot 4 + 3 \cdot 2}{4 + 2 + 1}$ *Let $x = 4$ and $y = 2$*

   $= \dfrac{8 + 6}{4 + 2 + 1}$ *Multiply*

   $= \dfrac{14}{7}$ *Add*

   $= 2$ *Divide*

   (b) $\dfrac{2x + 3y}{x + y + 1}$

   $= \dfrac{2 \cdot 1 + 3 \cdot 5}{1 + 5 + 1}$ *Let $x = 1$ and $y = 5$*

   $= \dfrac{2 + 15}{1 + 5 + 1}$ *Multiply*

   $= \dfrac{17}{7}$ *Add*

29. (a) $\dfrac{x^2 + y^2}{x + y}$

   $= \dfrac{4^2 + 2^2}{4 + 2}$ *Let $x = 4$ and $y = 2$*

   $= \dfrac{16 + 4}{4 + 2}$ *Use exponents*

   $= \dfrac{20}{6}$ *Add*

   $= \dfrac{10}{3}$ *Lowest terms*

   (b) $\dfrac{x^2 + y^2}{x + y}$

   $= \dfrac{1^2 + 5^2}{1 + 5}$ *Let $x = 1$ and $y = 5$*

   $= \dfrac{1 + 25}{1 + 5}$ *Use exponents*

   $= \dfrac{26}{6}$ *Add*

   $= \dfrac{13}{3}$ *Lowest terms*

33. "Eight times a number" translates to $8 \cdot x$ or $8x$.

37. "A number subtracted from eight" translates to $8 - x$. (Note that the number following the word "from" in "subtracted from" always comes first in an expression like this.)

41. "Eight times a number" translates as $8x$. "Added to 52" means $+ 52$. So we have $8x + 52$.

45.   5m + 2 = 7
       5·2 + 2 = 7   *Replace m with 2*
       10 + 2 = 7
          12 = 7   *False*

The number 2 is not a solution of the equation.

49.   6p + 4p - 9 = 11
       6·2 + 4·2 - 9 = 11   *Replace p with 2*
       12 + 8 - 9 = 11
           20 - 9 = 11
               11 = 11   *True*

The number 2 is a solution of the equation.

53. $\frac{z + 4}{z - 2} = 2$

     $\frac{8 + 4}{8 - 2} = 2$ *Let z = 8*

     $\frac{12}{6} = 2$

     2 = 2   *True*

The number 8 is a solution to the equation.

57. "The sum of a number and 8 is 12" translates to

         x + 8 = 12.

Replace x with each number in the domain. The only true statement results as follows.

       4 + 8 = 12   *Let x = 4*
          12 = 12

If x = 4, the statement is true. The only solution is 4.

61. "Five more than twice a number is 13" translates to

         5 + 2x = 13

Replace x with each number in the domain.

       5 + 2·4 = 13   *Let x = 4*
          5 + 8 = 13
             13 = 13   *True*

The only solution is 4.

65. "The quotient of twenty and five times a number is 2" translates to

     $\frac{20}{5x} = 2$.

Replace x with each number in the domain.

     $\frac{20}{5·2} = 2$ *Let x = 2*

     $\frac{20}{10} = 2$

     2 = 2   *True*

The only solution is 2.

69. $\frac{2[4(x + 3) - x]}{2(x + 1)}$

     $= \frac{2[4(4 + 3) - 4]}{2(4 + 1)}$ *Let x = 4*

     $= \frac{2[4(7) - 4]}{2(5)}$ *Parentheses first*

     $= \frac{2[28 - 4]}{10}$ *Multiply in brackets*

     $= \frac{2[24]}{10}$ *Subtract in brackets*

     $= \frac{48}{10}$ *Multiply*

     $= \frac{24}{5}$ *Lowest terms*

Section 1.5 (page 27)

1. Since the sum -8 + 8 = 0, the additive inverse of 8 is -8.

5. The additive inverse of -2 is -(-2) = 2.

9. The value of $|-8|$ is 8; the additive inverse of this number is -8.

13. Since -12 is to the left of -4 on the number line, -12 is smaller than -4.

17. Since $|-4| = 4$, 3 is the smaller of the two numbers.

21. Since $-|-6| = -6$ and $-|-4| = -4$, $-|-6|$ is to the left of $-|-4|$ on the number line, so $-|-6|$ is the smaller of the two numbers.

25. Since -2 is to the left of -1 on the number line, -2 is smaller than -1, then -2 < -1 is true.

29. Since -20 is to the left of -15 on the number line, -20 is smaller than -15, then $-15 \leq -20$ is false.

33. Since $-(-4) = 4$, $0 \leq (-4)$ is true.

37. Since $-(-5) = 5$, $-4 < -(-5)$ is true.

41. Since $-|8| = -8$ and $|-9| = -(-9) = 9$, -8 is to the left of 9 on the number line. So -8 is smaller than 9.

    $-|8| > |-9|$ is false.

45. Since $|6 - 5| = |1| = 1$ and $|6 - 2| = |4| = 4$

    $|6 - 5| \geq |6 - 2|$ is false.

49. Graph the numbers 0, 3, -5, -6. See answer graph in the textbook.

53. Graph the numbers $\frac{1}{4}$, $2\frac{1}{2}$, $-3\frac{4}{5}$, -4, $-1\frac{5}{8}$.

    See answer graph in the textbook.

57. Examples are $2\frac{1}{2}$, $3\frac{1}{4}$, $4\frac{2}{3}$. Your answers will differ but they must be positive real numbers that are not integers.

61. Examples are π, $\sqrt{2}$, $\sqrt{7}$, or any square roots of numbers that are not perfect squares.

65. False. All integers are real numbers.

71. False. The whole numbers are included in the set of integers.

75. $|a + b| = -|a + b|$

    To make the statement true, a and b must be opposites of each other or a = -b.
    To make the statement false, choose values of a and b such that they are not opposites.

Section 1.6 (page 31)

1. 5 + (-3)

   Find the difference in the absolute values of both numbers:

   5 - 3 = 2

   Since the larger number in absolute value is 5, the answer is positive. Therefore, the answer is 2.

5. -6 + (-2)

   Since numbers with the same sign are being added, add the absolute values of both numbers:

   6 + 2 = 8.

Since both numbers are negative, the sign of the answer is negative:

$$-6 + (-2) = -8.$$

9. $12 + (-8)$

Find the difference in the absoulte values of both numbers:

$$12 - 8 = 4.$$

Since the larger number in absoulte value is 12, the answer is positive.
Therefore,

$$12 + (-8) = 4.$$

13. $8 + [-2 + (-1)]$
    $= 8 + (-3)$ *Work with brackets*
    $= 5$ *Add*

17. $-6 + [6 + (-9)]$
    $= -6 + (-3)$ *Work within brackets*
    $= -9$ *Add*

21. $-\dfrac{1}{6} + \dfrac{2}{3} = -\dfrac{1}{6} + \dfrac{4}{6}$ *Write each fraction with a common denominator*

    $= \dfrac{3}{6}$ *Add the numerators: $-1 + 4 = 3$*

    $= \dfrac{1}{2}$ *Lowest terms*

25. $2\dfrac{1}{2} + (-3\dfrac{1}{4})$

    $= \dfrac{5}{2} + (\dfrac{-13}{4})$ *Change each fraction to an improper fraction*

    $= \dfrac{10}{4} + (\dfrac{-13}{4})$ *Write each fraction with a common denominator*

    $= -\dfrac{3}{4}$ *Add the numerators: $10 + (-13) = -3$*

29. $[-3 + (-4)] + [5 + (-6)]$
    $= -7 + (-1)$ *Work within brackets*
    $= -8$ *Add*

33. $[-4 + (-6)] + [(-3) + (-8)] + [12 + (-11)]$
    $= -10 + (-11) + 1$ *Work in the brackets first*
    $= -20$ *Add*

37. $-9 + 5 + 6 = -2$
    $2 = -2$

    This statement is false.

41. $|-8 + 3| = 8 + 3$
    $|-5| = 11$
    $5 = 11$

    This statement is false.

45. $[4 + (-6)] + 6 = 4 + (-6 + 6)$
    $-2 + 6 = 4 + 0$
    $4 = 4$

    This statement is true.

49. $-5 + (-|-5|) = -10$
    $-5 + (-5) = -10$
    $-10 = -10$

    This statement is true.

In Exercises 53 and 57, mentally replace x with each number from the domain to determine which number makes the equation a true statement.

53. $x + 1 = -2$
    $-3 + 1 = -2$ *Let $x = -3$*
    $-2 = -2$ *True*

    The solution is -3.

57. $x + (-4) = -6$

   $-2 + (-4) = -6$ *Let x = -2*

   $-6 = -6$ *True*

   The solution is -2.

61.   "The sum of -9 and 2 and 6" is translated

   $-9 + 2 + 6 = -1.$

65.   "The sum of -11 and -4 increased by -5" is translated

   $[-11 + (-4)] + (-5) = -15 + (-5) = -20.$

69. $-15 - 120 = -15 + (-120)$

   $= -135$

   His altitude is -135 feet, or 135 feet below sea level.

73. $-22° + 35° = 13°$

   At noon, the temperature was 13°.

77.   Since $17 + (-9) = 8$, the number we must add is 17.

Section 1.7 (page 35)

1. $3 - 6 = 3 + (-6)$ *Add the opposite of 6*

   $= -3$

5. $-6 - 2 = -6 + (-2)$ *Add the opposite of 2*

   $= -8$

9. $6 - (-3) = 6 + (3)$ *Add the opposite of (-3)*

   $= 9$

13. $2 - (3 - 5)$

   $= 2 - [3 + (-5)]$ *Add the opposite of 5*

   $= 2 - (-2)$ *Add the opposite of (-2)*

   $= 2 + 2$

   $= 4$

17. $-\frac{3}{4} - \frac{5}{8} = -\frac{3}{4} + (-\frac{5}{8})$ *Add the opposite of 5/8*

   $= -\frac{6}{8} + (-\frac{5}{8})$

   $= -\frac{11}{8}$

21. $3.4 - (-8.2) = 3.4 + (8.2) = 11.6$

25. $-4.1128 - (7.418 - 9.80632)$

   $= -4.1128 - (-2.38832)$

   $= -4.1128 + 2.38832$

   $= -1.72448$

29. $(4 - 6) + 12 = (-2) + 12 = 10$

33. $6 - (-8 + 3) = 6 - (-5)$

   $= 6 + (5)$

   $= 11$

37. $(-5 - 6) - (9 - 2)$

   $= [-5 + (-6)] - [9 + (-2)]$

   $= -11 - (7)$

   $= -11 + (-7)$

   $= -18$

41. $-9 - [(3 - 2) - (-4 - 2)]$

   $= -9 - [1 - (-6)]$

   $= -9 - (7) = -16$

45. $-9.1237 + [(-4.8099 - 3.2516) + 11.27903)$

   $= -9.1237 + (-8.0615 + 11.27903)$

   $= -9.1237 + 3.21753$

   $= -5.90617$

49.   "Subtract -6 from 12" can be read "from 12 subtract -6," which becomes

   $12 - (-6) = 12 + (6) = 18.$

53. To determine how much greater one number is than another, always subtract the smaller number from the larger. This exercise can now be written "from -24 subtract -27" which becomes

$$-24 - (-27) = -24 + (27)$$
$$= 3.$$

57. "Find the difference of 8 and -2" becomes

$$8 - (-2) = 8 + 2$$
$$= 10.$$

61. "From the sum of -12 and -3, subtract 4" becomes

$$[-12 + (-3)] - 4 = -15 - 4$$
$$= -19.$$

65. $14,494 - (-282) = 14,494 + 282$
$$= 14,776$$

The difference between the elevations is 14,776 feet.

69. $\$76,000 - (-\$29,000) = \$105,000$

The difference between the profits is $105,000.

73. $x + y - z$
$$= (-5) + (-4) - (8) \quad Let\ x = -5,$$
$$y = -4,\ z = 8$$
$$= -9 - (8) = -17$$

Section 1.8   (page 40)

1. $(-3)(-4) = (3 \cdot 4) = 12$

5. $(-10)(-12) = (10 \cdot 12) = 120$

9. $(15)(-11) = -(15 \cdot 11) = -165$

13. $(-1\frac{1}{4})(\frac{2}{15}) = -(1\frac{1}{4} \cdot \frac{2}{15})$
$$= -(\frac{5}{4} \cdot \frac{2}{15})$$
$$= -\frac{10}{60} = -\frac{1}{6}$$

17. $(-5.1)(.02) = -[(5.1)(.02)]$
$$= -.102$$

21. $(3.4)(-3.5) = -(3.4)(3.5)$
$$= -11.9$$

25. $(-8.91)(-4.725) = (8.91)(4.725)$
$$= 42.09975$$
$$= 42.100 \ (rounded)$$

29. $-9 - (-2) \cdot 3$
$$= -9 - (-6) \quad Do\ multiplication\ first$$
$$= -9 + (6) \quad Add\ the\ opposite\ of\ (-6)$$
$$= -3 \quad Add$$

33. $-6(2 - 4)$
$$= -6(-2) \quad Subtract\ inside\ parentheses\ first$$
$$= 12 \quad Multiply$$

37. $(2 - 5)(3 - 7)$
$$= (-3)(-4) \quad Subtract\ in\ parentheses\ first$$
$$Multiply$$

41. $5(-2) - 4 = -10 - 4 \quad Multiply$
$$= -14 \quad Subtract$$

45. $5x - 2y + 3a$
$$= 5(-2) - 2(3) + 3(-4) \quad Let\ x = -2$$
$$y = 3,\ a = -4$$
$$= -10 - 6 + (-12) \quad Multiply$$
$$= -10 + (-6) + (-12) \quad Add\ the\ opposite\ of\ 6$$
$$= -28 \quad Add$$

49. $(3x - 4y)(-5a)$

    $= [3(-2) - 4(3)][-5(-4)]$ *Let x = -2,*
                                     y = 3, a = -4

    $= (-6 - 12)(20)$ *Find the products*

    $= (-18)(20)$ *Subtract*

    $= -360$ *Multiply*

53. $-2y^2 + 3(a + 2)$

    $= -2(3)^2 + 3[(-4) + 2]$ *Let x = -2,*
                                       y = 3, a = -4

    $= -2(9) + 3[(-4) + 2]$ *Simplify exponent*

    $= -2(9) + 3(-2)$ *Add*

    $= -18 - 6$ *Multiply*

    $= -24$ *Subtract*

57. $2x = -4$

    $2(-2) = -4$ *Let x = -2*

        $-4 = -4$ *Multiply*

    True

    The solution is -2.

61. $-9r = 27$

    $-9(-3) = 27$ *Let r = -3*

         $27 = 27$

    True

    The solution is -3.

65. $-5t + 6 = 11$

    $-5(-1) + 6 = 11$ *Let t = -1*

          $5 + 6 = 11$

              $11 = 11$

    True

    The solution is -1.

69. $-4 - 2(-8 \cdot 2) = -4 - 2(-16)$

                      $= -4 + 32$

                      $= 28$

73. $(-9 - 1)(-2)^2 - (-6)$

    $= (-9 - 1)(4) - (-6)$

    $= (-10)(4) - (-6)$

    $= -40 - (-6)$

    $= -40 + 6$

    $= -34$

77. $|-3|(-2) + |-8| \cdot |5|$

    $= 3(-2) + 8 \cdot 5$

    $= -6 + 40$

    $= 34$

81. $a(b + c) = ab + ac$

    $2(3 + 4) = (2)(3) + (2)(4)$

        $2(7) = 6 + 8$

          $14 = 14$

    True

Section 1.9 (page 45)

1. Since $9 \cdot \frac{1}{9} = 1$, the multiplicative inverse is $\frac{1}{9}$.

5. The reciprocal of 0 is $\frac{1}{0}$, but $\frac{1}{0}$ is not defined, so 0 does not have a multiplicative inverse.

9. Write .8697 as $\frac{.8697}{1}$. The multiplicative inverse is

    $$\frac{.8697}{1} = \frac{1}{.8697} = 1.150 \quad (rounded)$$

13. $\frac{18}{-3} = 18 \cdot (-\frac{1}{3}) = -6$

17. $\frac{0}{-2} = 0 \cdot -\frac{1}{2} = 0$

21. $(-4.2) \div (-2) = -4.2 \cdot (-\frac{1}{2}) = 2.1$

25. $\frac{12}{2 - 5} = \frac{12}{-3} = 12 \cdot (-\frac{1}{3}) = -4$

29. $\frac{-40}{8 - (-8)} = \frac{-40}{16} = -40 \cdot \frac{1}{16} = -\frac{40}{16} = -\frac{5}{2}$

33. $\frac{-30 - (-8)}{-11} = \frac{-30 + 8}{-11} = \frac{-22}{-11}$

37. $\frac{-15(2) - 10}{-7 - 3} = \frac{-30 - 10}{-10} = \frac{-40}{-10}$

  $= -40 \cdot (\frac{-1}{10})$

  $= 4$

41. $\frac{6^2 + 4^2}{5(2 + 13)} = \frac{36 + 16}{5(15)}$

  $= \frac{52}{75}$

45. The factors of 32 are

  $-32, -16, -8, -4, -2,$

  $-1, 1, 2, 4, 8, 16, 32.$

49. The numbers that divide (with remainder 0) into 29 are

  $1, -1, 29, -29$

53. $\frac{t}{-2} = -2$

  $\frac{4}{-2} = -2$ *Let* $t = 4$

  $4 \cdot (-\frac{1}{2}) = -2$

  $-2 = -2$ *True*

  The solution is 4.

57. $\frac{y}{-1} = 2$

  $\frac{-2}{-1} = 2$ *Let* $y = -2$

  $-2 \cdot (-1) = 2$

  $2 = 2$ *True*

  The solution is -2.

61. "A number divided by -3 is -4" becomes

  $\frac{x}{-3} = -4$

  $\frac{12}{-3} = -4$ *Let* $x = 12$

  $-4 = -4.$ *True*

  The solution is 12.

65. "The square of a number divided by 3 is 12" becomes

  $\frac{x^2}{3} = 12$

  $\frac{(-6)^2}{3} = 12$

  $\frac{36}{3} = 12$

  $12 = 12.$ *True*

  A solution is -6.
  Also,

  $\frac{6^2}{3} = 12$

  $\frac{36}{3} = 12$

  $12 = 12$ *True*

  Another solution is 6.

69. "Subtract 3 from the quotient of -16 and 4" becomes

  $\frac{-16}{4} - 3 = -4 - 3$

  $= -7.$

73. $\dfrac{(-9)(-2) - [(-4)(-2) + 3]}{-2(3) - 2(2)}$

$= \dfrac{18 - [8 + 3]}{-6 - 4}$

$= \dfrac{18 - 11}{-10}$

$= -\dfrac{7}{10}$

77. $\dfrac{[1 - (.86)^2] + (2.5)^2}{(-1.43)^3 - [-3.76 + 6.45]}$

$= \dfrac{[1 - .7396] + 6.25}{-2.924207 - [2.69]}$

$= \dfrac{[.2604] + 6.25}{-5.614207}$

$= \dfrac{6.5104}{-5.614207}$

$= -1.15962949$

$= -1.160$ *(rounded)*

Section 1.10 (page 51)

1. $5(15 \cdot 8) = (5 \cdot 15)8$

The numbers are in the same order
but are grouped differently,
which indicates the associative
property of multiplication.

5. $2 + (p + r) = (p + r) + 2$

The order of the number and the
expression are added in a different order on both sides, which
indicates the commutative property
of addition.

9. $6 + (-6) = 0$

Since 6 and -6 are additive inverses, this is the additive
inverse property.

13. $3\left(\dfrac{1}{3}\right) = 1$

Since 3 and 1/3 are multiplicative
inverses, this is the multi-
cative inverse property.

17. $6(5 - 2x) = 6 \cdot 5 - 6(2x)$

Here the multiplication of 6 is
distributed over 5 and -2x, in-
dicating the distributive property.

21. $m + 0 = m$

25. $8 \cdot \dfrac{1}{8} = 1$

29. $5 + (-5) = -5 + 5$ *Add in the*
                          opposite
                          order
     $\qquad = 0$

33. $9 \cdot 1 = 9$

37. $5(m + 2) = 5 \cdot m + 5 \cdot 2 = 5m + 10$

41. $-8(k - 2) = -8k - (-8)(2)$
     $\qquad\quad = -8k + 16$

45. $(r + 8)4 = r \cdot 4 + 8 \cdot 4$
     $\qquad\quad = 4r + 32$

49. $2(5r + 6m) = 2 \cdot 5r + 2 \cdot 6m$
     $\qquad\qquad = 10r + 12m$

53. $5 \cdot 8 + 5 \cdot 9 = 5(8 + 9)$
     $\qquad\qquad = 5(17)$
     $\qquad\qquad = 85$

57. $9p + 9q = 9(p + q)$

61. $-(3k + 5) = -1 \cdot 3k + (-1)(5)$
     $\qquad\qquad = -3k - 5$

65. $-(-4 + p) = -1(-4) + (-1)(p)$
     $\qquad\qquad = 4 - p$

69. Taking a shower prior to getting out of bed would not be impossible but illogical. The events are not commutative.

73. $25 - (6 - 2) = 25 - (4)$
$$= 21$$
$(26 - 6) - 2 = 19 - 2$
$$= 17$$

Since $21 \neq 17$, subtraction is not associative.

77. $a + (b \cdot c)$
$= 3 + (2 \cdot 5)$ *Let $a = 3$, $b = 2$, $c = 5$*
$= 3 + 10$
$= 13$

$(a + b)(a + c) = (3 + 2)(3 + 5)$
$$= (5)(8)$$
$$= 40$$

Since $13 \neq 40$, $a + (b \cdot c) = (a + b)$ $(a + c)$ is false.

Chapter 1 Review Exercises (page 54)

1. $\dfrac{18}{54} = \dfrac{18 \div 18}{54 \div 18} = \dfrac{1}{3}$

5. $\dfrac{7}{10} \cdot \dfrac{1}{5} = \dfrac{7 \cdot 1}{10 \cdot 5} = \dfrac{7}{50}$

9. $\dfrac{1}{4} + \dfrac{1}{3} = \dfrac{1 \cdot 3}{4 \cdot 3} + \dfrac{1 \cdot 4}{3 \cdot 4}$
$= \dfrac{3}{12} + \dfrac{4}{12}$
$= \dfrac{7}{12}$

7/12 of the room was painted.

13. Since 2/3 is approximately equal to .666 and since .666 is less than .7, then either 2/3 < .7 or 2/3 $\leq$ 7 would be correct.

17. $70 < 4 - 9(6 + 2)$
$70 < 4 - 9(8)$
$70 < 4 - 72$
$70 < -68$

The statement is false.

21. $5^2 + 4^2 \leq 40$
$25 + 16 \leq 40$
$41 \leq 40$

The statement is false.

25. $\dfrac{3x^2 + 5y^2}{7x^2 - y^2}$

$= \dfrac{3 \cdot 2^2 + 5 \cdot 5^2}{7 \cdot 2^2 - 5^2}$ *Let $x = 2$ and $y = 5$*

$= \dfrac{3 \cdot 4 + 5 \cdot 25}{7 \cdot 4 - 25}$ *Use exponents*

$= \dfrac{12 + 125}{28 - 25}$ *Multiply*

$= \dfrac{137}{3}$ *Simplify numerator and denominator*

29. Since $|-7| = 7$, $|-7|$ is the smaller.

33. Since $-(-10) = 10$, and 9 is not greater than 10, the inequality is false.

37. Since $-|4| = -4$, $-|-3| = -3$, and -4 is to the left of -3 on the number line, then $-|4| > -|-3|$ is false.

41. $3\dfrac{1}{4}$, $-2\dfrac{4}{5}$, $-1\dfrac{1}{8}$, $\dfrac{2}{3}$

See answer graph in the textbook.

45. $\frac{7}{8} + (-\frac{3}{10})$

$= \frac{7 \cdot 5}{8 \cdot 5} + (-\frac{3 \cdot 4}{10 \cdot 4})$ *Use common deno-minator of 40*

$= \frac{35}{40} + (-\frac{12}{40})$ *Multiply*

$= \frac{35 - 12}{40}$ *Add numerators*

$= \frac{23}{40}$

49.
The amount	and	the amount	is
Tom has		he spends	
↓	↓	↓	↓
9	+	(-11)	=

his new
balance
↓
-2

His new balance is -$2.

53. $\frac{3}{4} - (-\frac{2}{3})$

$= \frac{3 \cdot 3}{4 \cdot 3} + \frac{2 \cdot 4}{3 \cdot 4}$ *Use common deno-minator of 12*

$= \frac{9}{12} + \frac{8}{12}$ *Multiply*

$= \frac{17}{12}$ *Add numerators*

57. $-\frac{4}{5}(-\frac{10}{7}) = (\frac{4}{5} \cdot \frac{10}{7}) = \frac{8}{7}$

61. $8(-9) - (6)(-2) = (-72) - (-12)$

$= -72 + 12$

$= -60$

65. $3z^2 - 4x^2$

$= 3(-3)^2 - 4(-5)^2$ *Let $x = -5$ and $z = -3$*

$= 3(9) - 4(25)$

$= 27 - 100$

$= -73$

69. $8.974 \cdot 1 = 8.974$

Multiplicative identity

73. $\frac{5}{8} \cdot \frac{8}{5} = 1$

Multiplicative inverse

77. $[-4) + 6 + (-9)] + [-3 + (-5)]$

$= [(-4 + 6) + (-9)] + [-3 + (-5)]$

$= [2 + (-9)] + [-3 + (-5)]$

$= -7 + (-8)$

$= -15$

81. $\frac{5(-3) - 8(3)}{(-5)(-4) + (-7)} = \frac{-15 - 24}{20 - 7}$

$= \frac{-39}{13} = -3$

85. $-11(-4) - (3)(-7) = 44 - (-21)$

$= 44 + 21$

$= 65$

89. $(-8 - 2) - [(-1 - 4) - (-1)]$

$= -10 - [-5 + 1]$

$= -10 - (-4)$

$= -10 + 4$

$= -6$

93. $\$28,000 + (-\$7000) = \$21,000$

$21,000 was spent on advertising the second year.

Chapter 1 Test   (page 56)

1. $\frac{84}{132} = \frac{84 \div 12}{132 \div 12} = \frac{7}{11}$

2. $\frac{3}{8} + \frac{7}{12} + \frac{11}{15}$

$= \frac{3 \cdot 15}{8 \cdot 15} + \frac{7 \cdot 10}{12 \cdot 10} + \frac{11 \cdot 8}{15 \cdot 8}$

$= \frac{45}{120} + \frac{70}{120} + \frac{88}{120}$

$= \frac{203}{120}$

3. $\frac{6}{5} \div \frac{19}{15} = \frac{6}{5} \cdot \frac{15}{19} = \frac{18}{19}$

4. $6 - |-4| \geq 10$

    $6 - 4 \geq 10$

      $2 \geq 10$

The statement is false.

5. $4[-20 + 7(-2)] \leq 135$

   $4[-20 - 14] \leq 135$

      $4(-34) \leq 135$

       $-136 \leq 135$

The statement is true.

6. $-2 \geq \frac{-36 - 3(-6)}{(-2)(-4) - (-1)}$

  $-2 \geq \frac{-36 - (-18)}{8 - (-1)}$

  $-2 \geq \frac{-18}{9}$

  $-2 \geq -2$

The statement is true.

7. $-14 < \frac{32 + 4(1 + 5)}{6(3 + 5) - 2}$

  $-14 < \frac{32 + 24}{48 - 2}$

  $-14 < \frac{56}{46}$

  $-14 < \frac{28}{3}$

The statement is true.

8. $(-3)^2 + 2^2 = 5^2$

    $9 + 4 = 25$

      $13 = 25$

The statement is false.

9. $5m + 2p^3 = 5 \cdot 6 + 2 \cdot 2^3$ *Let m = 6 and p = 2*

    $= 5 \cdot 6 + 2 \cdot 2 \cdot 2 \cdot 2$

    $= 30 + 16$

    $= 46$

10. $\frac{7m^2 - p^2}{m + 4} = \frac{7 \cdot 6^2 - 2}{6 + 4}$ *Let m = 6 and p = 2*

    $= \frac{7 \cdot 6 \cdot 6 - 2 \cdot 2}{6 + 4}$

    $= \frac{252 - 4}{10} = \frac{248}{10}$

    $= \frac{124}{5}$ *Lowest terms*

11. Since $-|-8| = -8$, $-|-8|$ is smaller than 6.

12. .705 is smaller than .742.

13. "Twice a number subtracted from 11" becomes

    $11 - 2 \cdot x$ or $11 - 2x$.

14. "The quotient of 9 and the difference of a number and 8" becomes

    $\frac{9}{x - 8}$.

15. $6m + m + 2$

  $= 6 \cdot 5 + 5 + 2$ *Replace m with 5*

  $= 30 + 5 + 2$

  $= 37$

Yes, since $37 = 37$, 5 is a solution.

16. $8(y - 3) + 2y = 8(4 - 3) + 2(4)$

        $= 8(1) + 2(4)$

        $= 8 + 8$

        $= 16$

No, since $16 \neq 18$, 4 is not a solution.

17. $-9 - (4 - 11) + (-5)$
     $= -9 - (-7) + (-5)$
     $= -9 + 7 + (-5)$
     $= -2 + (-5)$
     $= -7$

18. $-2\frac{1}{5} + 5\frac{1}{4} = -\frac{11}{5} + \frac{21}{4}$
     $= \frac{-11\cdot4}{5\cdot4} + \frac{21\cdot5}{4\cdot5}$
     $= \frac{-44}{20} + \frac{105}{20}$
     $= \frac{61}{20}$

19. $-6 - [-5 + (8 - 9)]$
     $= -6 - [-5 + (-1)]$
     $= -6 - (-6)$
     $= -6 + 6$
     $= 0$

20. $3^2 + (-7) - (2^3 - 5)$
     $= 3\cdot3 + (-7) - (2\cdot2\cdot2 - 5)$
     $= 9 + (-7) - (8 - 5)$
     $= 2 - 3$
     $= -1$

21. $|-6|\cdot(-5) + 2\cdot|8|$
     $= 6(-5) + 2\cdot8$
     $= -30 + 16$
     $= -14$

22. $\frac{-7 - (-5 + 1)}{-4 - (-3)} = \frac{-7 - (-4)}{-4 + 3}$
     $= \frac{-7 + 4}{-4 + 3}$
     $= \frac{-3}{-1} = 3$

23. $\frac{-6[5 - (-1 + 4)]}{-9[2 - (-1)] - 6(-4)}$
     $= \frac{-6[5 - 3]}{-9[2 + 1] + 24}$
     $= \frac{-6(2)}{-9(3) + 24}$
     $= \frac{-12}{-27 + 24}$
     $= \frac{-12}{-3} = 4$

24. $\frac{15(-4 - 2)}{16(-2) + (-7 - 1)(-3 - 1)}$
     $= \frac{15(-6)}{16(-2) + (-8)(-4)}$
     $= \frac{-90}{-32 + 32}$
     $= \frac{-90}{0}$

Not defined.

25. $\frac{p}{-3} = 3$

     $\frac{-9}{-3} = 3$ *Let p = -9*

     -9 is the solution.

26. $2x + 1 = -7$
     $2(-4) + 1 = -7$ *Let x = -4*
     $-8 + 1 = -7$
     $-7 = -7$

     -4 is the solution.

27. $-4x - 7 = 5$
     $-4(-3) - 7 = 5$ *Let x = -3*
     $12 - 7 = 5$
     $5 = 5$

     -3 is the solution.

28.   Commutative: A and E

29.   Associative: H

30.   Identity: C and I

31.   Inverse: B and G

32.   Distributive: D and F

33. $-(3 - 4m) = -1(3) + (-1)(-4m)$
$= -3 + 4m$

CHAPTER 2   SOLVING EQUATIONS
AND INEQUALITIES

Section 2.1   (page 61)

1. $\underset{\uparrow}{15y}$

   └── Numerical coefficient

5. $\underset{\uparrow}{35a^4b^2}$

   └── Numerical coefficient

9. $y^2 = \underset{\uparrow}{1} \cdot y^2$

   └── Numerical coefficient

13.   6m and -14m are like terms since
   the variables are the same.

17.   25y, -14y, and 8y are like terms
   since the variables are the same.

21. $9y + 8y = (9 + 8) = 17y$

25. $12b + b = 12b + 1b$
   $= (12 + 1)b$
   $= 13b$

29. $-5y + 3 - 1 + 5 + y - 7$
   $= -5y + 1y + 3 - 1 + 5 - 7$
   $= (-5 + 1)y + (3 - 1 + 5 - 7)$
   $= -4y + 0$
   $= -4y$

33. $16 - 5m - 4m - 2 + 2m$
   $= -5m - 4m + 2m + 16 - 2$
   $= (-5 - 4 + 2)m + 14$
   $= (-7)m + 14 = -7m + 14$

37. $1 + 7x + 11x - 1 + 5x$
   $= 7x + 11x + 5x + 1 - 1$
   $= (7 + 11 + 5)x + (1 - 1)$
   $= 23x + 0$
   $= 23x$

41. $2p^2 + 3p^2 - 8p^3 - 6p^3$
   $= (2 + 3)p^2 + (-8 - 6)p^3$
   $= 5p^2 + (-14)p^3$
   $= 5p^2 - 14p^3$

45. $6(5t + 11) = 6(5t) + 6(11)$
   $= 30t + 66$

49. $-3(2r - 3) + 2(5r + 3)$
   $= -3(2r) + (-3)(-3) + 2(5r) + 2(3)$
   $= -6r + 9 + 10r + 6$
   $= -6r + 10r + 9 + 6$
   $= (-6 + 10)r + (9 + 6)$
   $= 4r + 15$

53. $-2(-3k + 2) - (5k - 6) - 3k - 5$
   $= 6k - 4 - 5k + 6 - 3k - 5$
   $= (6 - 5 - 3)k + (-4 + 6 - 5)$
   $= -2k - 3$

57.   Think of this as "the sum of a
   number and 2 minus two times a
   number."

The sum of a number and 2	minus	two times a number.
↓	↓	↓
(x + 2)	-	$2x$

   $(x + 2) - 2x = 2 - x$ *Simplify*

61.   "Nine is multiplied times the sum
   of five times a number and 4" becomes

   $9 \cdot (5x + 4)$ or $45x + 36$.

   "The result, (45x + 36), is subtracted from the difference of 4
   and twice the number"

   $(4 - 2x) - (45x + 36)$
   $= (4 - 2x) - 1(45x + 36)$
   $= 4 - 2x - 45x - 36$
   $= -47x - 32$

65. $-2p + p^2 - p + 4p^2 + 6p^2 + 8p + 1$

$= p^2 + 4p^2 + 6p^2 - 2p - p + 8p + 1$

$= (1 + 4 + 6)p^2 + (-2 - 1 + 8)p + 1$

$= 11p^2 + 5p + 1$

69. $z + 2(5 - z) - (2z + 3) - z^2$

$= z + 10 - 2z - 2z - 3 - z^2$

$= -z^2 + z - 2z - 2z + 10 - 3$

$= -z^2 - 3z + 7$

73.   The additive inverse of -4 is
$-(-4) = 4$.

77.   Since -6 is the additive inverse
of 6, then add -6 to get x.

$-6 + (x + 6) = -6 + x + 6$

$= x - 6 + 6$

$= x$

Section 2.2   (page 66)

1. $x - 3 = 7$

$x - 3 + 3 = 7 + 3$ *Add 3 on*
both sides

$x = 10$

5. $3r - 10 = 2r$

$3r - 10 - 2r = 2r - 2r$ *Subtract 2r*
from both
sides

$r - 10 = 0$

$r - 10 + 10 = 0 + 10$ *Add 10 on*
both sides

$r = 10$

9. $m + 5 = 0$

$m + 5 - 5 = 0 - 5$ *Subtract 5 from*
both sides

$m = -5$

13. $2p + 6 = 10 + p$

$2p + 6 - p = 10 + p - p$ *Subtract p*

$p + 6 = 10$ *Simplify*

$p + 6 - 6 = 10 - 6$ *Subtract 6*

$p = 4$

17. $x - 5 = 2x + 6$

$x - 5 - x = 2x + 6 - x$ *Subtract x*

$-5 = x + 6$

$-5 - 6 = x + 6 - 6$ *Subtract 6*

$-11 = x$

21. $2p = p + \frac{1}{2}$

$2p - p = p + \frac{1}{2} - p$ *Subtract p*

$p = \frac{1}{2}$

25. $-3t + 5t - 6t + 4 - 3 = -3t + 2$

$-4t + 1 = -3t + 2$
Simplify

$-4t + 1 + 4t = -3t + 2 + 4t$
Add 4t

$1 = t + 2$
Simplify

$1 - 2 = t + 2 - 2$
Subtract 2

$-1 = t$

29. $15y - 4y + 8 - 2 + 7 - 4 = 4y + 2 + 8y$

$11y + 9 = 12y + 2$
Simplify

$11y + 9 - 11y = 12y + 2 - 11y$
Subtract 11y

$9 = y + 2$
Simplify

$9 - 2 = y + 2 - 2$
Subtract 2

$7 = y$
Simplify

33.
$$2(k + 5) - 3k = 8$$
$$2(k) + 2(5) - 3k = 8 \quad \textit{Distributive property}$$
$$2k + 10 - 3k = 8$$
$$-k + 10 = 8 \quad \textit{Simplify}$$
$$-k + 10 + k = 8 + k \quad \textit{Add } k$$
$$10 = 8 + k$$
$$10 - 8 = 8 + k - 8 \quad \textit{Subtract 8}$$
$$2 = k$$

37.
$$1(15p - 3) - 2(7p + 1) = -3$$
$$1(15p) + 1(-3) - 2(7p) - 2(1) = -3 \quad \textit{Distributive property}$$
$$15p - 3 - 14p - 2 = -3$$
$$p - 5 = -3 \quad \textit{Simplify}$$
$$p - 5 + 5 = -3 + 5 \quad \textit{Add 5}$$
$$p = 2$$

41.
$$-5(3k - 3) + (1 + 16k) = 2$$
$$-5(3k - 3) + 1(1 + 16k) = 2$$
$$-5(3k) - 5(-3) + 1(1) + 1(16k) = 2 \quad \textit{Distributive property}$$
$$-15k + 15 + 1 + 16k = 2$$
$$k + 16 = 2 \quad \textit{Simplify}$$
$$k + 16 - 16 = 2 - 16 \quad \textit{Subtract 16}$$
$$k = -14$$

45.
$$-5(8 - 2z) + 4(7 - z) = 7(8 + z) - 3$$
$$-5(8) - 5(-2z) + 4(7) + 4(-z) = 7(8) + 7(z) - 3 \quad \textit{Distributive property}$$
$$-40 + 10z + 28 - 4z = 56 + 7z - 3 \quad \textit{Simplify}$$
$$6z - 12 = 53 + 7z$$
$$6z - 12 - 6z = 53 + 7z - 6z \quad \textit{Subtract 6z}$$
$$-12 = 53 + z \quad \textit{Simplify}$$
$$-12 - 53 = 53 + z - 53 \quad \textit{Subtract 53}$$
$$-65 = z$$

49.
$$-2 - \frac{3}{4}y = \frac{1}{4}y$$
$$-2 - \frac{3}{4}y + \frac{3}{4}y = \frac{1}{4}y + \frac{3}{4}y \quad \textit{Add } \frac{3}{4}y$$
$$-2 = y$$

53.
$$2.7a + 5 = 1.7a$$
$$2.7a + 5 - 1.7a = 1.7a - 1.7a \quad \textit{Subtract 1.7a}$$
$$a + 5 = 0 \quad \textit{Simplify}$$
$$a + 5 - 5 = 0 - 5 \quad \textit{Subtract 5}$$
$$a = -5$$

57. "If five times a number is added to three times the number, the result is the sum of seven times the number and 9" becomes

$$5 \cdot x + 3 \cdot x = 7 \cdot x + 9$$
$$5x + 3x = 7x + 9$$
$$8x = 7x + 9$$
$$8x - 7x = 7x + 9 - 7x$$
$$x = 9.$$

The number is 9.

61.
$$3\left(\frac{1}{3}m\right) = \left(3 \cdot \frac{1}{3}\right)m \quad \textit{Associative property}$$
$$= 1m \quad \textit{Inverse property}$$
$$= m$$

65.
$$\frac{-1}{9}(-9q) = \left(\frac{-1}{9}(-9)\right)q \quad \textit{Associative property}$$
$$= 1q \quad \textit{Inverse Property}$$
$$= q$$

Section 2.3 (page 71)

In Exercises 1-53, the answers should be checked by substituting in the original equation.

1.
$$5x = 25$$
$$\frac{5x}{5} = \frac{25}{5} \quad \textit{Divide both sides by 5}$$
$$1x = 5 \quad \textit{Simplify}$$
$$x = 5$$

5. $8s = -56$

$\dfrac{8s}{8} = \dfrac{-56}{8}$ *Divide both sides by 8*

$s = -7$

9. $-18z = 108$

$\dfrac{-18z}{-18} = \dfrac{108}{-18}$ *Divide both sides by -18*

$z = -6$

13. $-y = 6$

$-1 \cdot y = 6$

$(-1)(-1 \cdot y) = -1 \cdot 6$ *Multiply both sides by -1*

$(-1)(-1) \cdot y = -6$

$1y = -6$

$y = -6$

17. $2x + 3x = 20$

$5x = 20$ *Simplify*

$\dfrac{5x}{5} = \dfrac{20}{5}$ *Divide both sides by 5*

$x = 4$

21. $5m + 6m - 2m = 72$

$9m = 72$ *Simplify the left side*

$\dfrac{9m}{9} = \dfrac{72}{9}$ *Divide each side by 9*

$m = 8$

25. $3.5r - 5.8r = 6.9$

$-2.3r = 6.9$ *Simplify*

$\dfrac{-2.3r}{-2.3} = \dfrac{6.9}{-2.3}$ *Divide both sides by -2.3*

$r = -3$

29. $-7y + 8y - 9y = -56$

$-8y = -56$ *Simplify*

$y = 7$ *Divide each side by -8*

33. $\dfrac{2}{3}t = 6$

$\left(\dfrac{3}{2}\right)\left(\dfrac{2}{3}t\right) = \left(\dfrac{3}{2}\right)\left(\dfrac{6}{1}\right)$ *Multiply both sides by 3/2*

$1t = \dfrac{18}{2}$ *Simplify*

$t = 9$

37. $\dfrac{3}{4}p = -60$

$\left(\dfrac{4}{3}\right)\left(\dfrac{3}{4}p\right) = \left(\dfrac{4}{3}\right)\left(\dfrac{-60}{1}\right)$ *Multiply both sides by 4/3*

$1p = \dfrac{-240}{3}$ *Simplify*

$p = -80$

41. $\dfrac{-2}{7}p = -7$

$\left(\dfrac{-7}{2}\right)\left(\dfrac{-2}{7}p\right) = \left(\dfrac{-7}{2}\right)\left(\dfrac{-7}{1}\right)$ *Multiply both sides by -7/2*

$1p = \dfrac{49}{2}$ *Simplify*

$p = \dfrac{49}{2}$

45. $-4.2m = 25.62$

$\dfrac{-4.2m}{-4.2} = \dfrac{25.62}{-4.2}$ *Divide both sides by -4.2*

$1m = \dfrac{25.62}{-4.2}$

$m = -6.1$ *Divide*

49. $-9.273k = 10.2003$

$\dfrac{-9.273k}{-9.273} = \dfrac{10.2003}{-9.273}$ *Divide both sides by -9.273*

$k = -1.1$ *Divide*

53. $-p + 3p - 6 = 7p + 3 - 5 + p$

$2p - 6 = 8p - 2$ *Simplify*

$2p - 6 - 2p = 8p - 2 - 2p$ *Subtract 2p from both sides*

$-6 = 6p - 2$

$-6 + 2 = 6p - 2 + 2$ *Add 2 to both sides*

$-4 = 6p$

$\dfrac{-4}{6} = \dfrac{6p}{6}$ *Divide both sides by 6*

$-\dfrac{4}{6} = p$

$-\dfrac{2}{3} = p$ *Lowest terms*

57. "When a number is multiplied by 4, the result is 6" becomes

$$4x = 6.$$

$$\frac{4x}{4} = \frac{6}{4} \quad \textit{Divide both sides by 4}$$

$$x = \frac{3}{2}$$

The number is 3/2.

61. "Twice a number is divided by 1.74, producing -8.38 as a quotient" becomes

$$\frac{2x}{1.74} = -8.38.$$

$$\frac{2x}{(2)(.87)} = -8.38 \quad \textit{Factor the denominator}$$

$$\frac{x}{.87} = -8.38 \quad \textit{Simplify}$$

$$\frac{1}{.87}x = -8.38 \quad \textit{Definition of division}$$

$$(.87)(\frac{1}{.87})x = (.87)(-8.38) \quad \textit{Multiply both sides by .87}$$

$$x = -7.29 \quad \textit{(rounded)}$$

The number is -7.29.

65. $-4(5p - 1) + 6 = -4(5p) - 4(-1) + 6$
$$= -20p + 4 + 6$$
$$= -20p + 10$$

69. $6 - 3(4a + 3) = 6 - 3(4a) - 3(3)$
$$= 6 - 12a - 9$$
$$= -12a - 3$$

Section 2.4 (page 77)

1. $4h + 8 = 16$
$$4h + 8 - 8 = 16 - 8 \quad \textit{Subtract 8}$$
$$4h = 8$$
$$\frac{4h}{4} = \frac{8}{4} \quad \textit{Divide each side by 4}$$
$$h = 2$$

5. $12p + 18 = 14p$
$$12p + 12p + 18 = -12p + 14p \quad \textit{Subtract 12p}$$
$$18 = 2p$$
$$\frac{18}{2} = \frac{2p}{2} \quad \textit{Divide by 2}$$
$$9 = p$$

9. $2(2r - 1) = -3(r + 3)$
$$4r - 2 = -3 - 9 \quad \textit{Distributive property}$$
$$4r - 2 + 3r = -3r - 9 + 3r$$
$$7r - 2 = -9$$
$$7r - 2 + 2 = 9 + 2 \quad \textit{Add 2}$$
$$7r = -7$$
$$\frac{7r}{7} = \frac{-7}{7} \quad \textit{Divide each side by 7}$$
$$r = -1$$

13. $3(5 + 1.4x) = 3x$
$$15 + 4.2x = 3x \quad \textit{Distributive property}$$
$$15 + 4.2x - 3x = 3x - 3x \quad \textit{Subtract 3x}$$
$$15 + 1.2x = 0$$
$$-15 + 15 + 1.2x = -15 + 0 \quad \textit{Subtract 15}$$
$$1.2x = -15$$
$$\frac{1.2x}{1.2} = \frac{-15}{1.2} \quad \textit{Divide each side by 1.2}$$
$$x = -\frac{15}{1.2}$$
$$x = -12.5$$

17. $.291z + 3.715 = -.874z + 1.9675$
$$.874z + .291z + 3.715 = .874z - .874z + 1.9675 \quad \textit{Add .874z}$$
$$1.165z + 3.715 = 1.9675$$
$$-3.715 + 1.165z + 3.715 = -3.715 + 1.9675 \quad \textit{Subtract 3.715}$$
$$1.165z = -1.7475$$
$$\frac{1.165z}{1.165} = \frac{-1.7475}{1.165} \quad \textit{Divide by 1.165}$$
$$z = -1.5$$

21. $-5k - 8 = 2(k + 6) + 1$

        $-5k - 8 = 2k + 12 + 1$ *Distributive property*

        $-5k - 8 = 2k + 13$ *Simplify*

   $5k - 5k - 8 = 5k + 2k + 13$ *Add 5k*

           $-8 = 7k + 13$ *Simplify*

   $-13 - 8 = -13 + 7k + 13$ *Subtract 13*

       $-21 = 7k$ *Simplify*

      $\dfrac{-21}{7} = \dfrac{7k}{7}$ *Divide by 7*

        $-3 = k$

25. $5(4t + 3) = 6(3t + 2) - 1$

      $20t + 15 = 18t + 12 - 1$ *Distributive property*

      $20t + 15 = 18t + 11$ *Simplify*

  $-18t + 20t + 15 = -18t + 18t + 11$

                 Subtract 18t

       $2t + 15 = 11$

  $-15 + 2t + 15 = -15 + 11$

                 Subtract 15

          $2t = -4$

         $\dfrac{2t}{2} = \dfrac{-4}{2}$ *Divide by 2*

           $t = -2$

29. $-2(3s + 9) - 6 = -3(3s + 11) - 6$

    $-6s - 18 - 6 = -9s - 33 - 6$

        $-6s - 24 = -9s - 39$

  $9s - 6s - 24 = 9s - 9s - 39$

          $3s - 24 = -39$

   $3s - 24 + 24 = -39 + 24$

             $3s = -15$

           $\dfrac{3s}{3} = \dfrac{-15}{3}$

              $s = -5$

33. $3(m - 4) - 1(4m - 11) = -5$

    $3m - 12 - 4m + 11 = -5$

           $-1 - m = -5$

      $1 - 1 - m = 1 - 5$

             $-m = -4$

     $(-1)(-m) = (-1)(-4)$

               $m = 4$

37. $2x + 2(3x + 2) - 9 = 3x - 9 + 3$

     $2x + 6x + 4 - 9 = 3x - 6$

           $8x - 5 = 3x - 6$

    $8x - 5 - 3x = 3x - 6 - 3x$

           $5x - 5 = -6$

     $5x - 5 + 5 = -6 + 5$

             $5x = -1$

          $\dfrac{5x}{5} = \dfrac{-1}{5}$

            $x = \dfrac{-1}{5}$

41. $1.2(x + 5) = 3(2x - 8) + 23.28$

      $1.2x + 6.0 = 6x - 24 + 23.28$

                 Simplify

      $1.2x + 6.0 = 6x - .72$

  $-1.2x + 1.2x + 6.0 = -1.2x + 6x - .72$

                 Subtract 1.2x

         $6.0 = 4.8x - .72$

    $6.0 + .72 = 4.8x - .72 + .72$

                Add .72

        $6.72 = 4.8x$

      $\dfrac{6.72}{4.8} = \dfrac{4.8x}{4.8}$ *Divide by 4.8*

       $\dfrac{6.72}{4.8} = x$

        $1.4 = x$

45. $-3.2(1.4k + .8) - 1(2.97k - .3)$

         $= 1.32(2k - 1.8) - 16.028$

  $-4.48k - 2.56 - 2.97k + .3$

         $= 2.64k - 2.376 - 16.028$

  $-7.45k - 2.26 = 2.64k - 18.404$

  $7.45k - 7.45k - 2.26$

         $= 7.45k + 2.64k - 18.404$

       $-2.26 = 10.09k - 18.404$

  $-2.26 + 18.404 = 10.09k - 18.404 + 18.404$

     $16.144 = 10.09k$

    $\dfrac{16.144}{10.09} = \dfrac{10.09k}{10.09}$

      $1.6 = k$

49.   "-1 added to a number" becomes

$$-1 + x.$$

53.   "5 less than a number" becomes

$$x - 5.$$

57.   "The product of a number and 9" becomes

$$x9 \quad \text{or} \quad 9x.$$

61.   "A number subtracted from its reciprocal" becomes

$$\frac{1}{x} - x.$$

65.   "The product of 8 and the sum of a number and 3" becomes

$$8(x + 3).$$

69.   "Eight times the difference of a number and 8" becomes

$$8(x - 8).$$

73.   The total number of apples is "7 apples + x apples."

$$7 + x$$

77.   The number of five-dollar bills is "The number of dollars divided by 5."

$$\frac{t}{5}$$

Section 2.5 (page 82)

1.   Let x be the number.

6	added to	four times a number	is	42.
↓	↓	↓	↓	↓
6	+	4x	=	42

Solve the equation.

$$6 + 4x = 42$$
$$6 + 4x - 6 = 42 - 6$$
$$4x = 36$$
$$x = 9$$

The number is 9.

5.   Let x be the number.

Twice a number	decreased by	4	is
↓	↓	↓	↓
2x	-	4	=

the number	less	4.
↓	↓	↓
x	-	4

Solve the equation.

$$2x - 4 = x - 4$$
$$2x - 4 - x = x - 4 - x$$
$$x - 4 = -4$$
$$x - 4 + 4 = -4 + 4$$
$$x = 0$$

The number is 0.

9.   Let x be the number of tranquilizer prescriptions. Then 4/3x is the number of prescriptions for antibiotics.

Number of antibiotic prescriptions	and	number of tranquilizer prescriptions
↓	↓	↓
$\frac{4}{3}x$	+	x

is   total
number of
prescriptions.

↓   ↓

=   84

Solve the equation.

$$\frac{4}{3}x + x = 84$$

$$\frac{4}{3}x + \frac{3}{3}x = 84$$

$$\frac{7}{3}x = 84$$

$$\frac{3}{7}(\frac{7}{3}x) = \frac{3}{7}(84)$$

$$x = 36$$

She had 36 prescriptions for tran-
quilizers.

13. Let x be the smaller of two consecutive integers. Let (x + 1)
be the larger.

The smaller integer	added to	three times	the larger
↓	↓	↓	↓
x	+	3 ·	(x + 1)

is   43.

↓   ↓

=   43

Solve.

$$x + 3x + 3 = 43 \quad \textit{Distributive property}$$

$$4x + 3 = 43$$

$$4x + 3 - 3 = 43 - 3$$

$$4x = 40$$

$$\frac{4x}{4} = \frac{40}{4}$$

$$x = 10$$

The smaller integer is 10 and the
larger is 10 + 1 = 11.

17. Let x, x + 2, and x + 4 be the
three odd integers.

9	added to	the largest	equals
↓	↓	↓	↓
9	+	x + 4	=

the sum of the
first and second.

↓

x + (x + 2)

$$x + 13 = 2x + 2$$

$$-x + x + 13 = -x + 2x + 2$$

$$13 = x + 2$$

$$11 = x$$

The integers are 11, 13, and 15.

21. Let x be the first consecutive odd
integer; let x + 2 be the next odd
integer.

The first odd integer	added to	the next odd integer
↓	↓	↓
x	+	x + 2

equals   92.

↓   ↓

=   92

$$2x + 2 = 92$$

$$2x = 90$$

$$x = 45$$

The integers are 45 and 47.

25. Let x be the number.

5 times	the sum of a number and 8	is	60.
↓	↓	↓	↓
5 ·	(x + 8)	=	60

$$5(x + 8) = 60$$
$$5x + 40 = 60$$
$$5x + 40 - 40 = 60 - 40$$
$$5x = 20$$
$$\frac{5x}{5} = \frac{20}{5}$$
$$x = 4$$

The number is 4.

29. Let x be Bob's age now and 3x be Kevin's age now. Then (x - 3) was Bob's age three years ago and (3x - 3) was Kevin's age three years ago.

Bob's age   and   Kevin's age
3 years ago   3 years ago
  ↓   ↓   ↓
 x - 3   +   (3x - 3)

was   22.
 ↓   ↓
 =   22

Solve the equation.

$$x - 3 + (3x - 3) = 22$$
$$4x - 6 = 22$$
$$4x - 6 + 6 = 22 + 6$$
$$4x = 28$$
$$x = 7$$

Bob's age is 7 years now and Kevin's age is 3x = 21 years.

33. Let x be Paula's paycheck before deductions. Then .10x was Paula's deductions.

Paula's   less   deductions
paycheck
  ↓   ↓   ↓
  x   -   .10x

was   585.
 ↓   ↓
 =   585

Solve the equation.

$$1x - .10x = 585$$
$$(1 - .10)x = 585$$
$$.9x = 585$$
$$\frac{.9x}{.9} = \frac{585}{.9}$$
$$x = 650$$

Paula's pay check before deductions was $650.00.

37. Evaluate prt when p = 4000, r = .08, t = 2.

$$prt = (4000)(.08)(2)$$ *Replace variables with values*

$$= 640$$

Section 2.6   (page 89)

1. $V = \frac{1}{3}Bh$

    $V = \frac{1}{3}(20)(9)$ *Let B = 20, h = 9*

    $V = 60$

5. $A = \frac{1}{2}bh$

    $20 = \frac{1}{2}(5)h$ *Let A = 20, b = 5*

    $\frac{2}{5}(20) = \frac{2}{5}\left(\frac{5}{2}\right)h$ *Multiply both sides by 2/5*

    $8 = h$

9. $V = \frac{1}{3}Bh$

    $80 = \frac{1}{3}(24h)$ *Let V = 80, B = 24*

    $80 = 8h$ *Simplify*

    $\frac{80}{8} = \frac{8h}{8}$ *Divide both sides by 8*

    $10 = h$

13.
$$C = 2\pi r$$
$9.42 = 2(3.14)r$ *Let C = 9.42,*
                    π = 3.14

$9.42 = 6.28r$ *Multiply*

$\dfrac{9.42}{6.28} = \dfrac{6.28r}{6.28}$ *Divide by 6.28*

$1.5 = r$

17.
$$V = \frac{4}{3}\pi r^3$$

$V = (\frac{4}{3})(3.14)(3^3)$ *Let r = 3,*
                                π = 3.14

$V = \frac{4}{3}(3.14)(27)$ *Exponent first*

$V = \dfrac{339.12}{3}$ *Multiply*

$V = 113.04$ *Divide*

21.
$$V = LWH$$

$150 = (10)(5H)$ *Let V = 150,*
                   L = 10, W = 5

$150 = 50H$ *Simplify*

$\dfrac{150}{50} = \dfrac{50H}{50}$ *Divide both*
                                      sides by 50

$3 = H$

25.
$$V = \frac{1}{3}r^2h$$

$9.42 = \frac{1}{3}(3.14)(3^2)h$ *Let V = 9.42,*
                                  π = 3.14, r = 3

$9.42 = 9.42h$ *Simplify*

$\dfrac{9.42}{9.42} = \dfrac{9.42h}{9.42}$ *Divide both*
                                             sides by 9.42

$1 = h$

29.
$$V = LWH$$

$\dfrac{V}{LW} = \dfrac{LWH}{LW}$ *Divide both sides by LW*

$\dfrac{V}{LW} = H$

33.
$$P = 2L + 2W$$

$P - 2L = 2W$ *Subtract 2L*

$\dfrac{P - 2L}{2} = W$ *Divide by 2*

$\frac{1}{2}(P - 2L) = W$ *Either form of the*
                           result is correct

$\dfrac{P}{2} - L = W$

37.
$$S = 2\pi rh + 2\pi r^2$$

$S - 2\pi r^2 = 2\pi rh + 2\pi r^2 - 2\pi r^2$
                                   Subtract $2\pi r^2$
                                   from both sides

$S - 2\pi r^2 = 2\pi rh$

$\dfrac{S - 2\pi r^2}{2\pi r} = \dfrac{2\pi rh}{2\pi r}$ *Divide both*
                                                          sides by $2\pi r$

$\dfrac{S - 2\pi r^2}{2\pi r} = h$ *Either form of the*
                                    result is correct

$\dfrac{S}{2\pi r} - r = h$

41.
$$V = \frac{1}{3}\pi r^2 h$$

$V = \frac{1}{3}\pi h r^2$ *Commutative*
                            property

$V = \dfrac{\pi h}{3} r^2$ *Definition*
                            of division

$\dfrac{3}{\pi h}(V) = \dfrac{3}{\pi h}(\dfrac{\pi h}{3})r^2$ *Multiply both*
                                                              sides by 3/πh

$\dfrac{3V}{\pi h} = r^2$

45. To find the width, substitute
     L = 15 and P = 50 in the for-
     mula P = 2L + 2W.

$P = 2L + 2W$

$50 = (2)(15) + 2W$

$50 = 30 + 2W$

$50 - 30 = 30 + 2W - 30$

$20 = 2W$

$\dfrac{20}{2} = \dfrac{2W}{2}$

$10 = W$

The width is 10 inches.

49.
$$y = 6 - 5x$$

$y - 6 = 6 - 5x - 6$ *Subtract 6*
                      from both sides

$y - 6 = -5x$

$\dfrac{y - 6}{-5} = \dfrac{-5x}{-5}$ *Divide by -5*

$-\dfrac{y - 6}{5} = x$

$\dfrac{6 - y}{5} = x$

53.
$$3x - 5y = 15$$
$$3x - 5y + 5y = 15 + 5y \quad \textit{Add 5y to both sides}$$
$$3x = 15 + 5y$$
$$\frac{3x}{3} = \frac{15 + 5y}{3} \quad \textit{Divide by 3}$$
$$x = \frac{15 + 5y}{3}$$
$$x = \frac{5y}{3} + 5 \quad \textit{Either form is correct}$$

57.
$$y = ax + b$$
$$y - b = ax + b - b \quad \textit{Subtract b from both sides}$$
$$y - b = ax$$
$$\frac{y - b}{a} = \frac{ax}{a} \quad \textit{Divide by a}$$
$$\frac{y - b}{a} = x$$

61.
$$6x = 12$$
$$\frac{6x}{6} = \frac{12}{6} \quad \textit{Divide by 6}$$
$$x = 2$$

65.
$$-7z = 15$$
$$\frac{-7z}{-7} = \frac{15}{-7} \quad \textit{Divide by -7}$$
$$z = -\frac{15}{7}$$

Section 2.7 (page 95)

1. $\frac{30}{20} = \frac{3}{2}$

5. $\frac{6}{15} = \frac{2}{5}$

Here, 1 yard = 3 feet, so 5 yards
= (3)(5) = 15 feet.

9. $\frac{12}{120} = \frac{1}{10}$

Here, 1 hour = 60 minutes,
so 2 hours = (60)(2)
= 120 minutes.

13. $\frac{20}{120} = \frac{1}{6}$

Here, 1 day = 24 hours,
so   5 days = (24)(5)
= 120 hours.

17. $\frac{4}{7} = \frac{12}{21}$

(4)(21) = (7)(12)   *Find the cross products*

84 = 84

True

21. $\frac{7}{10} = \frac{82}{120}$

(7)(120) = (10)(82)   *Find the cross products*

840 = 820

False

25. $\frac{.612}{1.05} = \frac{1.0404}{1.785}$

(.612)(1.785) = (1.05)(1.0404)   *Find the cross products*

1.09242 = 1.09242

True

29. $\frac{35}{4} = \frac{k}{20}$

(35)(20) = (4)(k)   *Find the cross products*

700 = 4k

175 = k

33. $\frac{z}{80} = \frac{20}{100}$

(z)(100) = (80)(20)   *Find the cross products*

100z = 1600

z = 16

37.
$$\frac{5}{9} = \frac{z}{15}$$

$(5)(15) = (9)(z)$ *Find the cross products*

$75 = 9z$

$\frac{25}{3} = z$

41.
$$\frac{m}{m - 3} = \frac{5}{3}$$

$(m)(3) = (m - 3)(5)$ *Find the cross products*

$3m = 5m - 15$

$15 = 2m$

$\frac{15}{2} = m$

45.   Let x be the number of bars.

$$\frac{x \text{ bars}}{500 \text{ calories}} = \frac{1 \text{ bar}}{200 \text{ calories}}$$

Solve the equation.

$$\frac{x}{500} = \frac{1}{200}$$

$(x)(200) = (500)(1)$

$200x = 500$

$x = \frac{5}{2}$ or $2\frac{1}{2}$

You would need to eat 2 1/2 bars.

49.   Let x be the number of inches.

$$\frac{x \text{ inches}}{24 \text{ miles}} = \frac{3 \text{ inches}}{8 \text{ miles}}$$

Solve the equation.

$$\frac{x}{24} = \frac{3}{8}$$

$(x)(8) = (24)(3)$

$8x = 72$

$x = 9$

9 inches would represent 24 miles.

53.   Let x be the distance in miles.

$$\frac{x \text{ miles}}{15 \text{ inches}} = \frac{308 \text{ miles}}{11 \text{ inches}}$$

Solve the equation.

$$\frac{x}{15} = \frac{308}{11}$$

$(x)(11) = (15)(308)$

$11x = 4620$

$x = 420$

The two cities are 420 miles apart.

57.
$$\frac{3y - 2}{6y - 5} = \frac{5}{11}$$

$(11)(3y - 2) = (5)(6y - 5)$ *Find the cross products*

$33y - 22 = 30y - 25$ *Distributive property*

$3y - 22 = -25$ *Subtract 30y*

$3y = -3$ *Add 22*

$y = -1$ *Divide by 3*

61.   Let x be the amount needed for 8 dresses. Then the amount of material needed for 5 dresses is x - 7.2. Then

$$\frac{x \text{ yards}}{8 \text{ dresses}} = \frac{x - 7.2 \text{ yards}}{5 \text{ dresses}}$$

Solve the equation.

$$\frac{x}{8} = \frac{x - 7.2}{5}$$

$5x = (8)(x - 7.2)$

$5x = 8x - 57.6$

$-3x = -57.6$

$x = 19.2$

19.2 yards are need for 8 dresses.

65. To find the speed, substitute
d = 520, t = 13 in the formula
d = rt.

$$d = rt$$
$$520 = (r)(13)$$
$$40 = r$$

Tom travels at a speed of 40 miles per hour.

Section 2.8 (page 101)

1. Let s represent the length of a side.

Perimeter	is	seven times a side
↓	↓	↓
P	=	7s

decreased
   by
    ↓
   - 12,

or 7s - 12 = P. The perimeter of a square is given by P = 4s, so

$$7s - 12 = 4s.$$
$$7s - 4s - 12 = 4s - 4s$$
$$4s - 12 = 0$$
$$3s - 12 + 12 = 0 + 12$$
$$3s = 12$$
$$s = 4$$

The length of a side is 4.

5. Let r represent the radius of the circle. The formula for the circumference of a circle is C = 2πr.

Radius tripled	plus	8.2 cm added	is
↓	↓	↓	↓
3r	+	8.2	=

the
circumference.
    ↓
    C

Since C = 2πr,

$$3r + 8.2 = 2\pi r$$
$$3r + 8.2 = 2(3.14)r$$
$$3r + 8.2 = 6.28r$$
$$8.2 = 3.28r$$
$$2.5 = r.$$

The radius of the circle is 2.5 centimeters.

9. Let x be the number of 16¢ stamps. Then the number of 29¢ stamps is x + 2. The cost of the stamps is found by multiplying the value of the stamp by the number of stamps purchased.

Cost of 16¢ stamps	plus	cost of 29¢ stamps
↓	↓	↓
.16x	+	.29(x + 2)

is	total cost of the stamps.
↓	↓
=	8.68

$$.16x + .29x + .58 = 8.68$$
$$.45x + .58 = 8.68$$
$$.45x = 8.1$$
$$x = 18$$

He bought 18 16¢ stamps.

13. Let x = amount invested at 16%. Then x + 4000 = amount invested at 12%. The formula for simple interest is I = prt. Since the money was deposited for a year, t = 1. So

interest at 16% = I
$$= (x)(.16)(1) = .16x$$
interest at 12% = I
$$= (x + 4000)(.12)(1)$$
$$= .12x + 480.$$

The total interest is $3840.

Interest at 16%	plus	interest at 12%
↓	↓	↓
.16x	+	.12x + 480

is	total interest
↓	↓
=	3840

$$.28x + 480 = 3840$$
$$.28x = 3360$$
$$x = 12000$$

She invested $12,000 at 16%.

17. Let t represent the unknown number of hours. Use the formula d = rt to calculate the different distances.

Train	r	t	d
Northbound	60	t	60t
Southbound	80	t	80t

Distance traveled by Northbound train	plus
↓	↓
60t	+

distance traveled by Southbound train	is	280.
↓	↓	↓
80t	=	280

Solve the equation.

$$60t + 80t = 280$$
$$140t = 280$$
$$t = 2$$

In 2 hours, the trains will be 280 miles apart.

21. Let x = the number of gallons of 50% solution needed.

Strength	Gallons of solution	gallons pure antifreeze
50%	x	.05x
20%	80	16
40%	x + 80	.40x + 32

Pure antifreeze in 50% solution	plus	pure antifreeze in 20% solution
↓	↓	↓
.50x	+	16

is	pure antifreeze in 40% solution
↓	↓
=	.40x + 32

$$.10x + 16 = 32$$
$$.10x = 16$$
$$x = 160$$

Mix 160 gallons of 50% antifreeze.

25. Let x represent the number of days she can spend.

The cost for tickets = 15x.

The cost for lodging and meals = 60x.

She has only $281 to cover all costs, and transportation is $56.

Cost for tickets	plus	cost for lodging and meals
↓	↓	↓
15x	+	60x

plus	cost for transportation	equals
↓	↓	↓
+	56	=

amount available for trip.
↓
281

Solve the equation.

$$15x + 60x + 56 = 281$$
$$75x + 56 = 281$$
$$75x = 225$$
$$x = 3$$

She can spend 3 days at Disney-
land.

29. Let x represent the shortest side
of the triangle, then the medium
side is x + 2, and the longest
side is x + 5. The formula for
the perimeter of a triangle is

$$P = a + b + c.$$

$$55 = x + x + 2 + x + 5$$
Let P = 55, a = x,
b = a + 2, c = x + 5
$$55 = 3x + 7$$
$$55 - 7 = 3x + 7 - 7$$
$$48 = 3x$$
$$16 = x$$

The shortest side is 16 meters;
the medium side is 16 + 2 = 18
meters; and the longest side is
16 + 5 = 21 meters.

33. Let W represent the width of the
rectangle. Then the length L is
(8 + W).

$$P = 2L + 2W$$
$$P = 2(8 + W) + 2W$$

Perimeter	is	6	more than
↓	↓	↓	↓
2(8 + W) + 2W	=	6	+

five times
the width.
↓
5W

Solve the equation.

$$16 + 2W + 2W = 6 + 5W$$
$$16 + 4W = 6 + 5W$$
$$16 = 6 + W$$
$$10 = W$$

The width of the rectangle is 10
inches.

37. $-7 < 3$

41. $-8 > -10$

Section 2.9 (page 112)

1. The statement $x \leq 4$ says that x
can represent any number less
than or equal to 4. To show this
on a graph, place a dot at 4 and
draw an arrow to the left.
See answer graph in textbook.

5. The statement $-2 \leq x \leq 5$ is read
"-2 is less than or equal to x
and x is less than or equal to 5."
Then draw a line segment between
the two dots.
See answer graph in textbook.

9. $$a + 6 < 8$$
$$a + 6 - 6 < 8 - 6 \quad \textit{Subtract 6}$$
$$a < 2$$

13. $$-3 + k \geq 2$$
$$-3 + k + 3 \geq 2 + 3 \quad \textit{Add 3}$$
$$k \geq 5$$

17. $$-2k \leq 12$$
$$k \geq -6 \quad \textit{Divide by -2;}$$
$$\textit{symbol reversed}$$

21.
$$3n + 5 \le 2n - 6$$
$$3n + 5 - 2n \le 2n - 6 - 2n \quad \textit{Subtract } 2n$$
$$n + 5 \le -6$$
$$n + 5 - 5 \le -6 - 5 \quad \textit{Subtract 5}$$
$$n \le -11$$

See anwer graph in textbook.

25.
$$4k + 1 \ge 2k - 9$$
$$4k + 1 - 2k \ge 2k - 9 - 2k \quad \textit{Subtract 2k}$$
$$2k - 1 \ge -9$$
$$2k + 1 - 1 \ge -9 - 1 \quad \textit{Subtract 1}$$
$$2k \ge -10$$
$$\frac{2k}{2} \ge \frac{-10}{2} \quad \textit{Divide by 2, do not reverse symbol}$$
$$k \ge -5$$

See answer graph in textbook.

29.
$$4q + 1 - \frac{5}{3} < 8q + \frac{4}{3}$$
$$4q + \frac{3}{3} - \frac{5}{3} < 8q + \frac{4}{3}$$
$$4q - \frac{2}{3} < 8q + \frac{4}{3} \quad \textit{Simplify}$$
$$-4q - \frac{2}{3} < \frac{4}{3} \quad \textit{Subtract 8q}$$
$$-4q < \frac{6}{3} \text{ or } 2 \quad \textit{Add 2/3}$$
$$\frac{-4q}{-4} > \frac{2}{-4} \quad \textit{Divide by -4; symbol reversed}$$
$$q > -\frac{1}{2}$$

See anwer graph in textbook.

33.
$$-k + 4 + 5k \le -1 + 3k + 5$$
$$4k + 4 \le 3k + 4 \quad \textit{Simplify}$$
$$4k + 4 - 3k \le 3k + 4 - 3k \quad \textit{Subtract 3k}$$
$$k + 4 \le 4$$
$$k + 4 - 4 \le 4 - 4 \quad \textit{Subtract 4}$$
$$k \le 0$$

See anwer graph in textbook.

37.
$$-5 \le 2x - 3 \le 9$$
$$-5 + 3 \le 2x - 3 + 3 \le 9 + 3 \quad \textit{Add 3}$$
$$-2 \le 2x \le 12$$
$$\frac{-2}{2} \le \frac{2x}{2} \le \frac{12}{2} \quad \textit{Divide by 2}$$
$$-1 \le x \le 6$$

See answer graph in textbook.

41.
$$-1 \le 1 - 5q \le 16$$
$$-1 - 1 \le 1 - 5q - 1 \le 16 - 1 \quad \textit{Subtract 1}$$
$$-2 \le -5q \le 15 \quad \textit{Simplify}$$
$$\frac{-2}{-5} \ge \frac{-5q}{-5} \ge \frac{15}{-5} \quad \textit{Divide by -5; symbol reversed}$$
$$\frac{2}{5} \ge q \ge -3 \quad \textit{Simplify}$$
$$-3 \le q \le \frac{2}{5} \quad \textit{Rewrite with inequality symbols pointing left}$$

See answer graph in textbook.

45.
$$1 \le 3 + \frac{2}{3}p \le 7$$
$$1 - 3 \le 3 + \frac{2}{3}p - 3 \le 7 - 3 \quad \textit{Subtract 3}$$
$$-2 \le \frac{2}{3}p \le 4$$
$$\left(\frac{3}{2}\right)(-2) \le \left(\frac{3}{2}\right)\left(\frac{2}{3}p\right) \le \left(\frac{3}{2}\right)(4) \quad \textit{Multiply by 3/2}$$
$$-3 \le p \le 6$$

See answer graph in textbook.

49. Let x be the number. Then

one-half added to a number		is greater than or equal to
↓	↓ ↓	↓
$\frac{1}{2}x$	+ 5	$\ge$

$$-3.$$
↓
$$-3$$

Solve the inequality.

$$\frac{1}{2}x \geq -8$$

$$2\left(\frac{1}{2}\right)x \geq -8 \cdot 2$$

$$x \geq -16$$

Any number greater than or equal to -16 satisfies the condition.

53. Let x represent the score on the third test. To get an average of 80 or higher, the sum of all three scores divided by 3 must be greater than or equal to 80, or

sum of all three scores divided by 3	is greater than or equal to	80.
↓	↓	↓
$\frac{x + 75 + 82}{3}$	$\geq$	80

Solve the inequality.

$$3 \cdot \left(\frac{x + 157}{3}\right) \geq 80 \cdot 3$$

$$x + 157 \geq 240$$

$$x \geq 83$$

He must score greater than or equal to 83 on the third test to get an average of 80 or higher.

57. Let x be the employee's earnings during the fifth month. To average at least $1000 the sum of the five months earnings divided by 5 must be greater than or equal to 1000.

Sum of the five months divide by 5	is	1000.
↓	↓	↓
$\frac{900 + 1200 + 1040 + 760 + x}{5}$	$\geq$	1000

$$\frac{3900 + x}{5} \geq 1000$$

$$3900 + x \geq 5000$$

$$x \geq 1100$$

The employee must earn at least $1100 the fifth month.

61. $2(x - 5) + 3x < 4(x - 6) + 3$
$2x - 10 + 3x < 4x - 24 + 3$ *Distributive property*
$5x - 10 < 4x - 21$ *Simplify*
$x - 10 < 21$ *Subtract 4x*
$x < -11$ *Add 10*

65. $3(p+1) - 2(p-4) \geq 5(2p-3) + 2$
$3p + 3 - 2p + 8 \geq 10p - 15 + 2$ *Distributive property*
$p + 11 \geq 10p - 13$ *Simplify*
$-9p + 11 \geq -13$ *Subtract 10p*
$-9p \geq -24$ *Subtract 11*
$p \leq \frac{24}{9}$ *Divide by -9; symbol reversed*
$p \leq \frac{8}{3}$ *Lowest terms*

69. $5 \cdot 5 \cdot 5 \cdot 5 = 625$

73. $(2 \cdot 2 \cdot 2)(2 \cdot 2 \cdot 2 \cdot 2) = (8)(16) = 128$

77. $3 - (-2) = 3 + 2 = 5$

81. $-2 - [-4 - (3 - 2)]$
$= -2 - [-4 - (1)]$
$= -2 - [-4 + (-1)]$
$= -2 - [-5]$
$= -2 + 5$
$= 3$

Chapter 2 Review Exercises   (page 115)

1. $2m + 9m = (2 + 9)m$ *Distributive property*

$\qquad = 11m$

5. $7(2m + 3) - 2(8m - 4)$

$\qquad = 14m + 21 - 16m + 8$

$\qquad\qquad\qquad$ *Distributive property*

$\qquad = -2m + 29$

9. $\qquad 3k + 1 = 2k + 8$

$3k + 1 - 2k = 2k + 8 - 2k$

$\qquad\qquad\qquad$ *Subtract 2k*

$\qquad k + 1 = 8$

$k + 1 - 1 = 8 - 1$ *Subtract*

$\qquad\qquad k = 7$

13. $7k = 35$

$\dfrac{7k}{7} = \dfrac{35}{7}$ *Divide by 7*

$\qquad k = 5$

17. $\qquad \dfrac{5}{8}k = 8$

$\dfrac{8}{5}\left(\dfrac{5}{8}k\right) = \dfrac{8}{5}(8)$ *Multiply by 8/5*

$\qquad\qquad k = \dfrac{64}{5}$

21. Let x be the number.

Twice a number less 4 is 8.

$\quad\downarrow\qquad\qquad\quad\downarrow\quad\downarrow\;\;\downarrow$

$\quad 2x \qquad\qquad - \quad 4 \;\; = \;\; 8$

Solve the equation.

$\qquad 2x - 4 = 8$

$\quad 2x - 4 + 4 = 8 + 4$

$\qquad\quad 2x = 12$

$\qquad\quad \dfrac{2x}{2} = \dfrac{12}{2}$

$\qquad\qquad x = 6$

The number is 6.

25. $A = \dfrac{1}{2}bh$

$22 = \dfrac{1}{2}(4)h$ *Substitute A = 22, b = 4*

$22 = 2h$

$\dfrac{22}{2} = \dfrac{2h}{2}$ *Divide by 2*

$11 = h$

29. $A = LW$

$\dfrac{A}{L} = \dfrac{LW}{L}$ *Divide by L*

$\dfrac{A}{L} = W$

33. $\dfrac{45}{60} = \dfrac{3}{4}$

Here, since 1 foot = 12 inches,
5 feet = (5)(12) = 60 inches.

37. $\dfrac{38}{51} = \dfrac{722}{1020}$

$38(1020) = 51(722)$ *Cross products*

$38{,}760 = 36{,}822$

False

41. Let x represent the distance between towns that are 1.5 centimeters apart.

$\dfrac{x \text{ miles}}{1.5 \text{ centimeters}} = \dfrac{520 \text{ miles}}{2.6 \text{ centimeters}}$

$2.6x = 780$ *cross products*

$x = 300$ *Divide by 2.6*

The towns are 300 miles apart.

45. Let x = the number of five-dollar bills.
Then 2x = the number of ten-dollar bills.

Value of plus value of
the fives   the tens

$\quad\downarrow\qquad\quad\downarrow\qquad\quad\downarrow$

$\quad 5x \qquad + \qquad 10(2x)$

is $200.

$\downarrow\qquad\downarrow$

$=\qquad 200$

$$5x + 20x = 250$$
$$25x = 250$$
$$x = 10$$

The person has ten five-dollar bills.

49. The statement $m \geq -2$ says that m can represent any number greater than or equal to -2. To show this on a graph, place a dot at -2 and draw an arrow to the right. See the graph given with the answers in the textbooks.

53. $y + 5 \geq 2$
$y + 5 - 5 \geq 2 - 5$ *Subtract 5*
$y \geq -3$

57. $-6 \leq x + 2 \leq 0$
$-6 - 2 \leq x + 2 - 2 \leq 0 - 2$
                          Subtract 2
$-8 \leq x \leq -2$

61. $2 - 4p + 7p + 8 < 6p - 5p$
$3p + 10 < p$ *Simplify*
$2p + 10 < 0$ *Subtract p*
$2p < -10$ *Subtract 10*
$p < -5$ *Divide by 2*

65. $\dfrac{y}{y - 5} = \dfrac{7}{2}$

$(y)(2) = (y - 5)(7)$ *Find the cross products*

$2y = 7y - 35$
$2y - 2y = 7y - 35 - 2y$ *Subtract 2y*
$0 = 5y - 35$
$0 + 35 = 5y - 35 + 35$ *Add 35*
$35 = 5y$
$7 = y$

69. $2k - 5 = 4k + 7$
$-5 = 2k + 7$ *Subtract 2k*
$-12 = 2k$ *Subtract 7*
$-6 = k$ *Divide by 2*

73. Let x be the number of quarts of oil.

$$\frac{1 \text{ quart}}{24 \text{ quarts}} = \frac{x \text{ quarts}}{192 \text{ quarts}}$$

Solve the equation.

$\dfrac{1}{24} = \dfrac{x}{192}$

$1(192) = 24(x)$ *Cross products*

$192 = 24x$

$\dfrac{192}{24} = \dfrac{24x}{24}$ *Divide by 24*

$8 = x$

The amount of oil needed is 8 quarts.

77. Let s be the length of a side. The formula for the perimeter of a square is $P = 4s$.

The perimeter	cannot be greater than	200.
↓	↓	↓
$4s$	$\leq$	200

Solve the inequality.

$4s \leq 200$

$\dfrac{4s}{4} \leq \dfrac{200}{4}$

$s \leq 50$

The greatest possible length is 50 meters.

81. Let x represent the amount in-
    vested at 5%. Then the amount
    invested at 10% is 6000 + x.
    The formula for simple interest
    is I = prt.

    Interest   plus   interest
      at 5%   at 10%
        ↓   ↓   ↓
    x(.05)(1)   + (6000+x)(.10)(1)

    is   2100.
     ↓   ↓
    =   2100

    Solve the equation.

    .05x + .10(6000 + x) = 2100
      .05x + 600 + .10x = 2100
           .15x + 600 = 2100
     .15x + 600 - 600 = 2100 - 600
                 .15x = 1500
                    x = 10,000

    $10,000 is invested at 5% and
    $16,000 is invested at 10%.

Chapter 2 Test (page 118)

1. 9r + 3r - 4r - r - 8r
    = (9 + 3 - 4 - 1 - 8)r
                    Distributive
                    property
    = -r

2. 3z - 7z + 8 - 9 - (-5) + 4z
    = (3 - 7 + 4)z + 8 - 9 + 5
                    Distributive
                    property
    = 4

3. 4(2m - 1) - (m + 5) - 3(m - 5)
    = 8m - 4 - m - 5 - 3m + 15
                    Distributive
                    property
    = 4m + 6

4.   3(a + 12) = 1 - 2(a - 5)
        3a + 36 = 1 - 2a + 10
                    Distributive
                    property
        3a + 36 = 11 - 2a
     3a + 36 + 2a = 11 - 2a + 2a   *Add 2a*
        5a + 36 = 11
     5a + 36 - 36 = 11 = 36   *Subtract 36*
             5a = -25
          $\frac{5a}{5} = \frac{-25}{5}$ *Divide by 5*
              a = -5

5. 4k - 6k + 8(k - 3) = -2(k + 12)
    4k - 6k + 8k - 24 = -2k - 24
                    Distributive
                    property
        6k - 24 = -2k - 24
    6k - 24 + 2k = -2k - 24 + 2k
                    Add 2k
        8k - 24 = -24
    8k - 24 + 24 = -24 + 24
                    Add 24
             8k = 0
          $\frac{8k}{8} = \frac{0}{8}$ *Divide by 8*
              k = 0

6. $\frac{5}{4}m = -3$
    $(\frac{4}{5})(\frac{5}{4}m) = (\frac{4}{5})(-3)$ *Multiply by 4/5*
              $m = \frac{-12}{5}$

7. $\frac{1}{2}p + \frac{1}{3} = \frac{5}{2}p - \frac{4}{3}$
    $\frac{1}{2}p + \frac{1}{3} - \frac{5}{2}p = \frac{5}{2}p - \frac{4}{3} - \frac{5}{2}p$
                    Subtract 5/2p
        $-2p + \frac{1}{3} = \frac{-4}{3}$
    $-2p + \frac{1}{3} - \frac{1}{3} = \frac{-4}{3} - \frac{1}{3}$ *Subtract 1/3*
             $-2p = \frac{-5}{3}$
    $(-\frac{1}{2})(-2p) = (-\frac{1}{2})(\frac{-5}{3})$ *Multiply by -1/2*
              $p = \frac{5}{6}$

8. $-(y + 3) + 2y - 5 = 4 - 3y$

   $-y - 3 + 2y - 5 = 4 - 3y$ *Distributive property*

   $y - 8 = 4 - 3y$

   $y - 8 + 3y = 4 - 3y + 3y$ *Add 3y*

   $4y - 8 = 4$

   $4y - 8 + 8 = 4 + 8$ *Add 8*

   $4y = 12$

   $\dfrac{4y}{4} = \dfrac{12}{4}$ *Divide by 4*

   $y = 3$

9. Let x represent the number.

   4 minus 3 times the number
   ↓   ↓   ↓
   4 -   3x

   gives a result | 20 | more than | the number.
   ↓ | ↓ | ↓ | ↓
   = | 20 | + | x

   Solve the equation.

   $4 - 3x = 20 + x$

   $4 - 3x - x = 20 + x - x$

   $4 - 4x = 20$

   $4 - 4x - 4 = 20 - 4$

   $-4x = 16$

   $\dfrac{-4x}{-4} = \dfrac{16}{-4}$

   $x = -4$

   The number is −4.

10. Let x represent the cost for the tune-up on the Oldsmobile. Then the cost for the tune-up on the Bronco is 57 + x.

    Tune-up cost plus | tune-up cost
    Oldsmobile | Bronco
    ↓ | ↓ | ↓
    x | + | (57 + x)

    is 257.
    ↓ | ↓
    = | 257

Solve the equation.

$x + (57 + x) = 257$

$2x + 57 = 257$

$2x + 57 - 57 = 257 - 57$

$2x = 200$

$\dfrac{2x}{2} = \dfrac{200}{2}$

$x = 100$

It costs $100 for the tune-up on the Oldsmobile.

11. $V = LWH$

    $\dfrac{V}{LH} = \dfrac{LWH}{LH}$ *Divide by LH*

    $\dfrac{V}{LH} = W$

12. $A = \dfrac{1}{2}(b + B)h$

    $2A = 2(\dfrac{1}{2})(b + B)h$ *Multiply by 2*

    $2A = (b + B)h$ *Simplify*

    $2A = bh + BH$ *Distributive property*

    $2A - Bh = bh$ *Subtract Bh*

    $\dfrac{2A - Bh}{h} = b$ *Divide by h*

13. $\dfrac{15}{79} = \dfrac{465}{2449}$

    $15(2449) = 79(465)$ *Cross products*

    $36,735 = 36,735$

    True

14. $\dfrac{z}{16} = \dfrac{3}{48}$

    $z(48) = 16(3)$ *Cross products*

    $48z = 48$

    $\dfrac{48z}{48} = \dfrac{48}{48}$ *Divide by 48*

    $z = 1$

15.
$$\frac{y + 5}{y - 2} = \frac{1}{4}$$

$$(y + 5)(4) = (y - 2)(1)$$
Cross products

$$4y + 20 = y - 2$$
Distributive property

$$4y + 20 - y = y - 2 - y$$
Subtract y

$$3y + 20 = -2$$

$$3y + 20 - 20 = -2 - 20 \quad \textit{Subtract 20}$$

$$3y = -22$$

$$y = -\frac{22}{3} \quad \textit{Divide by 3}$$

16. Let x = be the cost of 32 hamburgers. Then

$$\frac{11 \text{ hamburgers}}{\$6.05} = \frac{32 \text{ hamburgers}}{\$x}.$$

Solve the equation.

$$\frac{11}{6.05} = \frac{32}{x}$$

$$11(x) = 6.05(32) \quad \textit{Cross products}$$

$$11x = 193.6$$

$$\frac{11x}{11} = \frac{193.6}{11} \quad \textit{Divide by 11}$$

$$x = 17.6$$

The cost is $17.60.

17. Let x represent the number of tens. Then the number of twenties is 10 + x.

Value of plus value of is $800.
  tens   twenties

$$10x \qquad + \qquad 20(10 + x) \qquad = \qquad 800$$

Solve the equation.

$$10x + 20(10 + x) = 800$$

$$10x + 200 + 20x = 800$$

$$30x + 200 = 800$$

$$30x + 200 - 200 = 800 - 200$$

$$30x = 600$$

$$\frac{30x}{30} = \frac{600}{30}$$

$$x = 20$$

There are 20 ten dollar bills.

18. Let t represent the time when the trains will be 360 miles apart. The formula for distance is d = rt.

Distance covered   plus
  by train A

$$50t \qquad\qquad\qquad +$$

distance covered   is   360.
  by train B

$$70t \qquad\qquad = \qquad 360$$

Solve the equation.

$$50t + 70t = 360$$

$$120t = 360$$

$$\frac{120t}{120} = \frac{360}{120}$$

$$t = 3$$

The trains will be 360 miles apart in 3 hours.

19. Let x represent the amount invested at 12%. Then the amount invested at 15% is 6000 + x. The formula for simple interest is I = prt.

Interest   plus   interest
  at 12%   at 15%

$$x(.12)(1) \quad + \quad (6000 + x)(.15)(1)$$

is $3870.

$$= \qquad 3870$$

Solve the equation.

$$.12x + .15(6000 + x) = 3870$$

$$.12x + 900 + .15x = 3870$$

$$.27x + 900 = 3870$$

$$.27x + 900 - 900 = 3870 - 900$$

$$.27x = 2970$$

$$\frac{.27x}{.27} = \frac{2970}{.27}$$

$$x = 11,000$$

The amount invested at 12% is $11,000.

20. Let x represent the number of liters of the 20% solution. Then the number of liters of the 50% mixture is x + 30.

Pure chemical solution in 20% solution	plus	pure chemical solution in 60% solution
↓	↓	↓
.20x	+	.60(30)

is	pure chemical solution in 50% solution.
↓	↓
=	.50(x + 30)

Solve the equation.

$$.20x + .60(30) = .50(x + 30)$$
$$.20x + 18 = .50x + 15$$
$$.20x + 18 - .50x = .50x + 15 - .50x$$
$$-.30x + 18 = 15$$
$$-.30x + 18 - 18 = 15 - 18$$
$$-.30x = -3$$
$$\frac{-.30x}{-.30} = \frac{-3}{-.30}$$
$$x = 10$$

10 liters of the 20% solution are needed.

21. $-2m < -14$

$$\frac{-2m}{-2} > \frac{-14}{-2} \quad \textit{Divide by -2 and reverse symbol}$$
$$m > 7$$

See the graph in the textbook.

22. $5(k - 2) + 3 \leq 2(k - 3) + 2k$

$$5k - 10 + 3 \leq 2k - 6 + 2k \quad \textit{Distributive property}$$
$$5k - 7 \leq 4k - 6$$
$$5k - 7 - 4k \leq 4k - 6 - 4k \quad \textit{Subtract 4k}$$
$$k - 7 \leq -6$$
$$k - 7 + 7 \leq -6 + 7 \quad \textit{Add 7}$$
$$k \leq 1$$

See the graph in the textbook.

23. $-4r + 2(r - 3) \geq 5r - (3 + 6r) - 7$

$$-4r + 2r - 6 \geq 5r - 3 - 6r + -7 \quad \textit{Distributive property}$$
$$-2r - 6 \geq -r - 10$$
$$-2r - 6 + r \geq -r - 10 + r \quad \textit{Add r}$$
$$-r - 6 \geq -10$$
$$-r - 6 + 6 \geq -10 + 6 \quad \textit{Add 6}$$
$$-r \geq -4$$
$$(-1)(-r) \leq (-1)(-4) \quad \textit{Multiply by -1 and reverse symbol}$$
$$r \leq 4$$

See the graph in the textbook.

24. $-8 < 3k - 2 \leq 12$

$$-8 + 2 < 3k - 2 + 2 \leq 12 + 2 \quad \textit{Add 2}$$
$$-6 < 3k \leq 14$$
$$\frac{-6}{3} < \frac{3k}{3} \leq \frac{14}{3} \quad \textit{Divide by 3}$$
$$-2 < k \leq \frac{14}{3}$$

See the graph in the textbook.

CHAPTER 3   EXPONENTS AND POLYNOMIALS
Section 3.1   (page 124)

1. In 5^{12}, 5 is the base.   The expo-
    nent is 12.

5. In $(-24)^2$, since -24 is in paren-
    theses under the exponent, -24 is
    the base, with exponent 2.

9. $3 \cdot 3 \cdot 3 \cdot 3 \cdot 3$
    3 is a factor 5 times, so 3 is the
    base with 5 the exponent: 3^5.

13. $\dfrac{1}{(-2)(-2)(-2)}$

    In the denominator, -2 is a factor
    3 times so we have $\dfrac{1}{(-2)^3}$.

17. $\dfrac{1}{y \cdot y \cdot y \cdot y}$

    Since y is a factor 4 times, we
    have $\dfrac{1}{y^4}$.

21. $\begin{aligned} 3^2 + 3^4 &= 3 \cdot 3 + 3 \cdot 3 \cdot 3 \cdot 3 \\ &= 9 + 81 \\ &= 90 \end{aligned}$

25. $\begin{aligned} 2^2 + 2^5 &= 2 \cdot 2 + 2 \cdot 2 \cdot 2 \cdot 2 \cdot 2 \\ &= 4 + 32 \\ &= 36 \end{aligned}$

29. $\begin{aligned} 4^2 \cdot 4^3 &= 4^{2+3} \quad \textit{Add exponents} \\ &= 4^5 \\ &= 1024 \end{aligned}$

33. $4^3 \cdot 4^5 \cdot 4^{10} = 4^{3+5+10} = 4^{18}$

37. $\begin{aligned} y^3 \cdot y^4 \cdot y^7 &= y^{3+4+7} \\ &= y^{14} \end{aligned}$

41. $\begin{aligned} (-9r^3)(7r^6) &= -9 \cdot 7 \cdot r^3 \cdot r^6 \\ &= -63r^{3+6} \\ &= -63r^9 \end{aligned}$

45. $\begin{aligned} 4m^3 + 9m^3 &= (4 + 9)m^3 \\ &= 13m^3 \\ (4m^3)(9m^3) &= (4 \cdot 9)m^{3+3} \\ &= 36m^6 \end{aligned}$

49. $\begin{aligned} 7r + 3r + 5r &= (7 + 3 + 5)r \\ &= 15r \\ (7r)(3r)(5r) &= (7 \cdot 3 \cdot 5)r^{1+1+1} \\ &= 105r^3 \end{aligned}$

53. $\begin{aligned} (6^3)^2 &= 6^{3 \cdot 2} \quad \textit{Use the power rule} \\ &= 6^6 \end{aligned}$

57. $\begin{aligned} (-5^2)^4 &= (-1 \cdot 5^2)^4 \quad \textit{Exponent 2 refers only to base 5} \\ &= (-1)^4 \cdot)5^2)^4 \quad \textit{Use the power rule} \\ &= 1 \cdot 5^{2 \cdot 4} \quad \textit{Use the power rule} \\ &= 1 \cdot 5^8 = 5^8 \end{aligned}$

61. $\begin{aligned} (5m)^3 &= (5^1 m^1)^3 \\ &= 5^{1 \cdot 3} m^{1 \cdot 3} \quad \textit{Use the power rule} \\ &= 5^3 m^3 \quad \text{or} \quad 125m^3 \end{aligned}$

65. $\begin{aligned} \left(\dfrac{-3x^5}{4}\right)^2 &= \dfrac{(-3)^2 (x^5)^2}{4^2} \\ &= \dfrac{9x^{5 \cdot 2}}{16} \\ &= \dfrac{9x^{10}}{16} \end{aligned}$

69. $\left(\frac{4}{3}\right)^5 \cdot (4)^3 = \frac{4^5}{3^5} \cdot \frac{4^3}{1}$

$= \frac{4^{5+3}}{3^5}$

$= \frac{4^8}{3^5}$ or $\frac{65536}{243}$

73. $(3m)^2(3m)^5 = (3m)^{2+5}$

$= (3m)^7$

$= 3^7 \cdot m^7$ or $2187m^7$

77. $(2m^2n)^3(mn^2) = 2^3m^2 \cdot {}^3n^3(mn^2)$

$= 8m^6n^3(mn^2)$

$= 8m^6mn^3n^2$

$= 8m^{6+1}n^{3+2}$

$= 8m^7n^5$

81. $5^r \cdot 5^{7r} = 5^{r+7r} = 5^{8r}$

85. $(2m)^p = 2^p m^p$

89. $\left(\frac{4^2}{3^3}\right)^r = \frac{4^{2 \cdot r}}{3^{3 \cdot r}} = \frac{4^{2r}}{3^{3r}}$ or $\frac{16^r}{27^r}$

93. (a) $-x^2 + 4x - 7 = -(2)^2 + 4 \cdot 2 - 7$

$= -4 + 8 - 7$

$= -3$

(b) $-x^2 + 4x - 7 = -(-3)^2 + 4(-3) - 7$

$= -(-3)(-3) - 12 - 7$

$= -9 - 12 - 7$

$= -28$

Section 3.2 (page 130)

1. $4^0 + 5^0 = 1 + 1$

$= 2$

5. $3^{-3} = \frac{1}{3^3} = \frac{1}{27}$

9. $\left(\frac{1}{2}\right)^{-5} = 2^5 = 32$

13. $2^{-1} + 3^{-1} = \frac{1}{2} + \frac{1}{3}$

$= \frac{3}{6} + \frac{2}{6}$

$= \frac{5}{6}$

17. $(.98)^{-2} = \frac{1}{(.98)^2}$

$= \frac{1}{.9604}$

$= 1.041$ (rounded)

21. $\frac{4^7}{4^2} = 4^{7-2}$ *Subtract exponents*

$= 4^5$ or 1024

25. $\frac{6^{-4}}{6^2} = 6^{-4-2} = 6^{-6} = \frac{1}{6^6}$

29. $\frac{x^6}{x^{-9}} = x^{6-(-9)}$ *Subtract exponents*

$= x^{15}$

33. $\frac{1}{2^{-5}} = \left(\frac{1}{2}\right)^{-5} = 2^5 = 32$

37. $\frac{4^3 \cdot 4^{-5}}{4^7} = \frac{4^{3+(-5)}}{4^7}$

$= \frac{4^{-2}}{4^7}$

$= 4^{-2-7}$

$= 4^{-9}$

$= \frac{1}{4^9}$

41. $\frac{64^6}{32^6} = \left(\frac{64}{32}\right)^6 = (2)^6 = 64$

45.
$$\left(\frac{5m^{-2}}{m^{-1}}\right) = (5m^{-2-(-1)})^2$$
$$= (5m^{-1})^2$$
$$= 5^2 m^{(-1)(2)}$$
$$= 5^2 m^{-2}$$
$$= 5^2 \cdot \frac{1}{m^2}$$
$$= \frac{25}{m^2}$$

49.
$$\frac{3^{-1}a^{-2}}{3^2 a^{-4}} = 3^{-1-2}a^{-2-(-4)}$$
$$= 3^{-3}a^{-2+4}$$
$$= 3^{-3}a^2$$
$$= \frac{1}{3^3}\cdot a^2$$
$$= \frac{a^2}{3^3} \quad \text{or} \quad \frac{a^2}{27}$$

53.
$$5^r \cdot 5^{7r}\cdot 5^{-2r} = 5^{r+7r+(-2r)}$$
$$= 5^{6r}$$

57.
$$\frac{a^{6y}}{a^{2y}} = a^{6y-2y}$$
$$= a^{4y}$$

61.
$$(6\cdot p^{-3})^{-y} = 6^{-y}\cdot p^{3y}$$
$$= \frac{1}{6^y}\cdot p^{3y}$$
$$= \frac{p^{3y}}{6^y}$$

65.
$$2\cdot 3^{-1} + 4\cdot 2^{-1} = 2\cdot \frac{1}{3} + 4\cdot \frac{1}{2}$$
$$= \frac{2}{3} + \frac{4}{2}$$
$$= \frac{4}{6} + \frac{12}{6}$$
$$= \frac{16}{6} = \frac{8}{3}$$

69.
$$\frac{(4a^2b^3)^{-2}(2ab^{-1})^3}{(a^3b)^{-4}}$$
$$= \frac{(4^{-2}\cdot a^{-4}\cdot b^{-6})(2^3a^3b^{-3})}{a^{-12}b^{-4}}$$
$$= \frac{\frac{1}{4^2}\cdot 2^3\cdot a^{-4}\cdot a^3\cdot b^{-6}\cdot b^{-3}}{a^{-12}b^{-4}}$$
$$= \frac{\frac{8}{16}\cdot a^{-1}b^{-9}}{a^{-12}b^{-4}}$$
$$= \frac{8}{16}\cdot a^{-1-(-12)}b^{-9-(-4)}$$
$$= \frac{1}{2}a^{11}b^{-5}$$
$$= \frac{1}{2}a^{11}\cdot \frac{1}{b^5} = \frac{a^{11}}{2b^5}$$

73.
$$\frac{(9^{-1}z^{-2}x)^{-1}(4z^2x^4)^{-2}}{(5z^{-2}x^{-3})^2}$$
$$= \frac{(9^1z^2x^{-1})(4^{-2}z^{-4}x^{-8})}{5^2z^{-4}x^{-6}}$$
$$= \frac{9}{4^2\cdot 5^2}\cdot \frac{z^{2-4}x^{-1-8}}{z^{-4}x^{-6}}$$
$$= \frac{9}{16\cdot 25}\cdot \frac{z^{-2}x^{-9}}{z^{-4}x^{-6}}$$
$$= \frac{9}{400}\cdot z^{-2+4}x^{-9+6}$$
$$= \frac{9z^2}{400x^3}$$

77. $1000(1.23) = 1230$

81. $237 \div 1000 = .237$

Section 3.3 (page 134)

1. 6,835,000,000

    Place a caret after the first non-zero digit and count from the caret to the decimal point.

    6ₐ835,000,000 *9 places*

Since moving the decimal point made the number smaller, the exponent on 10 is positive.

$$6.835 \times 10^9$$

5. 215

Place a caret after the first non-zero digit and count from the caret to the decimal point.

$2_\wedge 15$ *2 places*

Since moving the decimal point made the number smaller, the exponent on 10 is positive.

$$2.15 \times 10^2$$

9. .035

Place the caret and count to the decimal point.

$.03_\wedge 5$ *2 places*

Since moving the decimal point made the number larger, the exponent on 10 is negative.

$$3.5 \times 10^{-2}$$

13. .000012

Place caret. $.0001_\wedge 2$
Count. $.00001_\wedge 2$ *5 places*

$$1.2 \times 10^{-5}$$

17. $9.132 \times 10^6 = 9,132,000$

Move decimal point 6 places to the right.

21. $3.2 \times 10^{-4} = .00032$

Move decimal point 4 places to the left.

25. $(2 \times 10^8) \times (4 \times 10^{-3})$

$= (2 \times 4) \times (10^8 \times 10^{-3})$

$= 8 \times 10^{8-3}$

$= 8 \times 10^5$

$= 800,000$

29. $(7 \times 10^3) \times (2 \times 10^2) \times (3 \times 10^{-4})$

$= (7 \times 2 \times 3) \times (10^3 \times 10^2 \times 10^{-4})$

$= 42 \times 10^{3+2-4}$

$= 42 \times 10^1$

$= 420$

33. $\dfrac{9 \times 10^5}{3 \times 10^{-1}} = \dfrac{9}{3} \times \dfrac{10^5}{10^{-1}}$

$= 3 \times 10^{5-(-1)}$

$= 3 \times 10^6$

$= 3,000,000$

37. $\dfrac{2.6 \times 10^5}{2 \times 10^2} = \dfrac{2.6}{2} \times \dfrac{10^5}{10^2}$

$= 1.3 \times 10^{5-2}$

$= 1.3 \times 10^3$

$= 1300$

41. $.0004_\wedge$ *Count from right to left 4 places*

$.0004 = 4 \times 10^{-4}$ *Negative exponent*

$.0008_\wedge$ *Count from right to left 4 places*

$.0008 = 8 \times 10^{-4}$ *Negative exponent*

45. $3.5 \times 10^4 = 35,000$

Move the decimal point 4 places to the right.

49. $7m + 8m = (7 + 8)m$

$$= 15m$$

53. $5(2m - 1) - 2m = 10m - 5 - 3m$

$$= 10m - 3m - 5$$
$$= (10 - 3)m - 5$$
$$= 7m - 5$$

57. $x^2 + x^3 = (-4)^2 + (-4)^3$

$$= (-4)(-4) + (-4)(-4)(-4)$$
$$= 16 + (-64)$$
$$= -48$$

Section 3.4   (page 140)

1. $2r^5 + (-3r^5) = [2 + (-3)]r^5$

$$= -1r^5$$
$$= -r^5$$

5. $-4p^7 + 8p^7 - 5p^7 = (-4 + 8 - 5)p^7$

$$= -1p^7$$
$$= -p^7$$

9. $-5p^5 + 8p^5 - 2p^5 - 1p^5$

$$= (-5 + 8 - 2 - 1)p^5$$
$$= 0 \cdot p^5$$
$$= 0 \quad \textit{Zero times any}$$
$$\textit{number is zero}$$

13. $4z^5 - 9z^3 + 8z^2 + 10z^5$

$$= (4 + 10)z^5 - 9z^3 + 8z^2$$
$$= 14z^5 - 9z^3 + 8z^2$$

17. $5x^4 - 8x$ *Simplified form*

The highest power is 4; the degree is 4. It is (a) a binomial.

21. $x^8 + 3x^7 - 5x^4$ *Simplified form*

The highest power is 8; the degree is 8. It is (c) a trinomial.

25. $2m^8 - 5m^9$ *Simplified form*

The degree is 9. It is (b) a binomial.

29.   It is never true that a monomial has no coefficient. Sometimes the coefficient is understood to be 1 as in the case of x^2. Sometimes the monomial is itself the coefficient, for example, if the degree is 0 in a case such as 8(or $8x^0$).

33. $8x + 5x^2 + 2$

(a)   Let $x = 2$.

$$8x + 5x^2 + 2 = 8(2) + 5(2)^2 + 2$$
$$= 16 + 5(4) + 2$$
$$= 16 + 20 + 2$$
$$= 38$$

(b)   Let $x = -1$.

$$8x + 5x^2 + 2 = 8(-1) + 5(-1)^2 + 2$$
$$= -8 + 5(1) + 2$$
$$= -8 + 5 + 2$$
$$= -1$$

37. $-2x^2 + 3$

    (a) Let $x = 2$.

    $\begin{aligned} -2x^2 + 3 &= -2(2)^2 + 3 \\ &= -2(4) + 3 \\ &= -8 + 3 \\ &= -5 \end{aligned}$

    (b) Let $x = -1$.

    $\begin{aligned} -2x^2 + 3 &= -2(-1)^2 + 3 \\ &= -2(1) + 3 \\ &= -2 + 3 \\ &= 1 \end{aligned}$

41. $\begin{array}{l} 3m^2 + 5m \\ \underline{2m^2 - 2m} \\ 5m^2 + 3m \end{array}$ *Add column by column*

45. $\begin{array}{l} 2n^5 - 5n^3 + 6 \\ 3n^5 + 7n^3 + 8 \end{array}$

    Change all signs in the second row, then add.

    $\begin{array}{l} 2n^5 - 5n^3 + 6 \\ \underline{-3n^5 - 7n^3 - 8} \\ -n^5 - 12n^3 - 2 \end{array}$

49. $\begin{array}{l} 5a^4 - 3a^3 + 2a^2 \\ \quad a^3 - a^2 + a - 1 \end{array}$

    Change signs in the second row and add.

    $\begin{array}{l} 5a^4 - 3a^3 + 2a^2 \\ \underline{\quad - a^3 + a^2 - a + 1} \\ 5a^4 - 4a^3 + 3a^2 - a + 1 \end{array}$

53. $(x^2 + x) - (3x^2 + 2x - 1)$

    $\begin{aligned} &= (x^2 + x) + (-3x^2 - 2x + 1) \\ &= x^2 + x - 3x^2 - 2x + 1 \\ &= x^2 - 3x^2 + x - 2x + 1 \\ &= -2x^2 - x + 1 \end{aligned}$

57. $(7y^4 + 3y^2 + 2y) - (-18y^4 - 5y^2 - y)$

    $\begin{aligned} &= 7y^4 + 3y^2 + 2y + 18y^4 + 5y^2 + y \\ &= 7y^4 + 18y^4 + 3y^2 + 5y^2 + 2y + y \\ &= (7 + 18)y^4 + (3 + 5)y^2 + (2 + 1)y \\ &= 25y^4 + 8y^2 + 3y \end{aligned}$

61. The sum of $\quad\quad$ is not equal to 5.

    $\downarrow \quad\quad\quad\quad \downarrow \quad\quad \downarrow$

    $(5 + x^2) + (3 - 2x) \quad\quad \neq \quad\quad 5$

65. $(3.127m^2 - 5.148m - 3.947) - (-.259m^2 + 7.125m - 8.9)$

    $\begin{aligned} &= 3.127m^2 - 5.148m - 3.947 + \\ &\quad (.259m^2 - 7.125m + 8.9) \\ &= (3.127 + .259)m^2 + \\ &\quad (-5.148 - 7.125)m + (-3.947 + 8.9) \\ &= 3.386m^2 - 12.273m + 4.953 \end{aligned}$

69. $(10x^4 - 3x^3 + 2x + 1) + (3x^3 - 6x^2 + 8x - 2)$

    $\begin{aligned} &= 10x^4 - 3x^3 + 3x^3 - 6x^2 + 2x + 8x + 1 - 2 \\ &= 10x^4 - 6x^2 + 10x - 1 \end{aligned}$

73. $\begin{aligned} 5x^2(2x) &= (5 \cdot 2)(x^2 \cdot x^1) \\ &= 10x^3 \end{aligned}$

77. $\begin{aligned} 6p^5(5p^4) &= (6 \cdot 5)(p^5 \cdot p^4) \\ &= 30p^9 \end{aligned}$

Section 3.5 (page 144)

1. $(-4x^5)(8x^2) = (-4)(8)(x^5)(x^2)$

$= -32x^7$

5. $(15a^4)(2a^5) = (15)(2)(a^4)(a^5)$

$= 30a^9$

9. $(-6m^3)(3n^2) = (-6)(3)(m^3)(n^2)$

$= -18m^3n^2$

13. $3p(-2p^3 + 4p^2)$

$= (3p)(-2p^3) + (3p)(4p^2)$

$= -6p^4 + 12p^3$

17. $2y^3(3 + 2y + 5y^4)$

$= (2y^3)(3) + (2y^3)(2y) + (2y^3)(5y^4)$

$= 6y^3 + 4y^4 + 10y^7$

21. $3a^2(2a^2 - 4ab + 5b^2)$

$= (3a^3)(2a^2) + (3a^2)(-4ab) +$

$(3a^2)(5b^2)$

$= 6a^4 - 12a^3b + 15a^2b^2$

25.
$$
\begin{array}{r}
m + 5 \\
m + 7 \\
\hline
7m + 35 \quad \leftarrow 7(m+5) \\
m^2 + 5m \qquad\quad \leftarrow m(m+5) \\
\hline
m^2 + 12m + 35
\end{array}
$$

29.
$$
\begin{array}{r}
2x + 3 \\
6x - 4 \\
\hline
-8x - 12 \\
12x^2 + 18x \qquad \\
\hline
12x^2 + 10x - 12
\end{array}
$$

33.
$$
\begin{array}{r}
5a + 1 \\
2a + 7 \\
\hline
35a + 7 \\
10a^2 + 2a \qquad \\
\hline
10a^2 + 37a + 7
\end{array}
$$

37.
$$
\begin{array}{r}
5 - 3x \\
4 + x \\
\hline
5x - 3x^2 \\
20 - 12x \qquad \\
\hline
20 - 7x - 3x^2
\end{array}
$$

41.
$$
\begin{array}{r}
3x + 2y \\
5x - 3y \\
\hline
-9xy - 6y^2 \\
15x^2 + 10xy \qquad \\
\hline
15x^2 + xy - 6y^2
\end{array}
$$

45. $(9a + 2)(9a^2 + a + 1)$

$= 9a(9a^2) + 9a(a) + 9a(1) + 2(9a^2) +$

$2(a) + 2(1)$

$= 81a^3 + 9a^2 + 9a + 18a^2 + 2a + 2$

$= 81a^3 + 27a^2 + 11a + 2$

49. $(2x - 1)(3x^5 - 2x^3 + x^2 - 2x + 3)$

$= 2x(3x^5) + 2x(-2x^3) + 2x(x^2) +$

$2x(-2x) + 2x(3) - 1(3x^5) -$

$1(-2x^3) - 1(x^2) - 1(-2x) -$

$1(3)$

$= 6x^6 - 4x^4 + 2x^3 - 4x^2 + 6x - 3x^5 +$

$2x^3 - x^2 + 2x - 3$

$= 6x^6 - 3x^5 - 4x^4 + 4x^3 - 5x^2 + 8x - 3$

53. $(x + 7)^2 = (x + 7)(x + 7)$

$= x(x) + x(7) + 7(x) + 7(7)$

$= x^2 + 7x + 7x + 49$

$= x^2 + 14x + 49$

57. $(2p - 5)^2$

$= (2p - 5)(2p - 5)$

$= 2p(2p) + 2p(-5) - 5(2p) - 5(-5)$

$= 4p^2 - 10p - 10p + 25$

$= 4p^2 - 20p + 25$

61. $(m - 5)^3$

$= (m - 5)(m - 5)(m - 5)$

$= [m^2 - 5m - 5m + 25](m - 5)$

$= [m^2 - 10m + 25](m - 5)$

$= m^3 - 5m^2 - 10m^2 + 50m + 25m - 125$

$= m^3 - 15m^2 + 75m - 125$

65. $7(4m - 3) = 28m - 21$

$$\begin{array}{r} 2m + 1 \\ \hline 28m - 21 \\ 56m^2 - 42m \\ \hline 56m^2 - 14m - 21 \end{array}$$

69. $(3r - 2s)^4$

$= (3r - 2s)(3r - 2s)(3r - 2s)(3r - 2s)$

$= [9r^2 - 12rs + 4s^2][9r^2 - 12rs + 4s^2]$

$= 81r^4 - 108r^3s + 36r^2s^2 - 108r^3s +$
$\quad 144r^2s^2 - 48rs^3 + 36r^2s^2 -$
$\quad 48rs^3 + 16s^4$

$= 8r^4 - 216r^3s + 216r^2s^2 - 96rs^3 +$
$\quad 16s^4$

73. $-2x^5(3x^2 + 2x - 5)(4x + 2)$

$= [-2x^5(3x^2) - 2x^5(2x) - 2x^5(-5)] \cdot$
$\quad (4x + 2)$

$= [-6x^7 - 4x^6 + 10x^5](4x + 2)$

$= -6x^7(4x) - 6x^7(2) - 4x^6(4x) -$
$\quad 4x^6(2) + 10x^5(4x) + 10x^5(2)$

$= -24x^8 - 12x^7 - 16x^7 - 8x^6 + 40x^6 +$
$\quad 20x^5$

$= -24x^8 - 28x^7 + 32x^6 + 20x^5$

77. The numbers are -7 and 3, since

$$(-7)(3) = -21$$
and $\quad -7 + 3 = -4.$

Section 3.6 (page 149)

1. $(r - 1)(r + 3)$

$\qquad$ F $\quad$ O $\quad$ I $\quad$ L

$= (r)(r) + (r)(3) + (-1)(r) + (-1)(3)$

$= r^2 + 3r - 1r - 3$

$= r^2 + 2r - 3 \quad$ *Simplify*

5. $(2x - 1)(3x + 2)$

$= (2x)(3x) + (2x)(2) + (-1)(3x) + (-1)(2)$

$= 6x^2 + 4x - 3x - 2$

$= 6x^2 + x - 2$

9. $(2r - 1)(4r + 3)$

$= (2r)(4r) + (2r)(3) + (-1)(4r) + (-1)(3)$

$= 8r^2 + 6r - 4r - 3$

$= 8r^2 + 2r - 3$

13. $(-3 + 2r)(4 + r)$

$= (-3)(4) + (-3)(r) + (2r)(4) + (2r)(r)$

$= -12 - 3r + 8r + 2r^2$

$= -12 + 5r + 2r^2$

17. $(p + 3q)(p + q)$

$= (p)(p) + (p)(q) + (3q)(p) + (3q)(q)$

$= p^2 + pq + 3pq + 3q^2$

$= p^2 + 4pq + 3q^2$

21. $(8y - 9z)(y + 5z)$

$= (8y)(y) + (8y)(5z) + (-9z)(y) +$
$\quad (-9z)(5z)$

$= 8y^2 + 40yz - 9yz - 45z^2$

$= 8y^2 + 31yz - 45z^2$

25. $(8.17m - 2.4)(3.5m + 1.8)$

    $= (8.17m)(3.5m) + (8.17m)(1.8) +$
    $(-2.4)(3.5m) + (-2.4)(1.8)$

    $= 28.595m^2 + 14.706m - 8.4m - 4.32$

    $= 28.595m^2 + 6.306m - 4.32$

29. $(z - 5)^2$

    Use the formula for the square of a binomial.

    $= (z)^2 - 2(z)(5) + (5)^2$

    $= z^2 - 10z + 25$

33. $(8a - 3b)^2$

    $= (8a)^2 - 2(8a)(3b) + (3b)^2$

    $= 64a^2 - 48ab + 9b^2$

37. $(.67m - .17k)^2$

    $= (.67m)^2 - 2(.67m)(.17k) + (.17k)^2$

    $= .4489m^2 - .2278mk + .0289k^2$

41. $(4 - 3t)(4 + 3t)$

    Use the formula for sum and difference of two terms.

    $= (4)^2 - (3t)^2$

    $= 16 - 9t^2$

45. $(6a - p)(6a + p) = (6a)^2 - (p)^2$

    $= 36a^2 - p^2$

49. The square of 3 more than a number is 5.

    $\downarrow$ $\quad$ $\downarrow$ $\quad$ $\downarrow$

    $(x + 3)^2 \quad = \quad 5$

53. $(3p + \frac{4}{5}q)(2p - \frac{5}{3}q)$

    $= (3p)(2p) + (3p)(-\frac{5}{3}q) +$
    $(\frac{4}{5}q)(2p) + (\frac{4}{5}q)(-\frac{5}{3}q)$

    $= 6p^2 - \frac{15}{3}pq + \frac{8}{5}pq - \frac{20}{15}q^2$

    $= 6p^2 - \frac{75}{15}pq + \frac{24}{15}pq - \frac{4}{3}q^2$

    $= 6p^2 - \frac{51}{15}pq - \frac{4}{3}q^2$

    $= 6p^2 - \frac{17}{5}pq - \frac{4}{3}q^2$

57. $(.2x - 3y)^2$

    $= (.2x)^2 - 2 \cdot (.2x)(3y) + (3y)^2$

    $= .04x^2 - 1.2xy + 9y^2$

61. $(7y^2 + 10z)(7y^2 - 10z)$

    $= (7y^2)^2 - (10z)^2$

    $= 49y^4 - 100z^2$

65. $\frac{9y^4}{3y} = 3y^{4-1} = 3y^3$

69. $\frac{-8z^5}{10z^7} = -\frac{4}{5}z^{5-7} = -\frac{4}{5}z^{-2}$

    $= -\frac{4}{5} \cdot \frac{1}{z^2}$

    $= -\frac{4}{5z^2}$

Section 3.7 (page 152)

1. $\frac{4x^2}{2x} = \frac{4}{2} \cdot \frac{x^2}{x^1} = 2x^{2-1} = 2x$

5. $\frac{27k^4m^5}{3km^6} = \frac{27}{3} \cdot \frac{k^4}{k^1} \cdot \frac{m^5}{m^6}$

    $= 9k^{4-1}m^{5-6}$

    $= 9k^3m^{-1}$

    $= \frac{9k^3}{m}$

9. $\dfrac{60m^4 - 20m^2}{2m}$

$= \dfrac{60m^4}{2m^1} - \dfrac{20m^2}{2m^1}$

$= \dfrac{60}{2} \cdot m^{4-1} - \dfrac{20}{2} \cdot m^{2-1}$

$= 30m^3 - 10m$

13. $\dfrac{8m^5 - 4m^3 + 4m^2}{2m}$

$= \dfrac{8m^5}{2m} - \dfrac{4m^3}{2m} + \dfrac{4m^2}{2m}$

$= \dfrac{8}{2} \cdot \dfrac{m^5}{m^1} - \dfrac{4}{2} \cdot \dfrac{m^3}{m^1} + \dfrac{4}{2} \cdot \dfrac{m^2}{m^1}$

$= 4m^{5-1} - 2m^{3-1} + 2m^{2-1}$

$= 4m^4 - 2m^2 + 2m$

17. $\dfrac{2m^2 - 2m + 5}{2m} = \dfrac{2m^2}{2m} - \dfrac{2m}{2m} + \dfrac{5}{2m}$

$= m - 1 + \dfrac{5}{2m}$

21. $\dfrac{-40q^5 + 35q^3 - 20}{-5q}$

$= \dfrac{-40q^5}{-5q} + \dfrac{35q^3}{-5q} - \dfrac{20}{-5q}$

$= 8q^4 - 7q^2 + \dfrac{4}{q}$

25. $\dfrac{5q - 3q^2 + 2q - 7}{-5q}$

$= \dfrac{5q^3}{-5q} - \dfrac{3q^2}{-5q} + \dfrac{2q}{-5q} - \dfrac{7}{-5q}$

$= -q^2 + \dfrac{3q}{5} - \dfrac{2}{5} + \dfrac{7}{5q}$

29. $\dfrac{12x^4 + 3x^2 - 3x^3}{3x^2}$

$= \dfrac{12x^4}{3x^2} + \dfrac{3x^2}{3x^2} - \dfrac{3x^3}{3x^2}$

$= 4x^2 + 1 - x$

33. $\dfrac{x^3 + 6x^2 - x}{3x^2}$

$= \dfrac{x^3}{3x^2} + \dfrac{6x^2}{3x^2} - \dfrac{x}{3x^2}$

$= \dfrac{x}{3} + 2 - \dfrac{1}{3x}$

37. $\dfrac{100p^5 - 50p^4 + 30p^3 - 30p}{-10p^2}$

$= \dfrac{100p^5}{-10p^2} - \dfrac{50p^4}{-10p^2} + \dfrac{30p^3}{-10p^2} - \dfrac{30p}{-10p^2}$

$= -10p^3 + 5p^2 - 3p + \dfrac{3}{p}$

41. $(120x^{11} - 60x^{10} + 140x^9 - 100x^8) \div$

$(10x^{12})$

$= \dfrac{120x^{11} - 60x^{10} + 140x^9 - 100x^8}{10x^{12}}$

$= \dfrac{120x^{11}}{10x^{12}} - \dfrac{60x^{10}}{10x^{12}} + \dfrac{140x^9}{10x^{12}} - \dfrac{100x^8}{10x^{12}}$

$= \dfrac{12}{x} - \dfrac{6}{x^2} + \dfrac{14}{x^3} - \dfrac{10}{x^4}$

45. Multiplying the quotient by the divisor yields the original dividend.

$3x^2(4x^3 + 3x^2 - 4x + 2)$

$= 12x^5 + 9x^4 - 12x^3 + 6x^2$

49. Use $A = LW$ where $A = 10x^5 + 15x^4 + 40x^3$ and $W = 5x^3$. Substitute,

$10x^5 + 15x^4 + 40x^3 = L(5x^3)$

$\dfrac{10x^5 + 15x^4 + 40x^3}{5x^3} = \dfrac{L(5x^3)}{5x^3}$

$\dfrac{10x^5}{5x^3} + \dfrac{15x^4}{5x^3} + \dfrac{40x^3}{5x^3} = L$

$2x^2 + 3x + 8 = L$

53. $x(2x^2 - 5x + 1)$

$\qquad = (x)(2x^2) + (x)(-5x) + (x)(1)$

$\qquad = 2x^3 - 5x^2 + x$

57. $3m^5(2m^5 - 4m^3 + m^2)$

$\qquad = (3m^5)(2m^5) + (3m^5)(-4m^3) +$

$\qquad \quad (3m^5)(m^2)$

$\qquad = 6m^{10} - 12m^8 + 3m^7$

61. $6x^2 - 4$

$\underline{8x^2 + 7}$

Change signs and add.

$$\begin{array}{r} 6x^2 - 4 \\ \underline{-8x^2 - 7} \\ -2x^2 - 11 \end{array}$$

Section 3.8 (page 157)

1. $x - 3\overline{)x^2 - x - 6}$ *Subtract by*

$\qquad\quad \dfrac{x + 2}{}$

$\qquad\quad \underline{x^2 - 3x} \leftarrow$ *changing signs*

$\qquad\qquad\quad 2x - 6$ *in the second*

$\qquad\qquad\quad \underline{2x - 6} \leftarrow$ *row and then*

$\qquad\qquad\qquad\quad 0$ *adding*

There is no remainder. The
quotient is $x + 2$.

5. $p + 6\overline{)p^2 + 2p - 20}$

$\qquad\qquad \dfrac{p - 4}{}$

$\qquad\quad \underline{p^2 + 6p} \leftarrow$ *Change*

$\qquad\qquad -4p - 20$ *signs*

$\qquad\qquad \underline{-4p - 24} \leftarrow$ *and add*

$\qquad\qquad\qquad\;\; 4$

The remainder is 4.

The quotient is $p - 4$.

The result is $p - 4 + \dfrac{4}{p + 6}$.

9. $2m - 3\overline{)12m^2 - 20m + 3}$

$\qquad\qquad\qquad \dfrac{6m - 1}{}$

$\qquad\quad \underline{12m^2 - 18m} \leftarrow$ *Change*

$\qquad\qquad\quad -2m + 3$ *signs*

$\qquad\qquad\quad \underline{-2m + 3} \leftarrow$ *and add*

$\qquad\qquad\qquad\qquad 0$

There is no remainder. The
quotient is $6m - 1$.

13. $3r - 5\overline{)12r^2 - 17r + 5}$

$\qquad\qquad\qquad \dfrac{4r + 1}{}$

$\qquad\quad \underline{12r^2 - 20r} \leftarrow$ *Change*

$\qquad\qquad\quad 3r + 5$ *signs*

$\qquad\qquad\quad \underline{3r - 5} \leftarrow$ *and add*

$\qquad\qquad\qquad\; 10$

The remainder is 10. The quotient
is $4r + 1$.

The result is $4r + 1 + \dfrac{10}{3r - 5}$.

17. $\dfrac{2x^3 + 3x - x^2 + 2}{2x + 1}$

Rewrite the dividend with de-
cending powers.

$\qquad\qquad\qquad\quad \dfrac{x^2 - x^2 + 2}{}$

$2x + 1\overline{)2x^3 - x^2 + 3x + 2}$

$\qquad\quad \underline{2x^3 + x^2} \leftarrow$ *Change*

$\qquad\qquad -2x^2 + 3x$ *signs*

$\qquad\qquad \underline{-2x^2 - x} \leftarrow$ *and add*

$\qquad\qquad\qquad\; 4x + 2$

$\qquad\qquad\qquad\; \underline{4x + 2}$

No remainder. The quotient is

$x^2 - x + 2$.

21. $y + 1\overline{)3y^3 + y^2 + 4y + 1}$

$\qquad\qquad \dfrac{3y^2 - 2y + 6}{}$

$\qquad\quad \underline{3y^3 + 3y^2} \leftarrow$ *Change*

$\qquad\qquad -2y^2 + 4y$ *signs*

$\qquad\qquad \underline{-2y^2 - 2y} \leftarrow$ *and*

$\qquad\qquad\qquad\; 6y + 1$ *add*

$\qquad\qquad\qquad\; \underline{6y + 6}$

$\qquad\qquad\qquad\quad -5$

The remainder is -5.

The quotient is $3y^2 - 2y + 6$.

The result is $3y^2 + 6 + \dfrac{-5}{y + 1}$.

25.
$$
\require{enclose}
\begin{array}{r}
2p^3 - 6p^2 + 7p - 4 \\
3p + 1 \enclose{longdiv}{6p^4 - 16p^3 + 15p^2 - 5p + 10} \\
\end{array}
$$

$$6p^4 + 2p^3 $$
$$- 18p^3 + 15p^2$$
$$- 18p^3 - 6p^2$$
$$21p^2 - 5p$$
$$21p^2 + 5p$$
$$-12p + 10$$
$$-12p - 4$$
$$14$$

The remainder is 4.

The quotient is $2p^3 - 6p^2 + 7p - 4$.

The result is

$$2p^3 - 6p^2 + 7p - 4 + \frac{14}{3p + 1}.$$

29.
$$\frac{-m^3 - 9m^4 - 22m^2 + 4m^5 - 15}{4m^2 - m - 3}$$

Rewrite the dividend in descending powers and write 0 for any missing terms.

$$
\begin{array}{r}
m^3 - 2m^2 - 7 \\
4m^2 - m - 3 \enclose{longdiv}{4m^5 - 9m^4 - m^3 - 22m^2 + 0m - 15} \\
\end{array}
$$

$$4m^5 - m^4 - 3m^3$$
$$- 8m^4 + 2m^3 - 22m^2$$
$$- 8m^4 + 2m^3 + 6m^2$$
$$- 28m^2 + 0m - 15$$
$$- 28m^2 + 7m + 21$$
$$- 7m - 36$$

The remainder is $-7m - 36$. The quotient is $m^3 - 2m^2 - 7$.

The result is $m^3 - 2m^2 - 7 + \dfrac{-7m - 36}{4m^2 - m - 3}$.

33.
$$\frac{a^4 - 1}{a^2 + 1}$$

Rewrite with 0 for the missing terms.

$$
\begin{array}{r}
a^2 - 1 \\
a^2 + 0a + 1 \enclose{longdiv}{a^4 + 0a^3 + 0a^2 + 0a - 1} \\
\end{array}
$$

$$a^4 + 0a^3 + a^2$$
$$- a^2 + 0a - 1$$
$$- a^2 - 0a - 1$$

No remainder. The quotient is $a^2 - 1$.

37.
$$
\begin{array}{r}
3w + \dfrac{11}{3} \\
3w - 2 \enclose{longdiv}{9w^2 + 5w + 10} \\
\end{array}
$$

$$9w^2 - 6w$$
$$11w + 10$$
$$11w - \frac{22}{3}$$
$$10 + \frac{22}{3} = \frac{30}{3} + \frac{22}{3}$$
$$= \frac{52}{3}$$

The remainder is 52/3. The quotient is $3w + 11/3$.

The result is $3w + \dfrac{11}{3} + \dfrac{\frac{52}{3}}{3w - 2}$.

41. $1 \cdot 12 = 12$
$2 \cdot 6 = 12$
$3 \cdot 4 = 12$

$\{1, 2, 3, 4, 6, 12\}$

45. $1 \cdot 50 = 50$
$2 \cdot 25 = 50$
$5 \cdot 10 = 50$

$\{1, 2, 5, 10, 25, 50\}$

49. $2m(m^2 - m + 1)$
$$= (2m)(m^2) + (2m)(-m) + 2m(1)$$
$$= 2m^3 - 2m^2 + 2m$$

Chapter 3 Review Exercises (page 159)

1. $4^2 + 4^3 = 4 \cdot 4 + 4 \cdot 4 \cdot 4$
$$= 16 + 64$$
$$= 80$$

5. $(ab^2c^3)^4 = a^4b^{2 \cdot 4}c^{3 \cdot 4} = a^4b^8c^{12}$

9. $(5^{-2})^{-4} = 5^{(-2)(-4)}$ *Multiply Exponents*

$= 5^8$

13. $(6r^{-2})^{-1} = 6^{-1}(r^{-2})^{-1}$

$= 6^{-1}r^2$

$= \dfrac{r^2}{6}$

17. $.0004_\wedge 251$ *4 places*

Since moving the decimal point made the number larger, the exponent on 10 is negative.

$.004251 = 4.251 \times 10^{-4}$

21. $4.253 \times 10^{-4} = .0004253$

Move decimal point 4 places to the left.

25. $\dfrac{8 \times 10^4}{2 \times 10^{-2}} = (\dfrac{8}{2}) \times (\dfrac{10^4}{10^{-2}})$

$= 4 \times 10^{4-(-2)}$

$= 4 \times 10^6$

$= 4,000,000$

29. $-7y^5 - 8y^4 - 1y^5 + 1y^4 + 9y$

$= (-7 - 1)y^5 + (-8 + 1)y^4 + 9y$

$= -8y^5 - 7y^4 + 9y$

The degree is 5.

33. $(2m^3 - 8m^2 + 4) + (3m^3 + 2m^2 - 7)$

$= 2m^3 - 8m^2 + 4 + 3m^3 + 2m^2 - 7$

$= (2m^3 + 3m^3) + (-8m^2 + 2m^2) + (4-7)$

$= 5m^3 - 6m^2 - 3$

37.
$$
\begin{array}{r}
a^2 - 4a + 1 \\
a + 1 \\
\hline
2a^2 - 8a + 2 \\
a^3 - 4a^2 + a \\
\hline
a^3 - 2a^2 - 7a + 2
\end{array}
$$

41. $(a + 3b)(2a - b)$

$= (a)(2a) + (a)(-b) + (3b)(2a) + (3b)(-b)$

$= 2a^2 - ab + 6ab - 3b^2$

$= 2a^2 + 5ab - 3b^2$

45. $(6m - 5)(6m + 5) = (6m)^2 - (5)^2$

$= 36m^2 - 25$

49. $\dfrac{-10m^4 + 5m^3 + 6m^2}{5m^2}$

$= \dfrac{-10m^4}{5m^2} + \dfrac{5m^3}{5m^2} + \dfrac{6m^2}{5m^2}$

$= -2m^2 + m + \dfrac{6}{5}$

53.
$$
\begin{array}{r}
k^2 + k + \frac{7}{2} \\
2k^2 + k + 1 \overline{\smash{)}\ 2k^4 + 3k^3 + 9k^2 + 0k - 8} \\
\underline{2k^4 + k^3 + k^2} \\
2k^3 + 8k^2 + 0k \\
\underline{2k^3 + k^2 + k} \\
7k^2 - k - 8 \\
\underline{7k^2 + \frac{7}{2}k + \frac{7}{2}} \\
-\frac{9}{2}k - \frac{23}{2}
\end{array}
$$

The remainder is $-\dfrac{9}{2}k - \dfrac{23}{2}$.

The quotient is $k^2 + k + \dfrac{7}{2}$.

The result is

$k^2 + k + \dfrac{7}{2} + \dfrac{-\frac{9}{2}k - \frac{23}{2}}{2k^2 + k + 1}$.

57. $2^{-4} = \dfrac{1}{2^4} = \dfrac{1}{2\cdot 2\cdot 2\cdot 2} = \dfrac{1}{16}$

61. $(3k - 6)(2k^2 + 4k + 1)$

   $= 3k(2k^2) + 3k(4k) + 3k(1) - 6(2k^2)$
   $6(4k) - 6(1)$

   $= 6k^3 + 12k^2 + 3k - 12k^2 - 24k - 6$

   $= 6k^3 - 21k - 6$

65. $(2r + 5)(5r - 2)$

   $= (2r)(5r) + (2r)(-2) + (5)(5r) +$
   $(5)(-2)$

   $= 10r^2 - 4r + 25r - 10$

   $= 10r^2 + 21r - 10$

69. $(5^2)^4 = 5^{2 \cdot 4} = 5^8$

Chapter 3 Test   (page 161)

1. $\left(\frac{4}{3}\right)^{-3} = \frac{1}{\left(\frac{4}{3}\right)^3}$

   $= \frac{1}{\frac{4}{3} \cdot \frac{4}{3} \cdot \frac{4}{3}}$

   $= \frac{1}{\frac{64}{27}}$

   $= 1 \cdot \frac{27}{64}$

   $= \frac{27}{64}$

2. $(5)^{-2} = \frac{1}{5^2} = \frac{1}{25}$

3. $5^2 \cdot 5^6 \cdot 5 = 5^{2+6+1} = 5^9$

4. $\frac{(8^3)^2 \cdot 8^4}{8^3 \cdot 8^9} = \frac{8^{3 \cdot 2} \cdot 8^4}{8^{3+9}}$

   $= \frac{8^6 \cdot 8^4}{8^{12}}$

   $= \frac{8^{6+4}}{8^{12}}$

   $= \frac{8^{10}}{8^{12}}$

   $= \frac{1}{8^2}$

   $= \frac{1}{64}$

5. $\left(\frac{6q^{-2}}{q^{-3}}\right) = \frac{1}{\left(\frac{6q^{-2}}{q^{-3}}\right)^1}$

   $= 1 \cdot \frac{q^{-3}}{6q^{-2}}$

   $= \frac{q^{-3-(-2)}}{6}$

   $= \frac{q^{-1}}{6} = \frac{1}{6q}$

6. $\frac{(2p^2)^3(4p^4)^2}{(2p^5)^2} = \frac{2^3 p^6 \cdot 4^2 p^8}{2^2 p^{10}}$

   $= \frac{8p^6 \cdot 16p^8}{4p^{10}}$

   $= \frac{128p^{14}}{4p^{10}}$

   $= 32p^4$

7. .000379

   Place a caret after the first
   nonzero digit and count from
   the caret to the decimal point.

   .0003∧79   *4 places*

   Since moving the decimal point
   made the number larger, the
   exponent on 10 is negative.

   3.79×10^{-4}

8. $(6 \times 10^{-4}) \times (1.5 \times 10^6)$

$= (6 \times 1.5) \times (10^{-4} \times 10^6)$

$= 9 \times 10^{-4+6}$

$= 9 \times 10^2$

$= 900$

9. $\dfrac{5.6 \times 10^{-7}}{1.4 \times 10^{-3}} = \dfrac{5.6}{1.4} \times \dfrac{10^{-7}}{10^{-3}}$

$= 4 \times 10^{-7-(-3)}$

$= 4 \times 10^{-7+3}$

$= 4 \times 10^{-4}$

$= .0004$

10. $3x^2 + 6x - 4x^2 = 3x^2 - 4x^2 + 6x$

$= -x^2 + 6x$

The degree is 2.
The expression is (b) a binomial.

11. $11m^3 - m^2 + m^4 + m^4 - 7m^2$

$= 2m^4 + 11m^3 - m^2 - 7m^2$

$= 2m^4 + 11m^3 - 8m^2$

The degree is 4.
The expression is (a) a trinomial.

12. $-5m^3 + 2m^2 - 7m + 3$
     $8m^3 - 5m^2 + 9m - 5$

Change signs and add.

$-5m^3 + 2m^2 - 7m + 3$
$\underline{-8m^3 + 5m^2 - 9m + 5}$
$-13m^3 + 7m^2 - 16m + 8$

13. $(2x^5 - 4x + 7) - (x^5 + x^2 - 2x - 5)$

$= (2x^5 - 4x + 7) + (-x^5 - x^2 + 2x + 5)$

$= 2x^5 - 4x + 7 - x^5 - x^2 + 2x + 5$

$= 2x^5 - x^5 - x^2 - 4x + 2x + 7 + 5$

$= x^5 - x^2 - 2x + 12$

14. $(y^2 - 5y - 3) + (3y^2 + 2y) - (y^2 - y - 1)$

$= y^2 - 5y - 3 + 3y^2 + 2y - (y^2 - y - 1)$

$= y^2 + 3y^2 - 5y + 2y - 3 - (y^2 - y - 1)$

$= 4y^2 - 3y - 3 + (-y^2 + y + 1)$

$= 4y^2 - 3y - 3 - (y^2 + y + 1)$

$= 4y^2 - y^2 - 3y + y - 3 + 1$

$= 3y^2 - 2y - 2$

15. $6m^2(m^3 + 2m^2 - 3m + 7)$

$= (6m^2)(m^3) + (6m^2)(2m^2) + (6m^2)(-3m) +$

$(6m^2)(7)$

$= 6m^5 + 12m^4 - 18m^3 + 42m^2$

16. $(5m + 6)(3m - 1)$

$\quad$ F $\qquad$ O $\qquad$ I $\qquad$ L

$= (5m)(3m) + (5m)(-11) + (6)(3m) + (6)(-11)$

$= 15m^2 - 55m + 18m - 66$

$= 15m^2 - 37m - 66$

17. $(2t + 5s)(7t - 4s)$

$\quad$ F $\qquad$ O $\qquad$ I $\qquad$ L

$= (2t)(7t) + (2t)(-4s) + (5s)(7t) + (5s)(-4s)$

$= 14t^2 - 8ts + 35ts - 20s^2$

$= 14t^2 + 27ts - 20s^2$

18. $\quad 2k^2 - 7k + 8$
     $\quad 3k + 2$
     $\quad\underline{4k^2 - 14k + 16}$
     $6k^3 - 21k^2 + 24k$
     $\underline{6k^3 - 17k^2 + 10k + 16}$

19. $(2k + 5m)^2$

$= (2k)^2 + 2 \cdot (2k)(5m) + (5m)^2$

$= 4k^2 + 20km + 25m^2$

20. $(2r + \frac{1}{2}t)^2$

$= (2r)^2 + 2\cdot(2r)(\frac{1}{2}t) + (\frac{1}{2}t)^2$

$= 4r^2 + 2rt + \frac{1}{4}t^2$

21. $(6p^2 - 5r)(6p^2 + 5r)$

$= (6p^2)^2 - (5r)^2$

$= 6^2p^4 - 5^2r^2$

$= 36p^4 - 25r^2$

22. $\dfrac{-15y^5 - 8y^4 + 6y^3}{3y^2}$

$= \dfrac{-15y^5}{3y^2} - \dfrac{8y^4}{3y^2} + \dfrac{6y^3}{3y^2}$

$= -5y^3 - \dfrac{8y^2}{3} + 2y$

23. $(10r^3 + 25r^2 - 15r + 8) \div (5r^3)$

$= \dfrac{10r^3 + 25r^2 - 15r + 8}{5r^3}$

$= \dfrac{10r^3}{5r^3} + \dfrac{25r^2}{5r^3} - \dfrac{15r}{5r^3} + \dfrac{8}{5r^3}$

$= 2 + \dfrac{5}{r} - \dfrac{3}{r^2} + \dfrac{8}{5r^3}$

24.
$$
\begin{array}{r}
3x^2 + 4x + 2 \\
x - 2\overline{)3x^3 - 2x^2 - 6x - 4} \\
\underline{3x^3 - 6x^2} \\
4x^2 - 6x \\
\underline{4x^2 - 8x} \\
2x - 4 \\
\underline{2x - 4} \\
0
\end{array}
$$

There is no remainder.

The quotient is $3x^2 + 4x + 2$.

25.
$$
\begin{array}{r}
5r^2 + 2r - 5 \\
2r^2 + 0r - 3\overline{)10r^4 + 4r^3 - 25r^2 - 6r + 20} \\
\underline{10r^4 + 0r^3 - 15r^2} \\
4r^3 - 10r^2 - 6r \\
\underline{4r^3 + 0r^2 - 6r} \\
-10r^2 + 0r + 20 \\
\underline{-10r^2 + 0r + 15} \\
5
\end{array}
$$

The remainder is 5.

The quotient is $5r^2 + 2r - 5$.

The result is $5r^2 + 2r - 5 + \dfrac{5}{2r^2 - 3}$.

CHAPTER 4   FACTORING AND APPLICATIONS
Section 4.1   (page 166)

1. In factored form,

$$12y = 2 \cdot 2 \cdot 3 \cdot y \text{ and }$$
$$24 = 2 \cdot 2 \cdot 2 \cdot 3$$

To get the greatest common factor, take each prime the least number of times it appears in factored form. The least number of times the 2 appears is twice, and the 3 appears one time. y is not a factor of 24, so will not be in the greatest common factor. Thus

Greatest common factor = $2 \cdot 2 \cdot 3 = 12$.

5. In factored form,

$$18r = 2 \cdot 3 \cdot 3 \cdot r,$$
$$32y = 2 \cdot 2 \cdot 2 \cdot 2 \cdot 2 \cdot y$$
$$11z = 11 \cdot z$$

There is no common prime factor as seen in the above factorizations. However, 1 is a factor of every number, so 1 is the greatest common factor for the terms 18r, 32y, 11z.

9. In factored form,

$$32y^4x^5 = 2 \cdot 2 \cdot 2 \cdot 2 \cdot 2 \cdot y^4x^5$$
$$24y^7x = 2 \cdot 2 \cdot 2 \cdot 3 \cdot y^7x$$
$$36y^3x^5 = 2 \cdot 2 \cdot 3 \cdot 3 \cdot y^3x^5$$

The greatest common numerical factor is $2 \cdot 2 = 2^2 = 4$. We use the smallest exponent on each of the common variable factors to get y^3x. Thus, the greatest common factor is $4y^3x$.

13. $9m^4 = 3m^2(3m^2)$

Factor out $3m^2$ from $9m^4$ to obtain $3m^2$.

17. $x^2y^3 = xy(xy^2)$

Factor out xy from x^2y^3 to obtain xy^2.

21. $-16m^3n^3 - 4mn^2(-4m^2n)$

Factor out $4mn^2$ from $-16m^3n^3$ to obtain $-4m^2n$.

25. $49a^2 + 14a$

$= (7a)(7a) + (7a)(2)$ *Greatest common factor is 7a*

$= 7a(7a + 2)$

29. $121p^5 - 33p^4$

$= 11p^4(11p) - 11p^4(3)$ *Greatest common factor is $11p^4$*

$= 11p^4(11p - 3)$

33. $19y^3p^2 + 38y^2p^3$

$= (19y^2p^2)(y) + (19y^2p^2)(2p)$ *Greatest common factor is $19y^2p^2$*

$= 19y^2p^2(y + 2p)$

37. $45q^4p^5 - 36qp^6 + 81q^2p^3$

$= (9qp^3)(5q^3p^2) + (9qp^3)(-4p^3) + (9qp^3)(9q)$ *Greatest common factor is $9qp^3$*

$= 9qp^3(5q^3p^2 - 4p^3 + 9q)$

41. $7z^2 + 3zm + 14zm + 6m^2$

    The first two terms have a common factor of z, and the last two terms have a common factor of 2m.

    $7z^2 + 3zm + 14zm + 6m^2$
    $= z(7z + 3m) + 2m(7z + 3m)$.

    Now 7z + 3m is a common factor.

    $7z^2 + 3zm + 14zm + 6m^2$
    $= (7z + 3m)(z + 2m)$

45. $3a^3 + 3ab^2 + 2a^2b + 2b^3$

    The first two terms have a common factor of 3a, and the last two terms have a common factor of 2b.

    $3a^3 + 3ab^2 + 2a^2b + 2b^3$
    $= 3a(a^2 + b^2) + 2b(a^2 + b^2)$

    Now $a^2 + b^2$ is a common factor.

    $= (a^2 + b^2)(3a + 2b)$

49. $125z^5a^3 - 60z^4a^5 + 85z^3a^4$

    The greatest common factor is $5z^3a^3$.

    $125z^5a^3 - 60z^4a^5 + 85z^3a^4$
    $= 5z^3a^3(25z^2) + 5z^3a^3(-12za^2) +$
    $\quad 5z^3a^3(17a)$
    $= 5z^3a^3(25z^2 - 12za^2 + 17a)$

53. $36a^4b^3 + 32a^5b^2 - 48a^6b^3$

    The greatest common factor is $4a^4b^2$.

    $36^4b^3 + 32a^5b^2 - 48a^6b^3$
    $= 4a^4b^2(9b) + 4a^4b^2(8a) +$
    $\quad 4a^4b^2(-12a^2b)$
    $= 4a^4b^2(9b + 8a - 12a^2b)$

57. $(r + 5)(r - 9)$
    $= r^2 - 9r + 5r - 45$
    $= r^2 - 4r - 45$

61. $(a + 7)(a - 7)$
    $= a^2 - 7a + 7a - 49$
    $= a^2 - 49$

Section 4.2 (page 169)

1. $x^2 + 10x + 21 = (x + 7)(\quad)$

   Look for an integer whose product is 21 and whose sum with 7 is 10. That integer is 3.

   $x^2 + 10x + 21 = (x + 7)(x + 3)$

5. $t^2 - 14t + 24 = (t - 2)(\quad)$

   Look for an integer whose product with -2 is 24 and whose sum with -2 is -14. That integer is -12.

   $t^2 - 14t + 24 = (t - 2)(t - 12)$

9. $m^2 + 2m - 24 = (m - 4)(\quad)$

   Look for an integer whose product with -4 is -24 and whose sum with -4 is 2. That integer is 6.

   $m^2 + 2m - 24 = (m - 4)(m + 6)$

13. $x^2 + 6x + 5$

    Look for two integers whose product is 5 and whose sum is 6.

Product	Sum
(5)(1) = 5	5 + 1 = 6

    $x^2 + 6x + 5 = (x + 5)(x + 1)$ or
    $\qquad\qquad\quad (x + 1)(x + 5)$

17. $x^2 - 8x + 7$

Find two integers whose product is 7 and whose sum is -8.

Product	Sum	
$(7)(1) = 7$	$7 + 1 = 8$	*Incorrect*
$(-7)(-1) = 7$	$-7 + (-1) = -8$	*Correct*

$x^2 - 8x + 7 = (x - 7)(x - 1)$ or $(x - 1)(x - 7)$

21. $y^2 - 6y + 8$

Find two integers whose product is 8 and whose sum is -6.

Product	Sum	
$(-8)(-1) = 8$	$-8 + (-1) = -9$	*Incorrect*
$(-4)(-2) = 8$	$-4 + (-2) = -6$	*Correct*

$y^2 - 6y + 8 = (y - 4)(y - 2)$

25. $n^2 - 12n - 35$

Product	Sum	
$35(-1)$	$35 - 1 = 34$	*Incorrect*
$(-35)1$	$-35 + 1 = -34$	*Incorrect*
$7(-5)$	$7 - 2 = 2$	*Incorrect*
$(-7)5$	$-7 + 5 = -2$	*Incorrect*

This list does not product the required integers. Therefore,

$n^2 - 12n - 35$ is prime.

29. $k^2 - 10k + 25$

Product	Sum	
$-25(-1)$	$-25 - 1 = -26$	*Incorrect*
$-5(-5)$	$-5 - 5 = -10$	

$k^2 - 10k + 25 = (k - 5)(k - 5) = (k - 5)^2$

33. $y^2 - by - 30b^2$

Product	Sum	
$-30b(b)$	$-30b + b = -29b$	*Incorrect*
$-15b(2b)$	$-15b + 2b = -13b$	*Incorrect*
$-10b(3b)$	$-10b + 3b = -7b$	*Incorrect*
$-6b(5b)$	$-6b + 5b = -b$	*Correct*

$y^2 - by - 30b^2 = (y - 6b)(y + 5b)$

37. $r^2 - 2rs + s^2$

The only pair of terms whose product is s^2 and whose sum is $-2s$ is $-s$ and $-s$. Thus,

$r^2 - 2rs + s^2$

$= (r - s)(r - s) = (r - s)^2.$

41. $3m^3 + 12m^2 + 9m$

First, factor out the greatest common factor, $3m$.

$3m^3 + 12m^2 + 9m$

$= 3m(m^2 + 4m + 3)$

Now factor $m^2 + 4m + 3$. The integers 3 and 1 have a product of 3 and a sum of 4. The complete factored form is

$3m^3 + 12m^2 + 9m$

$= 3m(m + 3)(m + 1).$

45. $3r^3 - 30r^2 + 72r$

The greatest common factor is $3r$. So,

$3r^3 - 30r^2 + 72r$

$= 3r(r^2 - 10r + 24)$

Now factor $r^2 - 10r + 24$. The integers -6 and -4 have a product of 24 and a sum of -10.

So

$$3r^3 - 30r^2 + 72r$$
$$= 3r(r - 6)(r - 4).$$

49. $(2x + 4)(x - 3)$

$$\begin{array}{cccc} F & O & I & L \end{array}$$
$$= (2x)(x) + (2x)(-3) + (4)(x) + (4)(-3)$$
$$= 2x^2 - 6x + 4x - 12$$
$$= 2x^2 - 2x - 12$$

But $2x + 4$ has a greatest common factor of 2, so $2x + 4 = 2(x + 2)$. $2x^2 - 24 - 12$ is completely factored as $2(x + 2)(x - 3)$.

53. $a^5 + 3a^4b - 4a^3b^2$

The greatest common factor is a^3.

$$a^5 + 3a^4b - 4a^3b^2$$
$$= a^3(a^2 + 3ab - 4b^2)$$

Now factor the trinomial $(a^2 + 3ab - 4b^2)$. The integers 4 and -1 have a product of -4 and a sum of 3. So,

$$a^5 + 3a^4b - 4a^3b^2$$
$$= a^3(a + 4b)(a - b)$$

57. $z^{10} - 4z^9y - 21z^8y^2$

The greatest common factor is z^8.

$$z^{10} - 4z^9y - 21z^8y^2$$
$$= z^8(z^2 - 4zy - 21y^2)$$

Now factor the trinomial $(z^2 - 4zy - 21y^2)$. The integers -7 and $+3$ have a product of -21 and a sum of -4. So,

$$z^{10} - 4z^9y - 21z^8y^2$$
$$= z^8(z - 7y)(z + 3y)$$

61. $(2p + q)r^2 - 12(2p + q)r + 27(2p + q)$

The greatest common factor is $2p + q$.

$$(2p + q)r^2 - 12(2p + q)r + 27(2p + q)$$
$$= (2p + q)(r^2 - 12r + 27)$$

Now factor $r^2 - 12r + 27$. The integers -9 and -3 have a product of 27 and a sum of -12. So,

$$(2p + q)r^2 - 12(2p + q)r + 27(2p + q)$$
$$= (2p + q)(r - 9)(r - 3).$$

65. $(5z + 2)(3z - 2)$

$$= 15z^2 - 10z + 6z - 4$$
$$= 15z^2 - 4z - 4$$

Section 4.3 (page 175)

1. $2x^2 - x - 1 = (2x + 1)(\quad\quad)$

Since the first term of the trinomial is $2x^2$, the first term of the second factor must be x so that $2x \cdot x = 2x^2$. Since the last term of the trinomial is -1, the last term of the second factor is -1 so that $(1)(-1) = -1$.
Now check:

$$(2x + 1)(x - 1) = 2x^2 - 2x + x - 1$$
$$= 2x^2 - x - 1$$

5. $4y^2 + 17y - 15 = (y + 5)(\quad\quad)$

Since the first term of the trinomial is $4y^2$, the first term of the second factor muct be 4y so that $(y)(4y) = 4y^2$. Since the last term of the trinomial is -15, the last term of the second factor is -3 so that $(5)(-3) = -15$.

Now check:

$$(y + 5)(4y - 3) = 4y^2 - 3y + 20y - 15$$
$$= 4y^2 + 17y - 15$$

9. $2m^2 + 19m - 10 = (2m - 1)(\quad)$

Since the first term of the tri-onomial is $2m^2$, the first term of the second factor is m so that $(2m)(m) = 2m^2$. Since the last term of the trinomial is -10, the last term of the second factor is 10 so that $(-1)(10) = -10$. Now check:

$$(2m - 1)(m + 10) = 2m^2 + 20m - m - 10$$
$$= 2m^2 + 19m - 10$$

13. $4k^2 + 13km + 3m^2 = (4k + m)(\quad)$

Since the first term of the tri-nomial is $4k^2$, the first term of the second factor is k so that $(4k)(k) = 4k^2$. Since the last term of the trinomial is $3m^2$, the last term of the second factor is 3m so that $(m)(3m) = 3m^2$. Now check:

$$(4k + m)(k + 3m)$$
$$= 4k^2 + 12km + km + 3m^2$$
$$= 4k^2 + 13km + 3m^2$$

17. $6m^6 + 7m^5 - 20m^4$

$$= m^4(\quad) = m^4(3m - 4)(\quad)$$

First factor out the greatest common factor, m^4.

$$6m^6 + 7m^5 - 20m^4 = m^4(6m^2 + 7m - 20)$$

Since the first term of the tri-nomial is $6m^2$, the first term of the second factor is 2m so that $(3m)(2m) = 6m^2$. Since the last term of the trinomial is -20,

the last term of the second factor is 5 so that $(-4)(5) = -20$. Now check:

$$(3m - 4)(2m + 5)$$
$$= 6m^2 + 7m - 20.$$

So

$$6m^6 + 7m^5 - 20m^4 = m^4(3m - 4)(2m + 5).$$

21. $3a^2 + 10a + 7$

Since all signs are positive, the only possibilities are given.

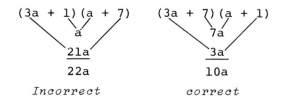

$$3a^2 + 10a + 7 = (3a + 7)(a + 1)$$

25. $15m^2 + m - 2$

Since -2 has fewer factors than $15m^2$, begin by factoring the (-2).

$$(\quad - 2)(\quad + 1)$$

Now try factors of $15m^2$

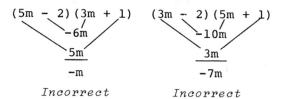

Now try $(\quad + 2)(\quad - 1)$

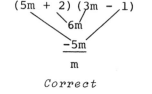

Correct

$$15m^2 + m - 2) = (5m + 2)(3m - 1)$$

29. $5a^2 - 6 - 7a$

Rewrite this trinomial as $5a^2 - 7a - 6$. Begin by factoring the $5a^2$ since $5a^2$ has fewer factors than -6. $5a^2 - 7a - 6 = (5a \quad)(a \quad)$ Now try factors of -6.

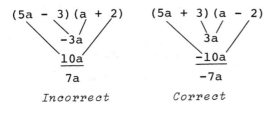

$(5a - 3)(a + 2)$ $(5a + 3)(a - 2)$
$\quad\quad -3a$ $\quad\quad 3a$
$\quad\quad \underline{10a}$ $\quad\quad \underline{-10a}$
$\quad\quad 7a$ $\quad\quad -7a$
Incorrect   *Correct*

$5a^2 - 6 - 7a = 5a^2 - 7a - 6$
$\quad\quad\quad\quad = (5a + 3)(a - 2)$

33. $4y^2 + 69y + 17$

Factor the 17 first since it has fewer factors than $4y^2$.
$(\quad + 17)(\quad + 1)$. Now try factors of $4y^2$.

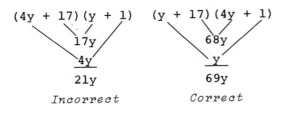

$(4y + 17)(y + 1)$ $(y + 17)(4y + 1)$
$\quad\quad 17y$ $\quad\quad 68y$
$\quad\quad \underline{4y}$ $\quad\quad \underline{y}$
$\quad\quad 21y$ $\quad\quad 69y$
Incorrect   *Correct*

$4y^2 + 69y + 17 = (y + 17)(4y + 1)$

37. $10x^2 + 11x - 6$

Both $10x^2$ and -6 have many factors. Try $(5x \quad)(2x \quad)$.

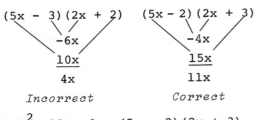

$(5x - 3)(2x + 2)$ $(5x - 2)(2x + 3)$
$\quad\quad -6x$ $\quad\quad -4x$
$\quad\quad \underline{10x}$ $\quad\quad \underline{15x}$
$\quad\quad 4x$ $\quad\quad 11x$
Incorrect   *Correct*

$10x^2 + 11x - 6 = (5x - 2)(2x + 3)$

41. $6q^2 + 23q + 21$

Start with $(2q \quad)(3q \quad)$. Use any positive integers for the factors of 21 since all the signs in $6q^2 + 23q + 21$ are positive. Try

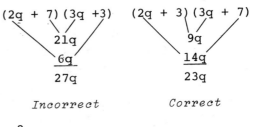

$(2q + 7)(3q + 3)$ $(2q + 3)(3q + 7)$
$\quad\quad 21q$ $\quad\quad 9q$
$\quad\quad \underline{6q}$ $\quad\quad \underline{14q}$
$\quad\quad 27q$ $\quad\quad 23q$
Incorrect   *Correct*

$6q^2 + 23q + 21 = (2q + 3)(3q + 7)$

Exercises 45-61 illustrate an alternate method of factoring trinomials in which the coefficient of the squared term is not 1.

45. $8k^2 + 2k - 15$

Look for integers whose product is $8(-15) = -120$ and whose sum is 2. The integers are 12 and -10.

$8k^2 + 2k - 15$

$= 8k^2 + 12k - 10k - 15$

$= 4k(2k + 3) - 5(2k + 3)$
$\quad\quad\quad\quad$ *Factor by grouping*

$= (2k + 3)(4k - 5)$

49. $8x^2 - 14x + 3$

Look for integers whose product is $8(3) = 24$ and whose sum is -14. The integers are -12 and -2.

$8x^2 - 14x + 3$

$= 8x^2 - 12x - 2x + 3$

$= 4x(2x - 3) - (2x - 3)$

$= (2x - 3)(4x - 1)$

53. $12p^2 + 7pq - 12q^2$

Look for integers whose product is $12(-12)$ or -144 and whose sum is 7.
The integers are 16 and -9.

$12p^2 + 7pq - 12q^2$

$= 12p^2 + 16pq - 9pq - 12q^2$

$= 4p(3p + 4q) - 3q(3p + 4q)$

$= (3p + 4q)(4p - 3q)$

57. $6a^2 - 7ab - 5b^2$

Look for integers whose product is $6(-5) = -30$ and whose sum is -7.

The integers are -10 and 3.

$6a^2 - 7ab - 5b^2$

$= 6a^2 - 10ab + 3ab - 5b^2$

$= 2a(3a - 5b) + b(3a - 5b)$

$= (3a - 5b)(2a + b)$

61. $32z^2w^4 - 20zw^4 - 12w^4$

$= 4w^4(8z^2 - 5z - 3)$
    Factor out the greatest common factor

Use the alternate method to factor the trinomial. Look for integers whose product is $8(-3) = -24$ and whose sum is -5.
The integers are -8 and 3.

$8z^2 - 5z - 3$

$= 8z^2 - 8z + 3z - 3$

$= 8z(z - 1) + 3(z - 1)$

$= (z - 1)(8z + 3)$

$32z^2w^4 - 20zw^4 - 12w^4$

$= 4w^4(z - 1)(8z + 3)$

65. $6m^6n + 7m^5n^2 + 2m^4n^3$

$= m^4n(6m^2 + 7mn + 2n^2)$
    Greatest common factor

Factor $6m^2 + 7mn + 2n^2$. Factor $2n^2$ first.

$(3m + 2n)(2m + n) = 6m^2 + 7mn + 2n^2$
    Correct

$6m^6n + 7m^5n^2 + 2m^4n^3$

$= m^4n(3m + 2n)(2m + n)$

69. $25q^2(m + 1)^3 - 5q(m + 1)^3 - 2(m + 1)^3$

$= (m + 1)^3(25q^2 - 5q - 2)$
    Greatest common factor

Factor $25q^2 - 5q - 2$.

$(5q + 2)(5q - 1)$

$= 25q^2 + 5q - 2$ *Incorrect*

$(5q - 2)(5q + 1)$

$= 25q^2 - 5q - 2$ *Correct*

$25q^2(m + 1)^3 - 5q(m + 1)^3 - 2(m + 1)^3$

$= (m + 1)^3(5q - 2)(5q + 1)$

73. $(x - 1)(x^2 + x + 1)$

$= (x)(x^2) + (x)(x) + (x)(1) +$

$(-1)(x^2) + (-1)(x) + (-1)(1)$
    Distributive property

$= x^3 + x^2 + x - x^2 - x - 1$
    Multiply

$= x^3 - 1$ *Simplify*

Section 4.4 (page 181)

1. $x^2 - 16 = (x)^2 - (4)^2$.

   $x^2 - 16 = (x + 4)(x - 4)$
   Difference of two squares

5. $9m^2 - 1 = (3m)^2 - (1)^2$

   $= (3m + 1)(3m - 1)$

9. The greatest common factor is 4.
   So

   $36t^2 - 16 = 4(9t^2 - 4)$
   Greatest common factor

   $9t^2 - 4 = (3t)^2 - (2)^2$
   Difference of two squares

   $= (3t + 2)(3t - 2)$

   Putting the above results together, we have

   $36t^2 - 16 = 4(3t + 2)(3t - 2)$

13. $x^2 + 16$ is not the <u>difference</u> of two squares, so cannot be factored and is prime.

17. $a^4 - 1 = (a^2)^2 - (1)^2$

   $= (a^2 + 1)(a^2 - 1)$

   Factor $a^2 - 1$.

   $a^2 - 1 = (a)^2 - (1)^2$

   $= (a + 1)(a - 1)$

   Putting the above results together, we have

   $a^4 - 1 = (a^2 + 1)(a + 1)(a - 1)$.

21. $a^2 + 4a + 4$

   The first term and the last term are perfect squares a^2 and 2^2. The middle term is positive. If this trinomial is a perfect square, the middle term is twice the product of the two terms of binomial

   $a + 2$

   or

   $2 \cdot a \cdot 2 = 4a$.

   Therefore,

   $a^2 + 4a + 4 = (a + 2)^2$

25. $49 + 14a + a^2$

   The first term, 49, and the last term, a^2, are perfect squares. The middle term is positive. If this trinomial is a perfect square, its the middle term is twice the product of the two terms of the binomial $7 + a$.

   $2 \cdot 7 \cdot a = 14a$

   Therefore,

   $49 + 14a + a^2 = (7 + a)^2$

29. $y^2 - 10y + 100$

   The first term $y^2 = (y)^2$ and the last term $100 = (10)^2$. The middle term is negative, so we try

   $(y - 10)^2$.

   The terms of the binomial are y and -10. Now, $2(y)(-10) = -20y$ which does <u>not</u> match the middle term -10y. So

   $y^2 - 10y + 100 \neq (y - 10)^2$.

There is no way to factor $y^2 - 10y + 100$ into the product of two binomials, so $y^2 - 10y + 100$ cannot be factored and is prime.

33. $4c^2 + 12cd + 9d^2$

The first and last terms are perfect squares. The middle term is twice the product of the first and last terms of the binomial 2c + 3d.

$$4c^2 + 12cd + 9d^2 = (2x + 3d)^2$$

37. $x^3y + 6x^2y^2 + 9xy^3$

$xy(x^2 + 6xy + 9y^2)$ *Greatest common factor*

Factor $x^2 + 6xy + 9y^2$

$$2 \cdot x \cdot 3y = 6xy$$

Therefore $x^2 + 6xy + 9y^2$ is a perfect square trinomial

$$x^2 + 7xy + 9t^2 = (x + 3y)^2$$

Putting the factors together, we have

$$x^3 + 6x^2y^2 + 9xy^3 = xy(x + 3y)^2.$$

41. $27x^3 - 125$

$= (3x) - 5^3$ *Difference of two cubes*

$= (3x - 5)[(3x)^2 + 3x \cdot 5 + 5^2]$

$= (3x - 5)(9x^2 + 15x + 25)$

45. $27a^3 - 64b^3$

$= (3a)^3 - (4b)^3$ *Difference of two cubes*

$= (3a - 4b)[(3a)^2 + 3a \cdot 4b + (4b)^2]$

$= (3a - 4b)(9a^2 + 12ab + 16b^2)$

49. $125m^3 - 8p^3$

$= (5m)^3 - (2p)^3$ *Difference of two cubes*

$= (5m - 2p)[(5m)^2 + 5m \cdot 2p + (2p)^2]$

$= (5m - 2p)(25m^2 + 10mp + 4p^2)$

53. $64y^6 + 1$

$= (4y^2)^3 + 1^3$ *Sum of two cubes*

$= (4y^2 + 1)[(4y^2)^2 - 4y^2 \cdot 1 + 1^2]$

$= (4y^2 + 1)(16y^4 - 4y^2 + 1)$

57. $1000a^3 - 343b^9$

$= (10a)^3 - (7b^3)^3$ *Difference of two cubes*

$= (10a - 7b^3) \cdot$
$\quad [(10a)^2 + 10a \cdot 7b^3 + (7b^3)^2]$

$= (10a - 7b^3)(100a^2 + 70ab^3 + 49b^6)$

61. $(a - b)^3 - (a + b)^3$ *Difference of two cubes*

Substitute into the rule using (a - b) for x and (a + b) for y.

$(a - b)^3 - (a + b)^3$

$= [(a - b) - (a + b)]$
$\quad [(a - b)^2 + (a - b)(a + b) + (a + b)^2]$

$= [a - b - a - b] \cdot$
$\quad [a^2 - 2ab + b^2 + a^2 - b^2 + a^2 + 2ab + b^2]$

$= [-2b][3a^2 + b^2]$

65. $(x^2 + 2x + 1) - 4$

Factor $x^2 + 2x + 1 = (x + 1)^2$, so

$(x^2 + 2x + 1) - 4 = (x + 1)^2 - (2)^2$
$\quad$ *A difference of squares*

Substitute into the rule using (x + 1) for x and 2 for y.

$(x + 1)^2 - (2)^2$

$= [(x+1) + (2)][(x + 1) - (2)]$

$= [x + 1 + 2][x - 1]$

$= [x + 3][x - 1]$

69. Find b such that $x^2 + bx + 25 = (x + 5)^2$.

$(x + 5)^2$ is a perfect square trinomial.

$(x + 5)^2 = (x)^2 + 2(x)(5) + (5)^2$

$= x^2 + 10x + 25$

Therefore, bx = 10x, and b = 10.

73. $m - 2 = 0$

$m - 2 + 2 = 0 + 2$

$m = 2$

77. $7a + 9 = 0$

$7a + 9 - 9 = 0 - 9$

$7a = -9$

$\dfrac{7a}{7} = \dfrac{-9}{7}$

$a = \dfrac{-9}{7}$

**Supplementary
Factoring Exercises (page 182)**

1. $a^2 - 4a - 12 = (a - 6)(a + 2)$

5. $6a + 12b + 18c$

$= 6(a + 2b + 3c)$ *Factor out the greatest common factor*

9. $10z^2 - 7z - 6$

$= 10z^2 - 12z + 5z - 6$
       Alternate method of factoring trinomials

$= 2z(5z - 6) + 1(5z - 6)$
       Factor by grouping

$= (5z - 6)(2z + 1)$

13. $8a^5 - 8a^4 - 48a^3$

$= 8a^3(a^2 - a - 6)$ *Factor out the greatest common factor*

$= 8a^3(a - 3)(a + 2)$ *Factor the trinomial*

17. $x^2 - 4x - 5x + 20$

$= x(x - 4) - 5(x - 4)$ *Factor by grouping*

$= (x - 5)(x - 4)$ *Common factor of x - 4*

21. $16x + 20 = 4(4x + 5)$ *Factor out the greatest common factor*

25. $6z^2 + 31z + 5 = (6z + 1)(z + 5)$
       Factor the trinomial

29. $54m^2 - 24z^2$

$= 6(9m^2 - 4z^2)$ *Factor out the greatest common factor*

$= 6(3m + 2z)(3m - 2z)$
       Difference of two squares

33. $14k^3 + 7k^2 - 70k$

$= 7k(2k^2 + k - 10)$ *Factor out the greatest common factor*

$= 7k(2k + 5)(k - 2)$ *Factor the trinomial*

37. $8m - 16m^2 = 8m(1 - 2m)$
       Factor out the greatest common factor

41. $k^2 + 9$ cannot be factored because it is not the difference of two squares.
The expression is prime.

45. $16r^2 + 24rm + 9m^2$

   $= (4r)^2 + 2 \cdot 4r \cdot 3m + (3m)^2$

   $= (4r + 3m)^2$ *Perfect square trinomial*

49. $k^2 - 11k + 30$

   $= (k - 6)(k - 5)$ *Factor the trinomial*

53. $1000p^3 + 27$ *Sum of cubes*

   Substitute into the rule using 10p for x and 3 for y.

   $1000p^3 + 27$

   $= (10p + 3)[(10p)^2 - (10p)(3) + (3)^2]$

   $= (10p + 3)(100p^2 - 30p + 9)$

57. $16z^2 - 8z + 1 = (4z - 1)^2$
   Perfect square trinomial

61. $64m^2 - 40mn + 25n^2$ is prime.

65. $20 + 5m + 12n + 3mn$

   $= 5(4 + m) + 3n(4 + m)$ *Factor by grouping*

   $= (4 + m)(5 + 3n)$ *Common factor of (4 + m)*

69. $a^3 - b^3 + 2a - 2b$

   $= (a - b)(a^2 + ab + b^2) + 2(a - b)$
   Factor by grouping. The first two terms form a difference of cubes.

   $= (a - b)(a^2 + ab + b^2 + 2)$
   Common factor of (a - b)

73. $8k^2 - 2kh - 3h^2$

   $= 8k^2 - 6kh + 4kh - 3h^2$
   Alternate method of factoring trinomials

   $= 2k(4k - 3h) + h(4k - 3h)$
   Factor by grouping

   $= (4k - 3h)(2k + h)$
   Common factor of (4k - 3h)

77. $10y^2 - 7yz - 6z^2$

   $= 10y^2 - 12yz + 5yz - 6z^2$
   Alternate method of factoring trinomials

   $= 2y(5y - 6z) + z(5y - 6z)$
   Factor by grouping

   $= (5y - 6z)(2y + z)$
   Common factor of (5y - 6z)

81. $9m^2 - 64 = (3m)^2 - 8^2$ *Difference of two squares*

   $= (3m + 8)(3m - 8)$

85. $a^2 + 8a + 16 = (a + 4)^2$
   Perfect square trinomial

Section 4.5 (page 187)

1. $(x - 2)(x + 4) = 0$

   Set each factor equal to 0.

   $x - 2 = 0$ or $x + 4 = 0$

   Solve each equation.

   $x - 2 + 2 = 0 + 2$ or $x + 4 - 4 = 0 - 4$
   $x = 2 \quad$ or $\quad x = -4$

   The solutions are 2 and −4.

5. $(5p + 1)(2p - 1) = 0$

   Set each factor equal to 0.

   $5p + 1 = 0$ or $2p - 1 = 0$

   Solve each equation.

   $5p + 1 - 1 = 0$ or $2p - 1 + 1 = 0 + 1$
   $5p = -1 \qquad\qquad 2p = 1$
   $p = \dfrac{-1}{5}$ or $\qquad p = \dfrac{1}{2}$

   The solutions are −1/5 and 1/2.

9. $(x - 1)(3x + 5) = 0$

    Set each factor equal to zero and solve.

    $x - 1 = 0$ or $3x + 5 = 0$
    $\qquad x = 1 \qquad\qquad 3x = -5$
    $\qquad\qquad\qquad\qquad\qquad x = \dfrac{-5}{3}$

    The solutions are 1 and -5/3.

13. $x^2 + 5x + 6 = 0$

    Factor the left side.

    $\qquad (x + 3)(x + 2) = 0$

    Set each factor equal to zero and solve.

    $x + 3 = 0$ or $x + 2 = 0$
    $\qquad x = -3$ or $\qquad x = -2$

    The solutions are -3 and -2.

17. $m^2 + 3m - 28 = 0$

    Factor the left side.

    $\qquad (m + 7)(m - 4) = 0$

    Set each factor equal to zero and solve.

    $m + 7 = 0$ or $m - 4 = 0$
    $\qquad m = -7$ or $\qquad m = 4$

    The solutions are -7 and 4.

21. $z^2 = -2 - 3z$

    Rewrite with all terms on the left side.

    $\qquad z^2 + 3z + 2 = 0$

    Factor the left side.

    $\qquad (z + 2)(z + 1) = 0$

    Set each factor equal to zero and solve.

    $z + 2 = 0$ or $z + 1 = 0$
    $\qquad z = -2$ or $\qquad z = -1$

    The solutions are -2 and -1.

25. $2k^2 - k - 10 = 0$

    Factor the left side.

    $\qquad (k + 2)(2k - 5) = 0$

    Set each factor equal to zero and solve.

    $k + 2 = 0$ or $2k - 5 = 0$
    $\qquad k = -2$ or $\qquad 2k = 5$
    $\qquad\qquad\qquad\qquad\qquad k = \dfrac{5}{2}$

    The solutions are -2 and 5/2.

29. $2z^2 + 3z = 20$

    Rewrite with all terms on the left side.

    $\qquad 2z^2 + 3z - 20 = 0$

    Factor the left side.

    $\qquad (2z - 5)(z + 4) = 0$

    Set each factor equal to zero and solve.

    $2z - 5 = 0$ or $z + 4 = 0$
    $\quad 2z = 5$
    $\qquad z = \dfrac{5}{2}$ or $\qquad z = -4$

    The solutions are 5/2 and -4.

33. $15r^2 = r + 2$

    Rewrite with all terms on the left side.

    $\qquad 15r^2 - r - 2 = 0$

    Factor the left side.

    $\qquad (5r - 2)(3r + 1) = 0$

Set each factor equal to zero and solve.

$$5r - 2 = 0 \quad \text{or} \quad 3r + 1 = 0$$
$$5r = 2 \qquad\qquad 3r = -1$$
$$r = \frac{2}{5} \quad \text{or} \qquad r = -\frac{1}{3}$$

The solutions are 2/5 and -1/3.

37. $16r^2 - 25 = 0$

Factor the left side.

$$(4r - 5)(4r + 5) = 0$$

Set each factor equal to zero and solve.

$$4r - 5 = 0 \quad \text{or} \quad 4r + 5 = 0$$
$$4r = 5 \qquad\qquad 4r = -5$$
$$r = \frac{5}{4} \quad \text{or} \qquad r = -\frac{5}{4}$$

The solutions are 5/4 and -5/4.

41. $m(m - 7) = -10$

$$m^2 - 7m = -10 \quad \textit{Simplify}$$

Rewrite with all terms on the left side.

$$m^2 - 7m + 10 = 0$$

Factor the left side.

$$(m - 5)(m - 2) = 0$$

Set each factor equal to zero and solve.

$$m - 5 = 0 \quad \text{or} \quad m - 2 = 0$$
$$m = 5 \quad \text{or} \qquad m = 2$$

The solutions are 5 and 2.

45. $3r(r + 1) = (2r + 3)(r + 1)$

Simplify each side.

$$3r^2 + 3r = 2r^2 + 5r + 3$$

Rewrite in standard form.

$$r^2 - 2r - 3 = 0$$

Factor the left side.

$$(r - 3)(r + 1) = 0$$

Set each factor equal to zero and solve.

$$r - 3 = 0 \quad \text{or} \quad r + 1 = 0$$
$$r = 3 \quad \text{or} \qquad r = -1$$

The solutions are 3 and -1.

49. $(2r - 5)(3r^2 - 16r + 5) = 0$

Factor $3r^2 - 16r + 5$ and rewrite.

$$(2r - 5)(3r - 1)(r - 5) = 0$$

Set each factor equal to zero and solve.

$$2r - 5 = 0 \quad \text{or} \quad 3r - 1 = 0 \quad \text{or} \quad r - 5 = 0$$
$$2r = 5 \qquad\qquad 3r = 1 \qquad\qquad r = 5$$
$$r = \frac{5}{2} \qquad\qquad r = \frac{1}{3}$$

The solutions are 5/2, 1/3, and 5.

53. $x^3 - 25x = 0$

Factor the left side.

$$x(x^2 - 25) = 0$$
$$x(x - 5)(x + 5) = 0$$

Set each factor equal to zero and solve.

$$x = 0 \quad \text{or} \quad x - 5 = 0 \quad \text{or} \quad x + 5 = 0$$
$$x = 5 \qquad\qquad x = -5$$

The solutions are 0, 5, and -5.

57. $r^3 - 2r^2 - 8r = 0$

Factor out r on the left side.

$r(r^2 - 2r - 8) = 0$ (Here, we do not divide by r because r is a variable and may equal zero.)

Factor $r^2 - 2r - 8$ as $(r - 4)(r + 2)$. Rewrite the original equation as

$\quad r(r - 4)(r + 2) = 0$

Set each factor equal to zero and solve.

$r = 0$ or $r - 4 = 0$ or $r + 2 = 0$
$\qquad\qquad\qquad r = 4 \qquad\qquad r = -2$

The solutions are 0, 4, and -2.

61. $r^4 = 2r^3 + 15r$

Rewrite with all terms on the left side.

$$r^4 - 2r^3 - 15r^2 = 0$$

Factor the left side.

$$r^2(r^2 - 2r - 15) = 0$$
$$r^2(r - 5)(r + 3) = 0$$

Set each factor equal to zero and solve.

$r^2 = 0$ or $r - 5 = 0$ or $r + 3 = 0$
$r = 0 \qquad\qquad r = 5 \qquad\qquad r = -3$

The solutions are 0, 5, and -3.

65. $(k + 3)^2 - (2k - 1) = 0$
$(k^2 + 6 + 9) - (4k^2 - 4k + 1) = 0$
$k^2 + 6k + 9 - 4k^2 + 4k - 1 = 0$
$\qquad -3k^2 + 10k + 8 = 0$
$\qquad\qquad\qquad\qquad\textit{Simplify}$
$(3k + 2)(-k + 4) = 0$
$\qquad\qquad\qquad\textit{Factor}$

Set each factor equal to zero and solve.

$3k + 2 = 0$ or $-k + 4 = 0$
$\quad 3k = -2 \qquad\qquad -k = -4$
$\quad k = -\dfrac{2}{3}$ or $\qquad k = 4$

The solutions are -2/3 and 4.

69. Let W = width of a rectangle.
W + 3 = length of a rectangle.

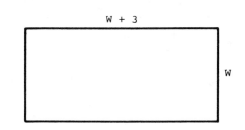

The perimeter is 34 meters. Use
$\quad P = 2L + 2W.$

$34 = 2(W + 3) + 2W$
$34 = 2W + 6 + 2W$
$34 = 4W + 6$
$28 = 4W$
$7 = W$

The width of the rectangle is 7 meters.

Section 4.6 (page 193)

1. Let W represent the width. Then W + 5 represents the length.

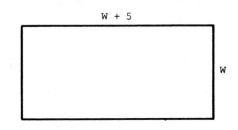

Use A = LW.

66 = (W + 5)W   *Substitute*
                    L = W + 5

Solve the equation.

$66 = W^2 + 5W$ *Simplify*

$0 = W^2 + 5W - 66$ *Get 0 alone*
                       on one side

$0 = (W + 11)(W - 6)$ *Factor*

Set each factor equal to zero
and solve.

W + 11 = 0   or   W - 6 = 0
       W = -11   or   W = 6

We reject -11 because width cannot be negative. So the width is
6 centimeters.

5. Let W represent the width.
    Then W + 3 represents the length.

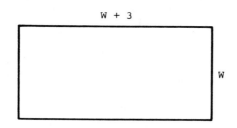

W + 3

W

Use the formula for the area of
a rectangle.

    A = LW
    A = (W + 3)W   *Substitute*
                      L = W + 3

Use the formula for the perimeter
of a rectangle.

    P = 2L + 2W
    P = 2(W + 3) + 2W   *Substitute*

The area   is numerically
     ↓   ↓
(W + 3)W   =

the perimeter   less 4.
     ↓   ↓ ↓
2(W +3) + 2   - 4.

Solve the equation.

(W + 3)W = 2(W + 3) + 2W - 4

$W^2 + 3W = 2W + 6 + 2W - 4$

$W^2 + 3W = 4W + 2$ *Simplify*

$W^2 + 3W - 4W - 2 = 0$ *Rewrite*

$W^2 - W - 2 = 0$ *Simplify*

(W - 2)(W + 1) = 0   *Factor*

W - 2 = 0   W + 1 = 0
   W = 2   W = -1 *Solve*

Reject -1 since width cannot be
negative. So the width of the
rectangle is 2 feet.

9. Let x represent the length of a
    side of the second square. Then
    x - 1 represents the length of a
    side of the first square.

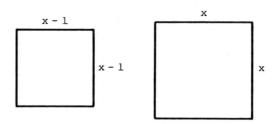

x - 1

x

x - 1

x

Use the formula

$$A = s^2.$$

The area of the first square is
$(x - 1)^2$.

The area of the second square is
x^2.

The difference of the areas is 37.
                    ↓   ↓ ↓
$x^2 - (x - 1)^2$ = 37

Solve

$$x^2 - (x - 1)^2 = 37.$$

$$x^2 - x^2 + 2x - 1 = 37$$

$$2x - 1 = 37 \quad \textit{Simplify}$$

$$2x = 38 \quad \textit{Rewrite}$$

$$x = 19$$

The length of a side of the second square is 19 feet.

13. Let x represent the length of the longer leg of the right triangle. Then x + 1 represents the hypotenuse. Also, x - 7 represents the length of the shorter leg of the triangle.

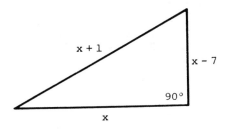

Use the Pythagorean formula

$$a^2 + b^2 = cz.$$

Substitute a = x, b = x - 7, and c = x + 1.

$$x^2 + (x - 7)^2 = (x + 1)^2$$

$$x^2 + x^2 - 14x + 49 = x^2 + 2x + 1$$

$$2x^2 - 14x + 49 = x^2 + 2x + 1$$

$$2x^2 - x^2 - 14x - 2x + 49 - 1 = 0$$

$$x^2 - 16x + 48 = 0$$

$$x - 12 = 0 \quad \text{or} \quad x - 4 = 0$$

$$x = 12 \quad \text{or} \quad x = 4$$

Reject 4 because if the longer leg is 4 meters long, by the conditions of the problem, the shorter leg is 4 - 7 or -3 meters which is impossible. So, the longer leg is 12 meters long.

17. Let x represent the first integer. Then x + 1 is the next consecutive integer.

Their product	is	2	more than	twice	their sum
↓	↓	↓	↓	↓	↓
x · (x + 1)	=	2	+	2 ·	(x + x + 1)

Solve the equation.

$$x^2 + x = 2 + 2(2x + 1)$$

$$x^2 + x = 2 + 4x + 2$$

$$x^2 + x = 4x \quad \textit{Simplify}$$

$$x^2 - 3x - 4 = 0 \quad \textit{Get 0 alone on one side}$$

$$(x - 4)(x + 1) = 0 \quad \textit{Factor}$$

$$x - 4 = 0 \quad \text{or} \quad x + 1 = 0$$

$$x = 4 \quad \text{or} \quad x = -1$$

We can use both solutions since we are not working with measurements here (such as feet or inches).

So the first integer is 4 or -1.

21. Let x represent the smaller number. Then x + 4 represents the larger number.

The square of the smaller	increased by	three times the larger	is	66.
↓	↓	↓	↓	↓
x^2	+	3(x + 4)	=	66

Solve the equation.

$$x^2 + 3(x + 4) = 66$$

$$x^2 + 3x + 12 = 66 \quad \textit{Simplify}$$

$$x^2 + 3x - 54 = 0 \quad \textit{Rewrite}$$

$$(x + 9)(x - 6) = 0 \quad \textit{Factor}$$

$$x + 9 = 0 \quad \text{or} \quad x - 6 = 0$$

$$x = -9 \quad \text{or} \qquad x = 6 \quad \textit{Solve}$$

If x = -9, then x + 4 = -5.
If x = 6, then 6 + 4 = 10.
The integers are -9 and -5   or
6 and 10.

25. Let x represent the length of the shorter leg. Then the hypotenuse is 2x + 1 and the longer leg is 2x - 1.

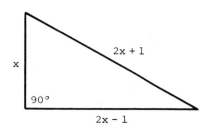

Use the Pythagorean formula. Let a = x, b = 2x - 1, and c = 2x + 1.

$$a^2 + b^2 = c^2$$

$$x^2 + (2x - 1)^2 = (2x + 1)^2$$
$$\textit{Substitute}$$

$$x^2 + 4x^2 - 4x + 1 = 4x^2 + 4x + 1$$

$$5x^2 - 4x + 1 = 4x^2 + 4x + 1$$
$$\textit{Simplify}$$

$$x^2 - 8x = 0$$
$$\textit{Get one side}$$
$$\textit{equal to zero}$$

$$x(x - 8) = 0 \quad \textit{Factor}$$

$$x = 0 \quad \text{or} \quad x - 8 = 0 \quad \textit{Solve}$$

$$x = 8$$

Reject 0 since a length cannot be 0. The length of the shorter leg is 8.

29. Let x be the numerical value of the area of the base. Then the height is x - 10. Use the formula for the volume of a pyramid.

$$V = \frac{1}{3}Bh$$

$$32 = \frac{1}{3}x(x - 10) \quad \textit{Substitute}$$

$$96 = x(x - 10) \quad \textit{Multiply both}$$
$$\textit{sides by 3}$$

$$96 = x^2 - 10x \quad \textit{Simplify}$$

$$0 = x^2 - 10x - 96 \quad \textit{Get one side}$$
$$\textit{equal to 0}$$

$$0 = (x - 16)(x + 16) \quad \textit{Factor}$$

$$x - 16 = 0 \quad \text{or} \quad x + 6 = 0 \quad \textit{Solve}$$

Since area cannot be negative, the area of the base is 16 square meters.

33. Use $d = \frac{1}{2}gt^2$ where g is 32 and d = 1600.

$$d = \frac{1}{2}gt^2$$

$$1600 = \frac{1}{2}(32)t^2 \qquad \textit{Substitute}$$

$$1600 = 16t^2 \qquad \textit{Simplify}$$

$$0 = 16t^2 - 1600 \quad \textit{Get one side}$$
$$\textit{equal to 0}$$

$$0 = 16(t^2 - 100) \quad \textit{Factor}$$

$$0 = 16(t - 10)(t + 10) \quad \textit{Factor}$$

$$t - 10 = 0 \quad \text{or} \quad t + 10 = 0 \quad \textit{Solve}$$

$$t = 10 \qquad\qquad t = -10$$

Since time cannot be negative, it takes 10 seconds for the object to fall.

37. Let v_0 be 64, t be 3 and use

$$h = v_0t - 16t^2$$

$$h = 64(3) - 16(3)^2 \quad \textit{Substitute}$$

$$= 192 - 16(9)$$

$$= 192 - 144$$

$$= 48$$

The height is 48 feet.

41.
$$x^2 - x + 4 \leq 0$$
$$(-2)^2 - (-2) + 4 \leq 0 \quad \text{\textit{Let }} x = -2$$
$$4 + 2 + 4 \leq 0$$
$$10 \leq 0$$

The inequality is false.

45.
$$(x - 1)(x^2 + 3x + 7) \leq 0$$
$$[(-2) - 1][(-2)^2 + 3(-2) + 7] \leq 0$$
$$\text{\textit{Let }} x = -2$$
$$(-3)(4 - 6 + 7) \leq 0$$
$$(-3)(5) \leq 0$$
$$-15 \leq 0$$

The inequality is true.

Section 4.7 (page 199)

In Exercises 1-29, see the answer graphs in the textbook.

1. $(m + 2)(m - 5) < 0$

First solve
$$(m + 2)(m - 5) = 0.$$
$$m + 2 = 0 \quad \text{or} \quad m - 5 = 0$$
$$m = -2 \quad \text{or} \quad m = 5$$

Use the solutions to divide a number line into three regions.

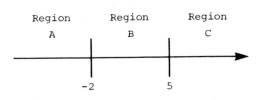

Now test any point from Region A, such as -3, in the inequality.
$$(m + 2)(m - 5) < 0$$
$$(-3 + 3)(-3 - 5) < 0 \quad \text{\textit{Let }} m = -3$$
$$(-1)(-8) < 0$$
$$8 < 0 \quad \text{\textit{False}}$$

No point in Region A is in the solution. Test 0 from Region B.
$$(0 + 2)(0 - 5) < 0 \quad \text{\textit{Let }} m = 0$$
$$2(-5) < 0$$
$$-10 < 0 \quad \text{\textit{True}}$$

All the points in Region are in the solution.

Test 6 from Region C.
$$(6 + 2)(6 - 5) < 0 \quad \text{\textit{Let }} m = 6$$
$$8(1) < 0$$
$$8 < 0 \quad \text{\textit{False}}$$

No point in Region C is in the solution.
Therefore, only points in Region B are in the solution. The endpoints are not in the solution. The solution is
$$-2 < m < 5.$$

5. $(a + 3)(a - 3) = 0$

Solve $(a + 3)(a - 3) = 0$, getting the solutions -3 and 3. Use these to divide the line into three regions.

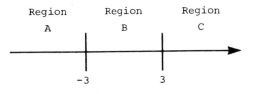

Test -4 from Region A in the inequality.
$$(-4 + 3)(-4 - 3) < 0$$
$$-1(-7) < 0$$
$$7 < 0 \quad \text{\textit{False}}$$

Region A is not part of the solution.

Test 0 from Region B.

$$(0 + 3)(0 - 3) < 0$$
$$3(-3) < 0$$
$$-9 < 0 \quad \textit{True}$$

Region B is part of the solution.

Test 4 from Region C.

$$(4 + 3)(4 - 3) < 0$$
$$7(1) < 0$$
$$7 < 0 \quad \textit{False}$$

Region C is not part of the solution,
The solution is

$$-3 < a < 3.$$

9. $m^2 + 5m + 6 > 0$

Solve

$$m^2 + 5m + 6 = 0$$
$$(m + 3)(m + 2) = 0 \quad \textit{Factor}$$
$$m = -3 \quad \text{or} \quad m = -2$$

Region A	Region B	Region C

$$\xleftarrow{\quad \overset{\displaystyle |}{-3} \quad \overset{\displaystyle |}{-2} \quad} \rightarrow$$

Test -4 from Region A.

$$m^2 + 5m + 6 > 0$$
$$(-4)^2 + 5(-4) + 6 > 0$$
$$16 - 20 + 6 > 0$$
$$2 > 0 \quad \textit{True}$$

Test -5/2 from Region B.

$$(-\tfrac{5}{2})^2 + 5(-\tfrac{15}{2}) + 6 > 0$$
$$\tfrac{25}{4} - \tfrac{25}{2} + 6 > 0$$
$$-\tfrac{1}{4} > 0 \quad \textit{False}$$

Test 0 from Region C.

$$0^2 + 5(0) + 6 > 0$$
$$6 > 0 \quad \textit{True}$$

The points in Region A and C are in the solution

$$m < -3 \quad \text{or} \quad m > -2.$$

13. $5m^2 + 3m - 2 < 0$

Solve

$$5m^2 + 3m - 2 = 0$$
$$(5m - 2)(m + 1) = 0$$
$$m = \tfrac{2}{5} \quad \text{or} \quad m = -1$$

Region A	Region B	Region C

$$\xleftarrow{\quad \overset{\displaystyle |}{-1} \quad \overset{\displaystyle |}{2/5} \quad} \rightarrow$$

Test -2 from Region A.

$$5m^2 + 3m - 2 < 0$$
$$5(-2)^2 + 3(-2) - 2 < 0$$
$$20 - 6 - 2 < 0$$
$$12 < 0 \quad \textit{False}$$

Test 0 from Region B.

$$5(0)^2 + 3(0) - 2 < 0$$
$$-2 < 0 \quad \textit{True}$$

Test 1 from Region C.

$$5(1)^2 + 3(1) - 2 < 0$$
$$5 + 3 - 2 < 0$$
$$6 < 0 \quad \textit{False}$$

Only points in Region B are in the solution

$$-1 < m < \tfrac{2}{5}.$$

17. $q^2 - 7q + 6 < 0$

Solve

$q^2 - 7q + 6 = 0$

$(q - 6)(q - 1) = 0$ *Factor*

$q = 6$ or $q = 1$

Region A	Region B	Region C

```
                 |         |
  ──────────────┼─────────┼──────────▶
                 1         6
```

In Region A, let $q = 0$.

$q^2 - 7q + 6 < 0$

$0^2 - 7(0) + 6 < 0$

$6 < 0$ *False*

Region A is not in the solution.
In Region B, let $q = 2$.

$q^2 - 7q + 6 < 0$

$(2)^2 - 7(2) + 6 < 0$

$4 - 14 + 6 < 0$

$-4 < 0$ *True*

Region B is in the solution.
In Region C, let $q = 7$.

$q^2 - 7q + 6 < 0$

$(7)^2 - 7(7) + 6 < 0$

$49 - 49 + 6 < 0$

$6 < 0$ *False*

Region C is not in the solution.
The solution is

$1 < q < 6$.

21. $12p^2 + 11p + 2 < 0$

Solve

$12p^2 + 11p + 2 = 0$

$(3p + 2)(4p + 1) = 0$ *Factor*

$p = \dfrac{-2}{3}$ or $p = -\dfrac{1}{4}$

Region A	Region B	Region C

```
                 |         |
  ──────────────┼─────────┼──────────▶
               -2/3      -1/4
```

In Region A, try $p = -1$.

$12p^2 + 11p + 2 < 0$

$12(-1)^2 + 11(-1) + 2 < 0$

$12 - 11 + 2 < 0$

$3 < 0$ *False*

Region A is not in the solution.
In Region B, try $p = -1/2$.

$12\left(-\dfrac{1}{2}\right)^2 + 11\left(-\dfrac{1}{2}\right) + 2 < 0$

$12\left(\dfrac{1}{4}\right) - \dfrac{11}{2} + 2 < 0$

$3 - \dfrac{11}{2} + 2 < 0$

$5 - \dfrac{11}{2} < 0$

$-\dfrac{1}{2} < 0$ *True*

Region B is in the solution.
In Region C, try $p = 0$.

$12(0)^2 + 11(0) + 2 < 0$

$2 < 0$ *False*

Region C is not in the solution.
The solution is

$\dfrac{-2}{3} < p < -\dfrac{1}{4}$.

25. $r^2 > 16$

Solve

$r^2 = 16$.

$r = \pm 4$

Region A	Region B	Region C

```
                 |         |
  ──────────────┼─────────┼──────────▶
                -4         4
```

Test -5 from Region A.

$(-5)^2 > 16$

$25 > 16$ *True*

Test 0 from Region B.

$$0^2 > 16$$
$$0 > 16 \quad \textit{False}$$

Test 5 from Region C.

$$5^2 > 16$$
$$25 > 16 \quad \textit{True}$$

The solution is

$$r < -4 \quad \text{or} \quad r > 4.$$

29. $(r - 2)(r^2 - 3r - 4) < 0$

Solve

$$(r - 2)(r^2 - 3r - 4) = 0$$
$$(r - 2)(r - 4)(r + 1) = 0$$
$$r = 2 \quad \text{or} \quad r = 4 \quad \text{or} \quad r = -1$$

They have four regions.

Region	Region	Region	Region
A	B	C	D

$$\xrightarrow{\quad\; |_{-1}\quad\;|_{2}\quad\;|_{4}\quad\;}$$

Test -2 from Region A.

$$(r - 2)(r^2 - 3r - 4) < 0$$
$$(-2 - 2)[(-2)^2 - 3(-2) - 4] < 0$$
$$(-4)(4 + 6 - 4) < 0$$
$$-24 < 0$$
$$\textit{True}$$

Test 0 from Region B.

$$(0 - 2)[0^2 - 3(0) - 4] < 0$$
$$-2(-4) < 0$$
$$8 < 0 \quad \textit{False}$$

Test 3 from Region C.

$$(3 - 2)[3^2 - 3(3) - 4] < 0$$
$$1(9 - 9 - 4) < 0$$
$$-4 < 0 \quad \textit{True}$$

Test from Region D.

$$(5 - 2)[5^2 - 3(5) - 4] < 0$$
$$3(25 - 15 - 4) < 0$$
$$18 < 0 \quad \textit{False}$$

Only points in Region A and C are in the solution

$$r < -1 \quad \text{or} \quad 2 < r < 4.$$

33. $\dfrac{14}{42} = \dfrac{1}{3}$ *Divide both numerator and denominator by 14*

37. $\dfrac{26}{156} = \dfrac{1}{6}$ *Divide both numerator and denominator by 26*

Chapter 4 Review Exercises (page 201)

1. $6 - 18r^5 + 12r^3$

The greatest common factor of

$6 - 18r^5 + 12r^3$ is 6.

$$6 - 18r^5 + 12r^3 = 6(1 - 3r^5 + 2r^3)$$

5. $r^2 - 6r - 27 = (r - 9)(r + 3)$

9. $p^7 - p^6q - 2p^5q^2$

$$= p^5(p^2 - pq - 2q^2)$$
$$= p^5(p - 2q)(p + q)$$

13. $6r^2 - 5r - 6$

Two integers with product 6(-6) or -36 and sum -5 are -9 and 4.

$$= 6r^2 - 9r + 4r - 6$$
$$= 3r(2r - 3) + 2(2r - 3)$$
$$= (2r - 3)(3r + 2)$$

17. $100a^2 - 9 = (10a)^2 - 3^2$

$$= (10a + 3)(10a - 3)$$

21. $16m^2 + 40mn + 25n^2$

$= (4m)^2 + 2(4m)(5n) + (5n)^2$

$= (4m + 5n)^2$

25. $343x^3 + 64$

$= (7x - 4)(49x^2 - 28x + 16)$

29.
$$p^2 = 12(p - 3)$$
$$p^2 = 12p - 36$$
$$p^2 - 12p + 36 = 0$$
$$(p - 6)^2 = 0$$
$$p - 6 = 0$$
$$p = 6$$

The only solution is 6.

33. Let x represent the smaller even integer.

Then x + 2 represents the next consecutive even integer.

Their product	is	4	more then	twice their sum
↓	↓	↓		↓
x(x + 2)	=	4	+	2(x + x + 2)

$$x^2 + 2x = 4 + 2(2x + 2)$$
$$x^2 + 2x = 4 + 4x + 4$$
$$x^2 + 2x = 8 + 4x$$
$$x^2 + 2x - 4x - 8 = 0$$
$$x^2 - 2x - 8 = 0$$
$$(x - 4)(x + 2) = 0$$
$$x - 4 = 0 \quad \text{or} \quad x = 2 = 0$$
$$x = 4 \quad \text{or} \quad x = -2$$

If x = 4, then x + 2 = 6
If x = -2, then x + 2 = 0
The integers are 4 and 6 or -2 and 0.

37. $m^2 - 5m + 6 \leq 0$

Find the solution of the corresponding quadratic equation,

$$m^2 - 5m + 6 = 0$$
$$(m - 3)(m - 2) = 0 \qquad \textit{Factor}$$
$$m - 3 = 0 \quad \text{or} \quad m - 2 = 0 \qquad \textit{Solve}$$
$$m = 3 \quad \text{or} \qquad m = 2$$

The values 3 and 2 determine three regions on the number line.

Try the point 1 from Region A.

$$(1 - 3)(1 - 2) \leq 0$$
$$(-2)(-1) \leq 0$$
$$2 \leq 0 \qquad \textit{False}$$

Region A is not part of the solution.

Try $2\frac{1}{2}$ from Region B.

$$(2\frac{1}{2} - 3)(2\frac{1}{2} - 2) \leq 0$$
$$(-\frac{1}{2})(\frac{1}{2}) \leq 0$$
$$-\frac{1}{4} \leq 0 \qquad \textit{True}$$

Region B is part of the solution.
Try 4 Region C.

$$(4 - 3)(4 - 2) \leq 0$$
$$(1)(2) \leq 0$$
$$2 \leq 0 \qquad \textit{False}$$

Region C is not part of the solution.
The endpoints 2 and 3 are in the solution. The solution is written

$$2 \leq m \leq 3.$$

41. $r^2 - 4rs - 96s^2 = (r - 12s)(r + 8s$

45. $m^2 + 9$ is a prime polynomial.

49. $y^2 - 8yz + 15z^2 = (y - 5z)(y - 3z)$

53. $15m^2 + 20mp - 12mp - 16p^2$

$= 5m(3m + 4p) - 4p(3m + 4p)$
Factor by grouping

$= (3m + 4p)(5m - 4p)$

57. Let x represent the height.
Then x + 2 represents the base.
Use $A = \frac{1}{2}bh$.

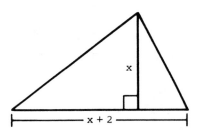

Substitute A = 12, b = x + 2,
h = x

$12 = \frac{1}{2}(x + 2)x$

$24 = (x + 2)x$

$24 = x^2 + 2x$

$x^2 + 2x - 24 = 0$

$(x + 6)(x - 4) = 0$

$x + 6 = 0$ or $x - 4 = 0$

$x = -6$ or $x = 4$

Reject x = -6. The height is 4
meters and the base is 4 + 2 or
6 meters.

Chapter 4 Test   (page 202)

1. $6ab - 36ab^2 = 6ab(1 - 6b)$
Factor out the greatest common factor 6ab

2. $15k^2t + 25kt^2$

$= 5kt(3k + 5t)$ *Factor out the greatest common factor 5kt*

3. $16m^2 - 24m^3 + 32m^4$

$= 8m^2(2 - 3m + 4m^2)$
Factor out the greatest common factor $8m^2$

4. $28pq + 14p + 56p^2q^3$

$= 14p(2q + 1 + 4pq^3)$
Factor out the greatest common factor 14p

5. $m^2 - 9m - 3m + 27$

$= m(m - 9) - 3(m - 9)$
The first two terms have a common factor of m, and the last two terms have a common factor of -3

$= (m - 9)(m - 3)$ *Now, m - 9 is a common factor*

6. $12 - 6a + 2b - ab$

$= 6(2 - a) + b(2 - a)$
The first two terms have a common factor of 6, and the last two terms have a common factor of b

$= (2 - a)(6 + b)$ *Now, 2 - a is a common factor*

7. $x^2 - 4x - 45 = (x - 9)(x + 5)$

8. $3p^4q + 18p^3q - 21p^2q$

$= 3p^2q(p^2 + 6p - 7)$
Factor out the greatest common factor $3p^2q$

$= 3p^2q(p + 7)(p - 1)$

9. $3a^2 + 13a - 10 = (3a - 2)(a + 5)$

10. $30z^5 - 6pz^4 - 15z^3$

$= 3z^3(10z^2 - 23z - 5)$
Factor out the greatest common factor $3z^3$

$= 3z^3(2z - 5)(5z + 1)$

11. $12r^2p^2 + 19rp^2 + 5p^2$

$= p^2(12r^2 + 19r + 5)$
Factor out the greatest common factor p^2

$= p^2(3r + 1)(4r + 5)$

12. $6t^2 - tx - 2x^2$

$= (3t - 2x)(2t + x)$

13. $50m^2 - 98$

$= 2(25m^2 - 49)$ *Factor out the common factor 2*

$= 2(5m + 7)(5m - 7)$ *Difference of two squares*

14. $144a^2 - 169b^2$

$= (12a + 13b)(12a - 13b)$
Difference of two squares

15. $a^4 - 625$

$= (a^2 + 25)(a^2 - 25)$
Difference of two squares

$= (a^2 + 25)(a + 5)(a - 5)$
Again, difference of two squares

16. $4p^2 + 12p + 9$

$= (2p)^2 + 2(2p)(3) + (3)^2$

$= (2p + 3)^2$ *Perfect square trinomial*

or factor like any trinomial:

$4p^2 + 12p + 9 = (2p + 3)(2p + 3)$

$= (2p + 3)^2$

17. $25z^2 - 10z + 1$

$= (5z)^2 - 2(5z)(1) + (1)^2$

$= (5z - 1)^2$ *Perfect square trinomial*

or

$25z^2 - 10z + 1 = (5z - 1)(5z - 1)$

$= (5z - 1)^2$

18. $4y^3 + 16y^2 + 16y$

$= 4y(y^2 + 4y + 4)$
Factor out common factor 4y

$= 4y(y + 2)(y + 2)$

$= 4y(y + 2)^2$ *Perfect square trinomial*

19. $8p^3 - 125$

$= (2p - 5)[(2p)^2 + (2p)(5) + (5)^2]$
Difference of two cubes

$= (2p - 5)(4p^2 + 10p + 25)$

20. $27r^3 + 64t^6$

$= (3r + 4t^2)[(3r)^2 - (3r)(4t^2) + (4t^2)^2]$
Sum of two cubes

$= (3r + 4t^2)(9r^2 - 12rt^2 + 16t^4)$

21. $m^2 - n^2 - 4m - 4n$

$= (m - n)(m + n) - 4(m + n)$
The first two terms form a difference of squares and the last two have a common factor of -4.

$= (m + n)(m - n - 4)$
Now $(m + n)$ is a common factor

$= (m - n - 4)(m + n)$
Either form is correct

22.
$$3x^2 + 5x = 2$$
$$3x^2 + 5x - 2 = 0$$
$$(3x - 1)(x + 2) = 0$$
$$3x - 1 = 0 \quad \text{or} \quad x + 2 = 0$$
$$3x = 1 \qquad\qquad x = -2$$
$$x = \frac{1}{3}$$

The solutions are 1/3 and -2.

23.
$$p(2p + 3) = 20$$
$$2p^2 + 3p = 20 \quad \textit{Get 0 alone on one side}$$
$$2p^2 + 3p - 20 = 0$$
$$(2p - 5)(p + 4) = 0$$
Factor the left side
$$2p - 5 = 0 \quad \text{or} \quad p + 4 = 0$$
Set each factor equal to zero and solve
$$2p = 5 \quad \text{or} \qquad p = -4$$
$$p = \frac{5}{2}$$

The solution is 5/2.

24. $(m - 3)(6m^2 - 11m - 10) = 0$

Factor $6m^2 - 11m - 10$ as $(2m - 5) \cdot (3m + 2)$.

$$(m - 3)(2m - 5)(3m + 2) = 0$$

Set each factor equal to zero and solve.

$$m - 3 = 0 \quad \text{or} \quad 2m - 5 = 0 \quad \text{or} \quad 3m + 2 = 0$$
$$m = 3 \qquad\qquad 2m = 5 \qquad\qquad 3m = -2$$
$$m = \frac{5}{2} \qquad\qquad m = \frac{-2}{3}$$

The solution is 3, 5/2, and -2/3.

25.
$$z^3 = 16z$$
$$z^3 - 16z = 0$$
$$z(z^2 - 16) = 0$$
$$z(z + 4)(z - 4) = 0$$

$$z = 0 \quad \text{or} \quad z + 4 = 0 \quad \text{or} \quad z - 4 = 0$$
$$z = -4 \qquad\qquad z = 4$$

The solutions are 0, -4, and 4.

26.   Let x represent the width.
Then 2x - 1 represents the length.

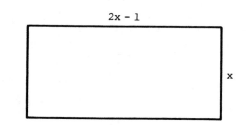

2x - 1

x

Use A = LW.
Substitute A = 15, L = 2x - 1, and W = x

$$15 = (2x - 1)(x)$$
$$15 = 2x^2 - x$$
$$2x^2 - x - 15 = 0$$
$$2x^2 + 5x - 6x - 15 = 0$$
$$x(2x + 5) - 3(2x + 5) = 0$$
$$(2x + 5)(x - 3) = 0$$
$$2x + 5 = 0 \qquad \text{or} \quad x - 3 = 0$$
$$2x = -5 \qquad\qquad x = 3$$
$$x = -5/2$$

Reject x = -5/2 because the width cannot be negative.
If x = 3, then 2x - 1 = 5.
The width of the rectangle is 3 inches.

27.   Let x represent the small number.
Then x + 9 represents the large number.

Their product	is	11 more		5 times	their sum
↓	↓	↓	↓	↓	↓
x(x + 9)	=	11	+	5 ·	(x + x + 9).

Solve the equation.

$$x^2 + 9x = 11 + 5(2x + 9)$$

$$x^2 + 9x = 11 + 10x + 45$$

$$x^2 + 9x = 10x + 56 \quad \textit{Simplify}$$

$$x^2 - x - 56 = 0 \quad \textit{Get 0 alone on one side}$$

$$(x - 8)(x + 7) = 0 \quad \textit{Factor}$$

$$x - 8 = 0 \quad \text{or} \quad x + 7 = 0$$
Set each factor equal to zero and solve

$$x = 8 \quad \text{or} \quad x = -7$$

When the small number is 8, the large number is 8 + 9 = 17. Also, when the small number is -7, the large number is -7 + 9 = 2.

28. Let x represent the length of the shorter leg.
Then the hypotenuse is 3x - 7 and the longer leg is 2x - 1.

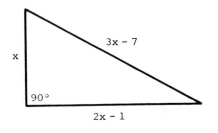

Use the Pythagorean formula
$$a^2 + b^2 = c^2 \text{ where}$$
$$a = x, \ b = 2x - 1, \text{ and } c = 3x - 7.$$

$$x^2 + (2x - 1)^2 = (3x - 7)^2$$

$$x^2 + 4x^2 - 4x + 1 = 9x^2 - 42x + 49$$
Simplify

$$0 = 4x^2 - 38x + 48$$
Get one side equal to zero

$$0 = 2(2x^2 - 19x + 24)$$

$$0 = 2(x - 8)(2x - 3)$$
Factor

$$x - 8 = 0 \quad \text{or} \quad 2x - 3 = 0$$
Set the factors equal to zero

$$x = 8 \qquad x = \frac{3}{2}$$

Reject x = 3/2 since then the hypotenuse (3x - 7) would be negative. The length of the shorter leg is 8.

29. $2p^2 + 5p - 3 \leq 0$

Solve the quadratic equation

$$2p^2 + 5p - 3 = 0$$
$$(2p - 1)(p + 3) = 0$$

$$2p - 1 = 0 \quad \text{or} \quad p + 3 = 0$$
$$2p = 1 \qquad\qquad p = -3$$
$$p = \frac{1}{2}$$

The solutions -3 and 1/2 determine 3 Regions on the answer line.

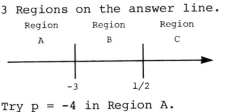

Try p = -4 in Region A.

$$[2(-4) - 1][-4 + 3] \leq 0$$
$$[-9](-1) \leq 0$$
$$9 \leq 0 \quad \textit{False}$$

Region A is not part of the solution.
Try p = 0 in Region B.

$$[2(0) - 1][0 + 3] \leq 0$$
$$[-1][3] \leq 0$$
$$-3 \leq 0 \quad \textit{True}$$

Region B is part of the solution.
Try p = 1 in Region C.

$$[2(1) - 1][1 + 3] \leq 0$$
$$[1][4] \leq 0$$
$$4 \leq 0 \quad \textit{False}$$

Region C is not part of the solution.

The solution is

$$-3 \leq p \leq \frac{1}{2}.$$

30. $m^2 + 2m - 24 > 0$

Solve the corresponding quadratic equation.

$$m^2 + 2m - 24 = 0$$
$$(m + 6)(m - 4) = 0$$
$$m + 6 = 0 \quad \text{or} \quad m - 4 = 0$$
$$m = -6 \qquad\qquad m = 4$$

The solutions -6 and 4 determine 3 Regions on the number line.

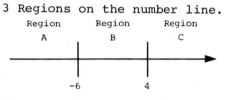

Try m = -7 in Region A.

$$(-7 + 6)(-7 - 4) > 0$$
$$(-1)(-11) > 0$$
$$11 > 0 \quad \textit{True}$$

Region A is part of the solution.
Try m = 0 in Region B.

$$(0 + 6)(0 - 4) > 0$$
$$(6)(-4) > 0$$
$$-24 > 0 \quad \textit{False}$$

Region B is not part of the solution.
Try m = 5 in Region C.

$$(5 + 6)(5 - 4) > 0$$
$$(11)(1) > 0$$
$$11 > 0 \quad \textit{True}$$

The solution is

$$m < -6 \quad \text{or} \quad m > 4.$$

CHAPTER 5 RATIONAL EXPRESSIONS

Section 5.1 (page 208)

1. The denominator 4x will be zero when x = 0. So $\frac{3}{4x}$ is x = 0.

5. To find the values for which the expression is undefined, set the denominator equal to zero and solve for a.

$$a^2 - 8a + 15 = 0$$
$$(a - 5)(a - 3) = 0 \quad \textit{Factor}$$
$$a - 5 = 0 \quad \text{or} \quad a - 3 = 0$$
$$a = 5 \qquad\qquad a = 3$$

The expression is undefined for 3 and 5.

9. (a) $\dfrac{4x - 2}{3x} = \dfrac{4 \cdot 2 - 2}{3 \cdot 2} \quad \textit{Let } x = 2$

$$= \frac{8 - 2}{6}$$

$$= \frac{6}{6}$$

$$= 1$$

(b) $\dfrac{4x - 2}{3x} = \dfrac{4(-3) - 2}{3(-3)} \quad \textit{Let } x = -3$

$$= \frac{-12 - 2}{-9}$$

$$= \frac{-14}{-9}$$

$$= \frac{14}{9}$$

13. (a) $\dfrac{(-8x)^2}{3x + 9} = \dfrac{(-8 \cdot 2)^2}{3 \cdot 2 + 9} \quad \textit{Let } x = 2$

$$= \frac{(-16)^2}{6 + 9}$$

$$= \frac{256}{15}$$

(b) $\dfrac{(-8x)^2}{3x + 9} = \dfrac{(-8) \cdot (-3)^2}{3(-3) + 9} \quad \textit{Let } x = -3$

$$= \frac{(24)^2}{-9 + 9} \quad \textit{Simplify}$$

$$= \frac{(24)^2}{0}$$

The expression is undefined for x = -3.

17. (a) $\dfrac{5x^2}{6 - 3x - x^2}$

$$= \frac{5(2)^2}{6 - 3(2) - (2)^2} \quad x = 2$$

$$= \frac{5(4)}{6 - 6 - (4)} \quad \textit{Simplify}$$

$$= \frac{20}{-4}$$

$$= -5$$

(b) $\dfrac{5x^2}{6 - 3x - x^2}$

$$= \frac{5(-3)^2}{6 - 3(-3) - (-3)^2} \quad \begin{array}{l}\textit{Let}\\ x = -3\end{array}$$

$$= \frac{5(9)}{6 + 9 - 9} \quad (-3)^2 = -3(-3)$$

$$= \frac{45}{6} \quad \textit{Simplify}$$

$$= \frac{15}{2}$$

21. $\dfrac{12k^2}{6k} = \dfrac{2 \cdot 2 \cdot 3 \cdot k \cdot k}{2 \cdot 3 \cdot k} \quad \textit{Factor}$

$$= \frac{(2 \cdot 3 \cdot k) 2 \cdot k}{(2 \cdot 3 \cdot k)}$$

$$= 2k \quad \textit{Fundamental property}$$

25. $\dfrac{6(y + 2)}{8(y + 2)} = \dfrac{2 \cdot 3(y + 2)}{2 \cdot 2 \cdot 2(y + 2)} \quad \textit{Factor}$

$$= \frac{3}{2 \cdot 2} \quad \begin{array}{l}\textit{Fundamental}\\ \textit{property}\end{array}$$

$$= \frac{3}{4}$$

29. $\dfrac{12m^2 - 9}{3} = \dfrac{3(4m^2 - 3)}{3}$ *Factor*

$= 4m^2 - 3$ *Fundamental property*

33. $\dfrac{2q - 6}{5q - 10} = \dfrac{2(q - 3)}{5(q - 2)}$

This expression cannot be written in simpler form.

37. $\dfrac{5m^2 - 5m}{10m - 10} = \dfrac{5m(m - 1)}{10(m - 1)}$

$= \dfrac{5m(m - 1)}{2 \cdot 5(m - 1)}$ *Factor*

$= \dfrac{m}{2}$ *Fundamental property*

41. $\dfrac{m^2 - 4m + 4}{m^2 + m - 6}$

$= \dfrac{(m - 2)(m - 2)}{(m - 2)(m + 3)}$ *Factor*

$= \dfrac{m - 2}{m + 3}$ *Fundamental property*

45. $\dfrac{m - 5}{5 - m} = \dfrac{-1(5 - m)}{(5 - m)}$ *Factor*

$= 1$ *Fundamental property*

49. $\dfrac{x^2 - 1}{1 - x}$

$= \dfrac{(x + 1)(x - 1)}{-1(x - 1)}$ *Factor*

$= \dfrac{x + 1}{-1}$ *Fundamental property*

$= -(x + 1)$ or $-x - 1$

53. $\dfrac{a + b + a^2 + ba}{ab + b^2}$

$= \dfrac{1(a + b) + a(a + b)}{b(a + b)}$ *Factor*

$= \dfrac{(a + b)(1 + a)}{b(a + b)}$

$= \dfrac{1 + a}{b}$ *Fundamental property*

57. $\dfrac{b^3 - a^3}{a^2 - b^2}$

$= \dfrac{(b - a)(b^2 + ab + a^2)}{(a - b)(a + b)}$ *Factor*

$= \dfrac{-1(a - b)(b^2 + ab + a^2)}{(a - b)(a + b)}$

$= \dfrac{-1(b^2 + ab + a^2)}{a + b}$ *Fundamental property*

or $- \dfrac{b^2 + ab + a^2}{a + b}$

61. $\dfrac{3}{4} \cdot \dfrac{5}{8} = \dfrac{3 \cdot 5}{4 \cdot 8}$

$= \dfrac{15}{32}$

65. $\dfrac{6}{5} \div \dfrac{3}{10} = \dfrac{6}{5} \cdot \dfrac{10}{3}$

$= \dfrac{6 \cdot 10}{5 \cdot 3}$

$= \dfrac{3 \cdot 2 \cdot 2 \cdot 5}{5 \cdot 3}$

$= 2 \cdot 2$

$= 4$

Section 5.2   (page 213)

1. $\dfrac{9m^2}{16} \cdot \dfrac{4}{3m} = \dfrac{9m^2 \cdot 4}{16 \cdot 3m}$

$= \dfrac{36m^2}{48m}$ *Multiply*

$= \dfrac{3m}{4}$

5. $\dfrac{8a^4}{12a^3} \cdot \dfrac{9a^5}{3a^2} = \dfrac{8a^4 \cdot 9a^5}{12a^3 \cdot 3a^2}$

$= \dfrac{72a^9}{36a^5}$ *Multiply*

$= 2a^4$

9. $\dfrac{3m^2}{(4m)^3} \div \dfrac{9m^3}{32m^4} = \dfrac{3m^2}{64m^3} \cdot \dfrac{32m^4}{9m^3}$

Multiply by the reciprocal

$= \dfrac{96m^6}{576m^6}$

$= \dfrac{1}{6}$

13. $\dfrac{a + b}{2} \cdot \dfrac{12}{(a + b)^2} = \dfrac{12(a + b)}{2(a + b)^2}$

$= \dfrac{6}{a + b}$

17. $\dfrac{9y - 18}{6y + 12} \cdot \dfrac{3y + 6}{15y - 30}$

$= \dfrac{9(y - 2) \cdot 3(y + 2)}{6(y + 2) \cdot 15(y - 2)}$ *Factor*

$= \dfrac{27(y - 2)(y + 2)}{90(y + 2)(y - 2)}$ *Multiply*

$= \dfrac{3}{10}$ *Fundamental property*

21. $\dfrac{y^2 - 16}{y + 3} \div \dfrac{y - 4}{y^2 - 9}$

$= \dfrac{(y + 4)(y - 4)}{y + 3} \div \dfrac{y - 4}{(y + 3)(y - 3)}$

Factor

$= \dfrac{(y + 4)(y - 4)}{y + 3} \cdot \dfrac{(y + 3)(y - 3)}{y - 4}$

Multiply by reciprocal

$= \dfrac{(y + 4)(y - 4)(y + 3)(y - 3)}{(y + 3)(y - 4)}$

$= (y + 4)(y - 3)$

25. $\dfrac{2 - y}{8} \cdot \dfrac{7}{y - 2}$

$= \dfrac{-1(y - 2)}{8} \cdot \dfrac{7}{y - 2}$ *Factor out -1*

$= \dfrac{-7(y - 2)}{8(y - 2)}$ *Multiply*

$= -\dfrac{7}{8}$ *Fundamental property*

29. $\dfrac{m^2 - 16}{4 - m} \cdot \dfrac{-4 + m}{-4 + m}$

$= \dfrac{(m - 4)(m + 4)}{-1(m - 4)} \cdot \dfrac{m - 4}{-1(m + 4)}$

Factor

$= m - 4$ *Fundamental property*

33. $\dfrac{z^2 - z - 6}{z^2 - 2z - 8} \cdot \dfrac{z^2 + 7z + 12}{z^2 - 9}$

$= \dfrac{(z - 3)(z + 2) \cdot (z + 4)(z + 3)}{(z - 4)(z + 2) \cdot (z + 3)(z - 3)}$

Factor

$= \dfrac{z + 4}{z - 4}$ *Fundamental property*

37. $\dfrac{m^2 + 2mp - 3p^2}{m^2 - 3mp + 2p^2} \div \dfrac{m^2 + 4mp + 3p^2}{m^2 + 2mp - 8p^2}$

$= \dfrac{m^2 + 2mp - 3p^2}{m^2 - 3mp + 2p^2} \cdot \dfrac{m^2 + 2mp - 8p^2}{m^2 + 4mp + 3p^2}$

Multiply by recripocal

$= \dfrac{(m + 3p)(m - p)}{(m - p)(m - 2p)} \cdot \dfrac{(m + 4p)(m - 2p)}{(m + 3p)(m + p)}$

Factor

$= \dfrac{m + 4p}{m + p}$ *Fundamental property*

41. $\left(\dfrac{x^2 + 10x + 25}{x^2 + 10x} \cdot \dfrac{10x}{x^2 + 15x + 50}\right) \div \dfrac{x + 5}{x + 10}$

$= \left(\dfrac{x^2 + 10x + 25}{x^2 + 10x} \cdot \dfrac{10x}{x^2 + 15x + 50}\right) \cdot \dfrac{x + 10}{x + 5}$

$= \left(\dfrac{(x + 5)(x + 5)}{x(x + 10)} \cdot \dfrac{10x}{(x + 10)(x + 5)}\right) \cdot \dfrac{x + 10}{x + 5}$

$= \dfrac{(x + 5)(x + 5) \cdot 10x}{x(x + 10)(x + 10)(x + 5)} \cdot \dfrac{x + 10}{x + 5}$

$= \dfrac{(x + 5)(x + 5)(10x) \cdot (x + 10)}{x(x + 10)(x + 10)(x + 5) \cdot (x + 5)}$

$= \dfrac{x(x + 5)(x + 5)(x + 10)(10)}{x(x + 5)(x + 5)(x + 10)(x + 10)}$

$= \dfrac{10}{x + 10}$ *Fundamental property*

45. $\dfrac{-x^3 - y^3}{x^2 - 2xy + y^2} \div \dfrac{3y^2 - 3xy}{x^2 - y^2}$

$= \dfrac{-1(x^3 + y^3)}{x^2 - 2xy + y^2} \cdot \dfrac{x^2 - y^2}{3y^2 - 3xy}$

*Factor out -1
and multiply
by reciprocal*

$= \dfrac{-1(x+y)(x^2 - xy + y^2)}{(x - y)(x - y)} \cdot \dfrac{(x-y)(x+y)}{3y(y - x)}$

Factor

$= \dfrac{-1(x+y)(x^2 - xy + y^2)(x-y)(x+y)}{-1(x - y)(x - y)(3y)(x - y)}$

Multiply

$= \dfrac{(x + y)^2(x^2 - xy + y^2)}{3y(x - y)^2}$

*Fundamental
property*

49. $72 = 3 \cdot 3 \cdot 2 \cdot 2 \cdot 2 = 3^2 \cdot 2^3$

53. $2y^2 + 5y - 3 = (2y - 1)(y + 3)$

Section 5.3 (page 217)

1. Factor each denominator.
   $12 = 2 \cdot 2 \cdot 3 \quad 10 = 2 \cdot 5$

   Take each factor the greatest
   number of times it appears:
   Least common denominator

   $= 2 \cdot 2 \cdot 3 \cdot 5 = 60.$

5. Factor each denominator.

   $100 = 5 \cdot 5 \cdot 2 \cdot 2 \quad 120 = 2 \cdot 2 \cdot 2 \cdot 5 \cdot 3$
   $180 = 3 \cdot 3 \cdot 2 \cdot 2 \cdot 5$

   Take each factor the greatest
   number of times it appears:
   Least common denominator

   $= 5 \cdot 5 \cdot 3 \cdot 3 \cdot 2 \cdot 2 \cdot 2$
   $= 1800.$

9. Factor each denominator.

   $5p = 5 \cdot p \quad 6p = 2 \cdot 3 \cdot p$

   Take each factor the greatest
   number of times it appears:
   Least common denominator

   $= 2 \cdot 3 \cdot 5 \cdot p$
   $= 30p.$

13. Factor each denominator.

    $5a^2 b^3 = 5 \cdot a \cdot a \cdot b \cdot b \cdot b$

    $15a^5 b = 3 \cdot 5 \cdot a \cdot a \cdot a \cdot a \cdot a \cdot b$

    Least common denominator

    $= 3 \cdot 5 \cdot a \cdot a \cdot a \cdot a \cdot a \cdot b \cdot b \cdot b$
    $= 15a^5 b^3$

17. Factor each denominator.

    $32r^2 = 2 \cdot 2 \cdot 2 \cdot 2 \cdot 2 \cdot r \cdot r;$
    $16r - 32 = 16(r - 2)$
    $\qquad\quad = 2 \cdot 2 \cdot 2 \cdot 2(r - 2)$

    Least common denominator

    $= 2 \cdot 2 \cdot 2 \cdot 2 \cdot 2 \cdot r \cdot r(r - 2)$
    $= 32r^2(r - 2)$

21. $12p + 60 = 12(p + 5)$
    $\qquad\qquad = 2 \cdot 2 \cdot 3 \cdot (p + 5);$

    Least common denominator
    $= 2 \cdot 2 \cdot 3 \cdot p \cdot (p + 5)$
    $= 12p(p + 5)$

25. $m - 3 = -1(3 - m)$
    $3 - m = -1(-3 + m)$
    $\qquad\quad = -1(m - 3)$

    Least common denominator
    $= -1(m - 3)$
    $= 3 - m$

    Note the least common denominator
    may also be m - 3.

29. $a^2 + 6a = a(a + 6);$

$a^2 + 3a - 18 = (a + 6)(a - 3)$

Least common denominator

$= a(a + 6)(a - 3)$

33. $2y^2 + 7y - 4 = (2y - 1)(y + 4);$

$2y^2 - 7y + 3 = (2y - 1)(y - 3)$

Least common denominator

$= (y - 3)(y + 4)(2y - 1)$

37. $\dfrac{7}{11} = \dfrac{}{66}$

$\dfrac{7}{11} = \dfrac{7}{11} \cdot \dfrac{6}{6}$

$= \dfrac{42}{66}$

41. $\dfrac{12}{35y} = \dfrac{}{70y^3}$

$\dfrac{12}{35y} = \dfrac{12}{35y} \cdot \dfrac{2y^2}{2y^2}$

$= \dfrac{24y^2}{70y^3}$

45. $\dfrac{19z}{2z - 6} = \dfrac{}{6z - 18}$

$\dfrac{19z}{2(z - 3)} = \dfrac{}{6(z - 3)}$ *Factor denominator*

$\dfrac{19z}{2(z - 3)} \cdot \dfrac{3}{3} = \dfrac{57z}{6z - 18}$ *Multiply by 3/3*

49. $\dfrac{6}{k^2 - 4k} = \dfrac{}{k(k - 4)(k + 1)}$

$\dfrac{6}{k(k - 4)} = \dfrac{}{k(k - 4)(k + 1)}$
Factor first denominator

$\dfrac{6}{k(k - 4)} \cdot \dfrac{k + 1}{k + 1} = \dfrac{6(k + 1)}{k(k - 4)(k + 1)}$

53. $\dfrac{a + 2b}{2a^2 + ab - b^2} = \dfrac{}{2a^3b + a^2b^2 - ab^3}$

$\dfrac{a + 2b}{2a^2 + ab - b^2} = \dfrac{}{ab(2a^2 + ab - b^2)}$
Factor second denominator

$\dfrac{a + 2b}{2a + ab - b^2} \cdot \dfrac{ab}{ab} = \dfrac{ab(a + 2b)}{ab(2a^2 + ab - b^2)}$
Multiply by ab/ab

$= \dfrac{a^2b + 2ab^2}{2a^3b + a^2b^2 - ab^3}$

57. $\dfrac{2(z - y)}{y^2 + yz + z^2} = \dfrac{}{y^4 - 2^3y}$

$\dfrac{2(z - y)}{y^2 + yz + z^2} = \dfrac{}{y(y^3 - z^3)}$
Factor second denominator

$\dfrac{2(z - y)}{y^2 + yz + z^2} = \dfrac{}{y(y - z)(y^2 + yz + z^2)}$

$\dfrac{2(z - y)}{y^2 + yz + z^2} \cdot \dfrac{y(y - z)}{y(y - z)} = \dfrac{2y(z - y)(y - z)}{y(y - z)(y^2 + yz + z^2)}$
Multiply by [y(y - z)][y(y - z)]

$= \dfrac{-2y^3 + 4y^2z - 2yz^2}{y^4 - 2^3y}$

61. $\dfrac{1}{2} + \dfrac{2}{5} = \dfrac{1 \cdot 5}{2 \cdot 5} + \dfrac{2 \cdot 2}{5 \cdot 2}$

$= \dfrac{5}{10} + \dfrac{4}{10}$

$= \dfrac{9}{10}$

65. $\dfrac{5}{24} + \dfrac{1}{18} = \dfrac{5 \cdot 3}{24 \cdot 3} + \dfrac{1 \cdot 4}{18 \cdot 4}$

$= \dfrac{15}{72} + \dfrac{4}{72}$

$= \dfrac{19}{72}$

Section 5.4 (page 223)

1. $\dfrac{2}{p} + \dfrac{5}{p} = \dfrac{2 + 5}{p} = \dfrac{7}{p}$

5. $\dfrac{y}{y + 1} + \dfrac{1}{y + 1} = \dfrac{y + 1}{y + 1}$
$$= 1$$

9. $\dfrac{m^2}{m + 6} + \dfrac{6m}{m + 6}$

$= \dfrac{m^2 + 6m}{m + 6}$

$= \dfrac{m(m + 6)}{m + 6}$ *Factor*

$= m$

13. $\dfrac{m}{3} + \dfrac{1}{2}$

$= \dfrac{m \cdot 2}{3 \cdot 2} + \dfrac{1 \cdot 3}{2 \cdot 3}$

$= \dfrac{2m}{6} + \dfrac{3}{6}$ *Find least common denominator*

$= \dfrac{2m + 3}{6}$

17. $\dfrac{5m}{6} - \dfrac{2m}{3} = \dfrac{5m}{6} - \dfrac{2m \cdot 2}{3 \cdot 2}$

$= \dfrac{5m}{6} - \dfrac{4m}{6}$

$= \dfrac{5m - 4m}{6} = \dfrac{m}{6}$

21. $\dfrac{m + 2}{m} + \dfrac{m + 3}{4m}$

$= \dfrac{(m + 2) \cdot 4}{m \cdot 4} + \dfrac{m + 3}{4m}$

$= \dfrac{4m + 8}{4m} + \dfrac{m + 3}{4m}$

$= \dfrac{4m + 8 + m + 3}{4m}$

$= \dfrac{5m + 11}{4m}$

25. $\dfrac{-1}{x^2} + \dfrac{3}{xy}$

$= \dfrac{-1 \cdot y}{x^2 \cdot y} + \dfrac{3 \cdot x}{xy \cdot x}$

$= \dfrac{-y}{x^2 y} + \dfrac{3x}{x^2 y}$

$= \dfrac{-y + 3x}{x^2 y}$

29. $\dfrac{2x}{x + y} - \dfrac{3x}{2x + 2y}$

Use least common denominator $2(x + y)$.

$\dfrac{2 \cdot 2x}{2(x + y)} - \dfrac{3x}{2(x + y)} = \dfrac{4x - 3x}{2(x + y)}$

$$= \dfrac{x}{2(x + y)}$$

33. $\dfrac{1}{m^2 - 1} - \dfrac{1}{m^2 + 3m + 2}$

Factor each denominator. The least common denominator is $(m + 1)(m - 1)(m + 2)$.

$\dfrac{1 \cdot (m + 2)}{(m + 1)(m - 1) \cdot (m + 2)} - \dfrac{1 \cdot (m - 1)}{(m + 1)(m + 2) \cdot (m - 1)}$

$= \dfrac{m + 2 - (m - 1)}{(m + 1)(m - 1)(m + 2)}$

$= \dfrac{m + 2 - m + 1}{(m + 1)(m - 1)(m + 2)}$

$= \dfrac{3}{(m + 1)(m - 1)(m + 2)}$

37. $\dfrac{3}{4p - 5} + \dfrac{9}{5 - 4p} = \dfrac{3}{4p - 5} + \dfrac{9}{-1(4p - 5)}$
Factor second denominator

The least common denominator is $4p - 5$.

$\dfrac{3}{4p - 5} - \dfrac{9}{4p - 5} = \dfrac{3 - 9}{4p - 5} = \dfrac{-6}{4p - 5}$ or

$$\dfrac{6}{5 - 4p}$$

41. $\dfrac{4}{r^2 - r} + \dfrac{6}{r^2 + 2r} - \dfrac{1}{r^2 + r - 2}$

Factor the denominators. The least common denominator is $r(r - 1)(r + 2)$.

$\dfrac{4 \cdot (r+2)}{r(r-1) \cdot (r+2)} + \dfrac{6 \cdot (r-1)}{r(r+2) \cdot (r-1)} -$

$\dfrac{r \cdot 1}{r \cdot (r + 2)(r - 1)}$

$= \dfrac{4r + 8 + 6r - 6 - r}{r(r - 1)(r + 2)}$

$= \dfrac{9r + 2}{r(r - 1)(r + 2)}$

45. $\dfrac{x + 3y}{x^2 + 2xy + y^2} + \dfrac{x - y}{x^2 + 4xy + 3y^2}$

$= \dfrac{x + 3y}{(x + y)(x + y)} + \dfrac{x - y}{(x + 3y)(x + y)}$

  Factor each denominator

$= \dfrac{(x + 3y)(x + 3y)}{(x + y)(x + y)(x + 3y)} +$

$\dfrac{(x - y)(x + y)}{(x + 3y)(x + y)(x + y)}$

  Write each term with a common denominator

$= \dfrac{x^2 + 6xy + 9y^2 + x^2 - y^2}{(x + y)(x + y)(x + 3y)}$

  Multiply and simplify

$= \dfrac{2x^2 + 6xy + 8y^2}{(x + y)(x + y)(x + 3y)}$

$= \dfrac{2(x^2 + 3xy + 4y^2)}{(x + y)^2(x + 3y)}$

49. $\dfrac{3p - 2}{1 - 4q^4} - \dfrac{p^2 + 2}{2pq^2 - 8q^2 + p - 4}$

Factor the denominators.

$= \dfrac{3p - 2}{(1 - 2q^2)(1 + 2q^2)} -$

$\dfrac{p^2 + 2}{2q^2(p - 4) + 1(p - 4)}$

$= \dfrac{3p - 2}{(1 - 2q^2)(1 + 2q^2)} - \dfrac{p^2 + 2}{(2q^2 + 1)(p - 4)}$

The common denominator is $(1 - 2q^2) \cdot (1 + 2q^2)(p - 4)$.

$= \dfrac{(3p - 2)(p - 4)}{(1 - 2q^2)(1 + 2q^2)(p - 4)} -$

$\dfrac{(p^2 + 2)(1 - 2q^2)}{(2q^2 + 1)(p - 4)(1 - 2q^2)}$

  Fundamental property

$= \dfrac{(3p - 2)(p - 4) - (p^2 + 2)(1 - 2q^2)}{(1 - 2q^2)(1 + 2q^2)(p - 4)}$

$= \dfrac{3p^2 - 14p + 8 - (p^2 - 2p^2q^2 + 2 - 4q^2)}{(1 - 2q^2)(1 + 2q^2)(p - 4)}$

$= \dfrac{3p^2 - 14p + 8 - p^2 + 2p^2q^2 - 2 + 4q^2}{(1 - 2q^2)(1 + 2q^2)(p - 4)}$

$= \dfrac{2p^2 + 2p^2q^2 + 4q^2 - 14p + 6}{(1 + 2q^2)(1 - 2q^2)(p - 4)}$

53. $\dfrac{k^2 + 4k + 16}{k + 4}\left(\dfrac{-5}{16 - k^2} + \dfrac{2k + 3}{k^3 - 64}\right)$

$= \dfrac{k^2 + 4k + 16}{k + 4}\left(\dfrac{-5}{(4 - k)(4 + k)} + \dfrac{2k + 3}{(k - 4)(k^2 + 4k + 16)}\right)$

  Factor the denominators

$= \dfrac{k^2 + 4k + 16}{k + 4}\left(\dfrac{-5}{-1(k - 4)(4 + k)} + \dfrac{2k + 3}{(k - 4)(k^2 + 4k + 16)}\right)$

The least common denominator is $(k - 4) \cdot (4 + k)(k^2 + 4k + 16)$.

$= \dfrac{k^2 + 4k + 16}{k + 4}\left(\dfrac{5(k^2 + 4k + 16)}{(k - 4)(4 + k)(k^2 + 4k + 16)} + \dfrac{(2k + 3)(4 + k)}{(k - 4)(4 + k)(k^2 + 4k + 16)}\right)$

  Fundamental property

$= \dfrac{k^2 + 4k + 16}{k + 4}\left(\dfrac{5k^2 + 20k + 80 + 2k^2 + 11k + 12}{(k - 4)(4 + k)(k^2 + 4k + 16)}\right)$ *Add*

$= \dfrac{k^2 + 4k + 16}{k + 4}\left(\dfrac{7k^2 + 31k + 92}{(k - 4)(4 + k)(k^2 + 4k + 16)}\right)$

$= \dfrac{(k^2 + 4k + 16)(7k^2 + 31k + 92)}{(k + 4)(k - 4)(4 + k)(k^2 + 4k + 16)}$ *Multiply*

$= \dfrac{7k^2 + 31k + 92}{(k - 4)(k + 4)^2}$ *Fundamental property*

57. $\dfrac{\dfrac{2}{3} + \dfrac{5}{3}}{\dfrac{3}{4} - \dfrac{1}{4}} = \dfrac{\dfrac{2+5}{3}}{\dfrac{3-1}{4}} = \dfrac{\dfrac{7}{3}}{\dfrac{2}{4}}$

$= \dfrac{7}{3} \div \dfrac{2}{4} = \dfrac{7}{3} \cdot \dfrac{4}{2} = \dfrac{28}{6} = \dfrac{14}{3}$

Section 5.5 (page 228)

1. $\dfrac{\dfrac{5}{8} + \dfrac{2}{3}}{\dfrac{7}{3} - \dfrac{1}{4}}$

Rewrite both the numerator and denominator as single fractions.

$= \dfrac{\dfrac{5 \cdot 3}{8 \cdot 3} + \dfrac{2 \cdot 8}{3 \cdot 8}}{\dfrac{7 \cdot 4}{3 \cdot 4} - \dfrac{1 \cdot 3}{4 \cdot 3}}$

$= \dfrac{\dfrac{15}{24} + \dfrac{16}{24}}{\dfrac{28}{12} - \dfrac{3}{12}}$

$= \dfrac{\dfrac{31}{24}}{\dfrac{25}{12}}$ *Add and subtract*

$= \dfrac{31}{24} \cdot \dfrac{12}{25}$ *Rule for divison*

$= \dfrac{31}{50}$ *Fundamental property*

5. $\dfrac{\dfrac{p}{q^2}}{\dfrac{p^2}{q}} = \dfrac{p}{q^2} \div \dfrac{p^2}{q}$ *Divide*

$= \dfrac{p}{q^2} \cdot \dfrac{q}{p^2}$ *Rule for division*

$= \dfrac{pq}{p^2 q^2}$

$= \dfrac{1}{pq}$ *Fundamental property*

9. $\dfrac{\dfrac{m^3 p^4}{5m}}{\dfrac{8mp^5}{p^2}} = \dfrac{m^3 p^4}{5m} \div \dfrac{8mp^5}{p^2}$ *Divide*

$= \dfrac{m^3 p^4}{5m} \cdot \dfrac{p^2}{8mp^5}$ *Rule for division*

$= \dfrac{m^3 p^6}{40m^2 p^5}$

$= \dfrac{mp}{40}$ *Fundamental property*

13. $\dfrac{\dfrac{3}{q}}{\dfrac{1-q}{6q^2}} = \dfrac{3}{q} \cdot \dfrac{6q^2}{1-q}$ *Rule for division*

$= \dfrac{18q^2}{(1-q)q}$

$= \dfrac{18q}{1-q}$ *Fundamental property*

Exercises 17-37 show the alternative method. Use the least common denominator of all the denominators appearing in the complex fraction.

17. $\dfrac{\dfrac{3}{y} + 1}{\dfrac{3+y}{2}}$

$= \dfrac{\dfrac{3}{y}(2y) + 1(2y)}{(\dfrac{3+y}{2}) \cdot 2y}$ *Least common denominator is 2y*

$= \dfrac{6 + 2y}{3y + y^2}$

$= \dfrac{2(3+y)}{y(3+y)} = \dfrac{2}{y}$

21. $\dfrac{x + \dfrac{1}{x}}{\dfrac{4}{x} + y} = \dfrac{(x + \dfrac{1}{x}) \cdot x}{(\dfrac{4}{x} + y) \cdot x}$

$= \dfrac{x(x) + \dfrac{1}{x}(x)}{\dfrac{4}{x}(x) + y(x)}$

$= \dfrac{x^2 + 1}{4 + xy}$

25. $\dfrac{\dfrac{2}{p^2} - \dfrac{3}{5p}}{\dfrac{4}{p} + \dfrac{1}{4p}}$

$= \dfrac{\left(\dfrac{2}{p^2} - \dfrac{3}{5p}\right) \cdot 20p^2}{\left(\dfrac{4}{p} + \dfrac{1}{4p}\right) \cdot 20p^2}$ *Least common denominator is 20p*

$= \dfrac{\dfrac{2}{p^2}(20p^2) - \dfrac{3}{5p}(20p^2)}{\dfrac{4}{p}(20p^2) + \dfrac{1}{4p}(20p^2)}$

$= \dfrac{40 - 12p}{80p + 5p}$

$= \dfrac{40 - 12p}{85p}$

29. $\dfrac{\dfrac{1}{4} - \dfrac{1}{a^2}}{\dfrac{1}{2} + \dfrac{1}{a}}$

$= \dfrac{\left(\dfrac{1}{4} - \dfrac{1}{a^2}\right) \cdot 4a^2}{\left(\dfrac{1}{2} + \dfrac{1}{a}\right) \cdot 4a^2}$

$= \dfrac{\dfrac{1}{4}(4a^2) - \dfrac{1}{a^2}(4a^2)}{\dfrac{1}{2}(4a^2) + \dfrac{1}{a}(4a^2)}$

$= \dfrac{a^2 - 4}{2a^2 + 4a}$

$= \dfrac{(a - 2)(a + 2)}{2a(a + 2)}$ *Factor*

$= \dfrac{a - 2}{2a}$ *Fundamental property*

33. $\dfrac{\dfrac{1}{m + 1} - 1}{\dfrac{1}{m + 1} + 1}$

$= \dfrac{\left(\dfrac{1}{m + 1} - 1\right) \cdot (m + 1)}{\left(\dfrac{1}{m + 1} + 1\right) \cdot (m + 1)}$

$= \dfrac{\dfrac{1}{m + 1}(m + 1) - 1(m + 1)}{\dfrac{1}{m + 1}(m + 1) + 1(m + 1)}$

$= \dfrac{1 - 1(m + 1)}{1 + 1(m + 1)}$

$= \dfrac{1 - m - 1}{1 + m + 1}$

$= \dfrac{-m}{m + 2}$

37. $1 - \dfrac{1}{1 + \dfrac{1}{1 + 1}} = 1 - \dfrac{1}{1 + \dfrac{1}{2}}$

$= 1 - \dfrac{1}{\dfrac{2}{2} + \dfrac{1}{2}}$

$= 1 - \dfrac{1}{\dfrac{3}{2}}$

$= 1 - 1 \cdot \dfrac{2}{3}$

$= 1 - \dfrac{2}{3}$

$= \dfrac{3}{3} - \dfrac{2}{3}$

$= \dfrac{1}{3}$

41. $9\left(\dfrac{4x}{3} + \dfrac{2}{9}\right) = 9 \cdot \dfrac{4x}{3} + 9 \cdot \dfrac{2}{9}$

$= 12x + 2$

45. $3x - 5 = 7x + 3$

$3x - 5 - 7x = 7x + 3 - 7x$

$-4x - 5 = 3$

$-4x - 5 + 5 = 3 + 5$

$-4x = 8$

$x = -2$

49. $9 - (5 - 3y) = 6$

$9 - 1 \cdot 5 + (-1)(-3y) = 6$

$9 - 5 + 3y = 6$

$4 + 3y = 6$

$3y = 2$

$y = \dfrac{2}{3}$

Section 5.6 (page 234)

1. $\dfrac{1}{4} = \dfrac{x}{2}$

$4\left(\dfrac{1}{4}\right) = 4\left(\dfrac{x}{2}\right)$ *Multiply both sides by the common denominator 4*

$1 = 2x$

$\dfrac{1}{2} = x$

5. $\dfrac{7}{y} = \dfrac{8}{3}$

$3y\left(\dfrac{7}{y}\right) = 3y\left(\dfrac{8}{3}\right)$ *Multiply both sides by the common denominator*

9. $\dfrac{x}{2} - \dfrac{x}{4} = 6$

$4\left(\dfrac{x}{2} - \dfrac{x}{4}\right) = 4 \cdot 6$ *Multiply both sides by 4*

$4\left(\dfrac{x}{2}\right) - 4\left(\dfrac{x}{4}\right) = 24$

$2x - x = 24$

$x = 24$

13. $\dfrac{2t}{7} - 5 = t$

$7\left(\dfrac{2t}{7} - 5\right) = 7 \cdot t$ *Multiply both sides by 7*

$7\left(\dfrac{2t}{7}\right) - 7(5) = 7t$

$2t - 35 = 7t$

$-35 = 5t$

$-7 = t$

17. $\dfrac{3m}{2} + m = 5$

$2\left(\dfrac{3m}{2} + m\right) = 2(5)$

$2\left(\dfrac{3m}{2}\right) + 2m = 2(5)$

$3m + 2m = 10$

$5m = 10$

$m = 2$

21. $\dfrac{m-2}{5} = \dfrac{m+8}{10}$

$10\left(\dfrac{m-2}{5}\right) = 10\left(\dfrac{m+8}{10}\right)$

$2(m-2) = m+8$

$2m - 4 = m + 8$

$m - 4 = 8$

$m = 12$

25. $\dfrac{a}{2} - \dfrac{17+a}{5} = 2a$

$10\left(\dfrac{a}{2} - \dfrac{17+a}{5}\right) = 10(2a)$

$10\left(\dfrac{a}{2}\right) - 10\left(\dfrac{17+a}{5}\right) = 10(2a)$

$5a - 2(17+a) = 20a$

$5a - 34 - 2a = 20a$

$3a - 34 = 20a$

$-34 = 17a$

$-2 = a$

29. $\dfrac{m+2}{5} - \dfrac{m-6}{7} = 2$

$35\left(\dfrac{m+2}{5} - \dfrac{m-6}{7}\right) = 35(2)$

$35\left(\dfrac{m+2}{5}\right) - 35\left(\dfrac{m-6}{7}\right) = 35(2)$

$7(m+2) - 5(m-6) = 70$

$7m + 14 - 5m + 30 = 70$

$2m + 44 = 70$

$2m = 26$

$m = 13$

33. $\dfrac{8k}{5} - \dfrac{3k-4}{2} = \dfrac{5}{2}$

$10\left(\dfrac{8k}{5} - \dfrac{3k-4}{2}\right) = 10\left(\dfrac{5}{2}\right)$

$10\left(\dfrac{8k}{5}\right) - 10\left(\dfrac{3k-4}{2}\right) = 10\left(\dfrac{5}{2}\right)$

$2(8k) - 5(3k-4) = 5 \cdot 5$

$16k - 15k + 20 = 25$

$k + 20 = 25$

$k = 5$

37. $\dfrac{5p+1}{3p+3} = \dfrac{5p-5}{5p+5} + \dfrac{3p-1}{p+1}$

$\dfrac{5p+1}{3(p+1)} = \dfrac{5p-5}{5(p+1)} + \dfrac{3p-1}{p+1}$

Factor each denominator

$15(p+1)\left(\dfrac{5p+1}{3(p+1)}\right)$

$\quad = 15(p+1)\left(\dfrac{5p-5}{5(p+1)} + \dfrac{3p-1}{p+1}\right)$

$\quad = 15(p+1)\left[\dfrac{5p-5}{5(p+1)}\right] + 15(p+1) \cdot$

$\quad\quad \left(\dfrac{3p-1}{p+1}\right)$

$$5(5p + 1) = 3(5p - 5) + 15(3p - 1)$$
$$25p + 5 = 15p - 15 + 45p - 15$$
$$25p + 5 = 60 - 30$$
$$-35p = -35$$
$$p = 1$$

41.
$$\frac{1}{r + 5} - \frac{3}{r - 5} = \frac{-10}{r^2 - 25}$$

$$\frac{1}{r + 5} - \frac{3}{r - 5} = \frac{-10}{(r - 5)(r + 5)}$$

$$(r - 5)(r + 5)\left(\frac{1}{r + 5} - \frac{3}{r - 5}\right)$$

$$= (r - 5)(r + 5)\left[\frac{-10}{(r - 5)(r + 5)}\right]$$

$$(r - 5)(r + 5)\left(\frac{1}{r + 5}\right) -$$

$$(r - 5)(r + 5)\left(\frac{3}{r - 5}\right) = -10$$

$$(r - 5) \cdot 1 - (r + 5) \cdot 3 = -10$$
$$r - 5 - 3r - 15 = -10$$
$$-2r - 20 = -10$$
$$-2r = -10$$
$$r = -5$$

-5 cannot be a solution because -5 makes the denominator of the first term in the original equation equal to 0.

This equation has no solution.

45.
$$\frac{5}{z - 2} + \frac{10}{z + 2} = 7$$

$$(z - 2)(z + 2) \cdot \frac{5}{z - 2} + (z - 2)(z + 2) \cdot \frac{10}{z + 2}$$

$$= (z - 2)(z + 2) \cdot 7$$

$$5(z + 2) + 10(z - 2) = 7(z^2 - 4)$$

$$5z + 10 + 10z - 20 = 7z^2 - 28$$

$$15z - 10 = 7z^2 - 28$$

$$0 = 7x^2 - 15z - 18$$

$$0 = (7z + 6)(z - 3)$$

$$7z + 6 = 0 \quad \text{or} \quad z - 3 = 0$$
$$7z = -6 \qquad\qquad z = 3$$
$$z = -\frac{6}{7}$$

49.
$$F = \frac{k}{r}$$

$$r \cdot F = r\left(\frac{k}{r}\right) \quad \textit{Multiply both sides by r}$$

$$rF = k$$

$$r = \frac{k}{F} \quad \textit{Divide both sides by F}$$

53.
$$S = \frac{a}{1 - r}$$

$$(1 - r)S = (1 - r)\left(\frac{a}{1 - r}\right) \quad \textit{Multiply by 1 - r}$$

$$S - rS = a$$

$$-rS = a - S \quad \textit{Get the term containing r alone on one side}$$

$$= r = \frac{a - S}{-S} \quad \textit{Divide}$$

or $\quad r = \frac{S - a}{S}$

57.
$$9x + \frac{3}{z} = \frac{5}{t}$$

$$yz\left(9x + \frac{3}{z}\right) = 5z\left(\frac{5}{y}\right)$$

$$yz(9x) + yz\left(\frac{3}{z}\right) = yz\left(\frac{5}{y}\right)$$

$$9xyz + 3y = 5z$$

$$9xyz - 5z = -3y \quad \textit{Get all the terms containing z on the left side}$$

$$z(9xy - 5) = -3y \quad \textit{Factor}$$

$$z = \frac{-3y}{9xy - 5} \quad \textit{Divide by 9xy - 5}$$

61.
$$\frac{8x + 3}{x} = 3x$$

$$x\left(\frac{8x + 3}{x}\right) = x(3x)$$

$$8x + 3 = 3x^2$$

$$-3x^2 + 8x + 3 = 0$$

$$3x^2 - 8x - 3 = 0 \quad \textit{Multiply both sides by -1}$$

$$(3x + 1)(x - 3) = 0 \quad \textit{Factor}$$

$$3x + 1 = 0 \quad \text{or} \quad x - 3 = 0$$
$$3x = -1 \qquad\qquad x = 3$$
$$x = -\frac{1}{3}$$

65.

$$\frac{m}{m^2+m-2}+\frac{m}{m^2-1}=\frac{m}{m^2+3m+2}$$

$$\frac{m}{(m+2)(m-1)}+\frac{m}{(m+1)(m-1)}=\frac{m}{(m+2)(m+1)}$$
Factor the denominators

Multiply both sides by the common denominator $(m+2)(m+1)(m-1)$

$$(m+2)(m+1)(m-1)\left(\frac{m}{(m+2)(m-1)}\right)+$$

$$(m+2)(m+1)(m-1)\left(\frac{m}{(m+1)(m-1)}\right)=$$

$$(m+2)(m+1)(m-1)\left(\frac{m}{(m+2)(m+1)}\right)$$

$$m(m+1)+m(m+2)=m(m-1)$$
$$m^2+m+m^2+2m=m^2-m$$

$$2m^2+3m=m^2-m$$
$$m^2+4m=0$$
$$m(m+4)=0 \quad \textit{Factor}$$

Set each factor equal to zero

$$m=0 \quad \text{or} \quad m+4=0$$
$$m=-4$$

69. Work = (rate)·(time)

Work = $\left(\frac{1 \text{ job}}{x \text{ hr}}\right)$(1 hr)

$$=\frac{1}{x}$$

Supplementary Exercises on Rational Expressions (page 236)

1. $\dfrac{6}{m}+\dfrac{2}{m}=\dfrac{6+2}{m}$

   $\phantom{\dfrac{6}{m}+\dfrac{2}{m}}=\dfrac{8}{m}$

5. $\dfrac{2r^2-3r-9}{2r^2-r-6}\cdot\dfrac{r^2+2r-8}{r^2-2r-3}$

   $=\dfrac{(2r+3)(r-3)}{(2r+3)(r-2)}\cdot\dfrac{(r+4)(r-2)}{(r-3)(r+1)}$

   $=\dfrac{r+4}{r+1}$

9. $\dfrac{5}{y-1}+\dfrac{2}{3y-3}$

   $=\dfrac{5}{y-1}+\dfrac{2}{3(y-1)}$

   $=\dfrac{3\cdot5}{3\cdot(y-1)}+\dfrac{2}{3(y-1)}$

   $=\dfrac{15+2}{3(y-1)}$

   $=\dfrac{17}{3(y-1)}$

13. $\dfrac{4}{9z}-\dfrac{3}{2z}=\dfrac{2\cdot4}{2\cdot9z}-\dfrac{9\cdot3}{9\cdot2z}$

    $=\dfrac{8}{18z}-\dfrac{27}{18z}$

    $=\dfrac{8-27}{18z}$

    $=-\dfrac{19}{18z}$

Section 5.7 (page 242)

1. Let x represent the number.

One half	of	a number	is	3 more than
↓	↓	↓	↓	↓
$\frac{1}{2}$	·	x	=	3 +

one sixth	of	the same number.
↓	↓	↓
$\frac{1}{6}$	·	x

Solve the equation.

$$6\left(\tfrac{1}{2}x\right)=6(3)+6\left(\tfrac{1}{6}\right)x$$
Multiply each term by the least common denominator 6

$$3x=18+x$$
$$2x=18$$
$$x=9$$

The number is 9.

5. Let the smaller number be x. Then the larger number is x + 3.

The smaller number	added to	two thirds	the larger
↓	↓	↓	↓
x	+	$\frac{2}{3}$ ·	(x + 3)

equals	four fifths	the sum of the original numbers.
↓	↓	↓
=	$\frac{4}{5}$ ·	(x + x + 3)

Solve the equation.

$$x + \frac{2}{3}(x + 3) = \frac{4}{5}(2x + 3)$$

$$15(x) + 15\left[\frac{2}{3}(x+3)\right] = 15\left[\frac{4}{5}(2x+3)\right]$$

Multiply both sides by the least common denominator 15

$$15x + 10(x + 3) = 12(2x + 3)$$
$$15x + 10x + 30 = 24x + 36$$
$$25x + 30 = 24x + 36$$
$$x = 6$$

The smaller number is 6 and the larger number is 6 + 3 = 9.

9. Let x represent the father's daily wage. The the son's wage is

$$\frac{2}{5}x = \frac{2x}{5},$$

and together they earn

$$x + \frac{2x}{5} = \frac{5x}{5} + \frac{2x}{5} = \frac{7x}{5}$$

each day. In 4 days they earn 4 times this amount, which is $672.

$$4\left(\frac{7x}{5}\right) = 672$$

$$5 \cdot 4\left(\frac{7x}{5}\right) = 5 \cdot 672$$ *Multiply both sides by the common denominator 5*

$$4(7x) = 3360$$
$$28x = 3360$$
$$x = 120$$

The father's daily wage is $120. Since

$$\frac{2x}{5} = \frac{2(120)}{5} = \frac{240}{5} = 48,$$

the son's wage is $48.

13. Let x represent the current. Sam's rate upstream is 4 - x and downstream it is 4 + x.

The information given is summarized in this chart.

	d	r	t
Downstream	24	4 + x	$\frac{24}{4 + x}$
Upstream	8	4 - x	$\frac{8}{4 - x}$

Since the times are equal, solve the equation.

$$\frac{8}{4 - x} = \frac{24}{4 + x}$$

$$(4-x)(4+x) \cdot \frac{8}{4-x} = (4-x)(4+x) \cdot \frac{24}{4+x}$$

$$8(4 + x) = 24(4 - x)$$
$$32 + 8x = 96 - 24x$$
$$32x = 64$$
$$x = 2$$

The current is 2 miles per hour.

17. Let x represent the number of hours it takes for Paul and Marco to tune the Toyota together. Since Paul can tune the car in 2 hours, then he can complete 1/2 of the tuneup in 1 hour. Also, since Marco can tune the car in 3 hours, he can complete 1/3 of the job in 1 hour. The amount of work Paul can do in one hour plus the amount of work Marco can do in one hour must equal the amount of work they can do together in one hour, or 1/x of the job. So,

$$\frac{1}{2} + \frac{1}{3} = \frac{1}{x}.$$

Solve the equation.

$$6x\left(\frac{1}{2}\right) + 6x\left(\frac{1}{3}\right) = 6x\left(\frac{1}{x}\right)$$

$$3x + 2x = 6$$

$$5x = 6$$

$$x = \frac{6}{5}$$

Working together, it takes Paul and Marco

$\frac{6}{5} = 1\frac{1}{2}$ hours = 1 hour 12 minutes

to tune the Toyota.

21. Let x represent the number of days it takes Sue to complete the job. Then she completes 1/x of the job in 1 day. Since Dennis can do the job in 4 days, then he does 1/4 of the job in 1 day. Finally, if it takes 2 1/3 = 7/3 days to complete the job working together, then they can complete 1/(7/3) = 3/7 of the job in 1 day.

$$\frac{1}{x} + \frac{1}{4} = \frac{3}{7}$$

Solve the equation.

$$28x\left(\frac{1}{x}\right) + 28x\left(\frac{1}{4}\right) = 28x\left(\frac{3}{7}\right)$$

$$28 + 7x = 12x$$

$$28 = 5x$$

$$\frac{28}{5} = x$$

It takes Sue 28/5 = 5 3/5 hours to complete the job.

25. $y = kx$

$2 = k \cdot 9$ *Let $x = 9$ and $y = 2$*

$\frac{2}{9} = k$

$y = kx$ becomes $y = \frac{2}{9}x.$

Now substitute.

$6 = \frac{2}{9}x$ *Let $y = 6$*

$54 = 2x$

$x = 27$

29. $p = \dfrac{k}{q^2}$

$4 = \dfrac{k}{\left(\frac{1}{2}\right)^2}$ *Let $p = 4$, $q = 1/2$*

$4 = \dfrac{k}{\frac{1}{4}}$

$\dfrac{1}{4}(4) = \dfrac{1}{4}\left(\dfrac{k}{\frac{1}{4}}\right)$

$1 = k$

$p = \dfrac{k}{q^2}$ becomes $p = \dfrac{1}{q^2}.$

Now substitute.

$p = \dfrac{1}{\left(\frac{3}{2}\right)^2}$ *Let $k = 1$, $q = 3/2$*

$p = \dfrac{1}{\frac{9}{4}}$

$p = \dfrac{4}{9}$

33. Let F represent the force and c the change in the length. The variation equation is F = kc.

$12 = k \cdot 3$ *Let $F = 12$, $c = 3$*

$4 = k$

Now, let c = 5 in F = 4c and solve for F.

$F = 4 \cdot 5$

$F = 20$

The force required is 20 pounds.

37. Let x represent the number.

Three times number	is added to	twice	its reciprocal	the answer is	5.
↓	↓	↓	↓	↓	↓
$3 \cdot x$	$+$	2	$\frac{1}{x}$	$=$	5

Solve the equation.

$$3x + \frac{2}{x} = 5$$

$$x(3x) + x(\frac{2}{x}) = 5x$$

$$3x^2 + 2 = 5x$$

$$3x^2 - 5x + 2 = 0$$

$$(3x - 2)(x - 1) = 0$$

$$3x - 2 = 0 \quad \text{or} \quad x - 1 = 0$$

$$3x = 2$$

$$x = \frac{2}{3} \quad \text{or} \quad x = 1$$

The solutions are 2/3 and 1.

41. Let x represent the average speed of the ferry. Use the formula d = rt to make a table.

	d	r	t
Seattle-Victoria	148	x	$\frac{148}{x}$
Victoria-Vancouver	74	x	$\frac{74}{x}$

The time for the Victoria-Vancouver trip is 4 hours less than the time for the Seattle-Victoria trip. Solve the equation.

$$\frac{74}{x} = \frac{148}{x} - 4$$

$$x(\frac{74}{x}) = x(\frac{148}{x} - 4)$$

$$74 = 148 - 4x$$

$$4x = 74$$

$$x = \frac{74}{4} = \frac{37}{2} = 18\frac{1}{2}$$

The average speed of the ferry is 37/2 or $18\frac{1}{2}$ miles per hour.

45. (a) Let x = 2.

$$y = 4x - 7 = 4 \cdot 2 - 7 = 8 - 7 = 1$$

(b) Let x = -4

$$y = 4(-4) - 7 = -16 - 7 = -23$$

49. 3x + 7y = 10

(a) Let x = 2.

$$3(2) + 7y = 10$$

$$6 + 7y = 10$$

$$7y = 4$$

$$y = \frac{4}{7}$$

(b) Let x = 4.

$$3(-4) + 7y = 10$$

$$-12 + 7y = 10$$

$$7y = 22$$

$$y = \frac{22}{7}$$

Chapter 5 Review Exercises (page 246)

1. $\frac{2}{7x}$ is undefined for x = 0.

5. (a) $\frac{x^2}{x + 2} = \frac{3^2}{3 + 2}$ *Let x = 3*

$$= \frac{9}{5}$$

(b) $\frac{x^2}{x + 2} = \frac{(-1)^2}{-1 + 2}$ *Let x = -1*

$$= \frac{1}{1}$$

$$= 1$$

9. $\frac{15p^2}{5p} = \frac{3 \cdot 5 \cdot p \cdot p}{5 \cdot p}$

$$= 3p \quad \textit{Fundamental property}$$

13. $\frac{10p^5}{5} \div \frac{3p^7}{20}$

$= \frac{10p^5}{5} \cdot \frac{20}{3p^7}$ *Multiply by the reciprocal*

$= \frac{10 \cdot 20 \cdot p^5}{5 \cdot 3 \cdot p^7}$

$= \frac{40}{3p^2}$

17. $\frac{2p^2 + 3p - 2}{p^2 + 5p + 6} \cdot \frac{p^2 - 2p - 15}{2p^2 - 7p - 15}$

$= \frac{(2p-1)(p+2)}{(p+3)(p+2)} \cdot \frac{(p-5)(p+3)}{(2p+3)(p-5)}$

$= \frac{(2p-1)(p+2)(p-5)(p+3)}{(2p+3)(p+2)(p-5)(p+3)}$

$= \frac{2p-1}{2p+3}$

21. Factor each denominator.

$y^2 + 2y = y(y+2)$

$y^2 + 6y + 8 = (y+2)(y+4)$

The least common denominator is

$y(y+2)(y+4)$.

25. $\frac{3}{8m^2} = \frac{3}{8m^2} \cdot \frac{3m}{3m} = \frac{9m}{24m^3}$

29. $\frac{11}{3r} - \frac{8}{3r} = \frac{11-8}{3r} = \frac{3}{3r} = \frac{1}{r}$

33. $\frac{2}{y+1} - \frac{3}{y-1}$

The least common denominator is

$(y+1)(y-1)$.

$= \frac{2(y-1)}{(y+1)(y-1)} - \frac{3(y+1)}{(y+1)(y-1)}$

$= \frac{2y - 2 - (3y + 3)}{(y+1)(y-1)}$

$= \frac{2y - 2 - 3y - 3}{(y+1)(y-1)}$

$= \frac{-y - 5}{(y+1)(y-1)}$

37. $\frac{\frac{6}{r} - 1}{\frac{6-r}{4r}}$

$= \frac{\left(\frac{6}{r} - 1\right) \cdot 4r}{\left(\frac{6-r}{4r}\right) \cdot 4r}$ *Multiply the numerator and denominator by the least common denominator 4r.*

$= \frac{24 - 4r}{6 - r}$

$= \frac{4(6-r)}{6-r}$ *Factor*

$= 4$

41. $\frac{y}{2} - \frac{y}{5} = 6$

$10\left(\frac{y}{2}\right) - 10\left(\frac{y}{5}\right) = 10 \cdot 6$

$5y - 2y = 60$

$3y = 60$

$y = 20$

45. $\frac{3y - 1}{y - 2} = \frac{5}{y - 2} + 1$

$(y-2)\left(\frac{3y-1}{y-2}\right) = (y-2)\left(\frac{5}{y-2} + 1\right)$ *Use least common denominator y - 2*

$3y - 1 = 5 + y - 2$

$3y - 1 = 3 + y$

$2y - 1 = 3$

$2y = 4$

$y = 2$

There is no solution since $y = 2$ makes the original denominator zero.

49. $x = \frac{3y}{2y + z}$

$(2y+z)x = (2y+z)\left(\frac{3y}{2y+z}\right)$

$2xy + xz = 3y$

$2xy - 3y = -xz$

$y(2x - 3) = -xz$ *Factor*

$y = \frac{-xz}{2x - 3}$ or $\frac{xz}{3 - 2x}$

53. Let x represent the speed of the plane in still air. Use the formula d = rt to fill in the table.

	d	r	t
With wind	400	x + 50	$\dfrac{400}{x + 50}$
Against wind	200	x - 50	$\dfrac{200}{x - 50}$

The times are the same.
Solve the equation.

$$\frac{400}{x + 50} = \frac{200}{x - 50}.$$

$$(x+50)(x-50) \cdot \frac{400}{x+50} = (x+50)(x-50)\frac{200}{x-50}$$

$$400(x - 50) = 200(x + 50)$$

$$400x - 20000 = 200x + 1000$$

$$200x = 30000$$

$$x = \frac{30000}{200} = 150$$

The speed of the plane is 150 kilometers per hour.

57. $r = \dfrac{k}{s}$ inversely

$$9 = \frac{k}{\frac{1}{2}} \qquad \textit{Let r = 9 and s = 1/2}$$

$$9 = k \cdot \frac{2}{1}$$

$$9 = 2k$$

$$\frac{9}{2} = k$$

$r = \dfrac{k}{s}$ becomes $r = \dfrac{9}{2s}$.

$$r = \frac{9}{2 \cdot 2} = \frac{9}{4} \qquad \textit{Let s = 2}$$

61. $\dfrac{z + \dfrac{1}{x}}{z - \dfrac{1}{x}} = \dfrac{(z + \dfrac{1}{x}) \cdot x}{(z - \dfrac{1}{x}) \cdot x}$

Multiply the numerator and denominator of the complex fraction by the least common denominator x

$$= \frac{zx + 1}{zx - 1}$$

65.
$$\frac{5 + m}{m} + \frac{3}{4} = \frac{-2}{m}$$

$$4m\left(\frac{5 + m}{m} + \frac{3}{4}\right) = 4m\left(\frac{-2}{m}\right)$$

$$4(5 + m) + 3m = 4(-2)$$

$$20 + 4m + 3m = -8$$

$$7m + 20 = -8$$

$$7m = -28$$

$$m = -4$$

69. Let x represent the number.

Five times a number	added to	three times the reciprocal	gives	$\dfrac{17}{2}$.
↓	↓	↓	↓	↓
5 · x	+	3 · $\dfrac{1}{x}$	=	$\dfrac{17}{2}$

$$5x + \frac{3}{x} = \frac{17}{2}$$

$$2x\left(5x + \frac{3}{x}\right) = 2x\left(\frac{17}{2}\right)$$

$$2x(5x) + 2x\left(\frac{3}{x}\right) = 2x\left(\frac{17}{2}\right)$$

$$10x^2 + 6 = 17x$$

$$10x^2 - 17x + 6 = 0$$

$$(5x - 6)(2x - 1) = 0$$

$$5x - 6 = 0 \quad \text{or} \quad 2x - 1 = 0$$

$$x = \frac{6}{5} \qquad\qquad x = \frac{1}{2}$$

Both numbers, 6/5 and 1/2, are solutions.

Chapter 5 Test   (page 248)

1. The expression $\dfrac{8k + 1}{k^2 - 4k + 3}$ is undefined when the denominator $k^2 - 4k + 3$ is zero.

$$k^2 - 4k + 3 = 0$$

$$(k - 1)(k - 3) = 0 \quad \textit{Factor}$$

$$k - 1 = 0 \quad \text{or} \quad k - 3 = 0$$

$$k = 1 \qquad\qquad k = 3$$

Thus, the values that make the expression undefined are k = 1 and k = 3.

2. (a) $\dfrac{6r + 1}{2r^2 - 3r - 20}$

    $= \dfrac{6(-1) + 1}{2(-1)^2 - 3(-1) - 20}$ *Let*
    r = -1

    $= \dfrac{-6 + 1}{2 \cdot 1 + 3 - 20}$

    $= \dfrac{-5}{-15}$

    $= \dfrac{1}{3}$

    (b) $\dfrac{6r + 1}{2r^2 - 3r - 20}$

    $= \dfrac{6(4) + 1}{2(4)^2 - 3(4) - 20}$

    $= \dfrac{24 + 1}{2 \cdot 16 - 12 - 20}$

    $= \dfrac{25}{32 - 32}$

    $= \dfrac{25}{0}$ which is undefined

3. $\dfrac{8m^2 p^2}{6m^3 p^5} = \dfrac{4}{3mp^3}$

4. $\dfrac{5y^3 - 5y}{2y + 2} = \dfrac{5y(y^2 - 1)}{2(y + 1)}$

    $= \dfrac{5y(y - 1)(y + 1)}{2(y + 1)}$

    $= \dfrac{5y(y - 1)}{2}$

5. $\dfrac{a^6 b}{a^3} \cdot \dfrac{b^2}{a^2 b^3} = \dfrac{a^6 b^3}{a^5 b^3}$

    $= a$

6. $\dfrac{8y - 16}{9} \div \dfrac{6 - 3y}{5}$

    $= \dfrac{8(y - 2)}{9} \div \dfrac{-3(y - 2)}{5}$

    $= \dfrac{8(y - 2)}{9} \cdot \dfrac{5}{-3(y - 2)}$

    $= -\dfrac{40}{27}$

7. $\dfrac{6m^2 - m - 2}{8m^2 + 10m + 3} \cdot \dfrac{4m^2 + 7m + 3}{3m^2 + 5m + 2}$

    $= \dfrac{(3m - 2)(2m + 1)}{(4m + 3)(2m + 1)} \cdot \dfrac{(4m + 3)(m + 1)}{(3m + 2)(m + 1)}$

    $= \dfrac{3m - 2}{3m + 2}$

8. $\dfrac{5a^2 + 7a - 6}{2a^2 + 3a - 2} \div \dfrac{5a^2 + 17a - 12}{2a^2 + 5a - 3}$

    $= \dfrac{(5a - 3)(a + 2)}{(2a - 1)(a + 2)} \div \dfrac{(5a - 3)(a + 4)}{(2a - 1)(a + 3)}$

    $= \dfrac{(5a - 3)(a + 2)}{(2a - 1)(a + 2)} \cdot \dfrac{(2a - 1)(a + 3)}{(5a - 3)(a + 4)}$

    $= \dfrac{a + 3}{a + 4}$

9. $10p^2 = 2 \cdot 5 \cdot p^2$

    $25p^2 = 5^2 \cdot p^3$

    $30p^5 = 2 \cdot 3 \cdot 5 \cdot p^5$

    Least common denominator

    $= 2 \cdot 3 \cdot 5^2 \cdot p^5$

    $= 105p^5$

10. $2r^2 + 7r + 6 = (2r + 3)(r + 2)$

    $2r^2 - 7r - 15 = (2r + 3)(r - 5)$

    Least common denominator

    $= (r + 2)(r - 5)(2r + 3)$

11. $\dfrac{11}{7r} = \dfrac{11}{7r} \cdot \dfrac{7r}{7r} = \dfrac{77r}{49r^2}$

12. $\dfrac{5}{8m - 16} = \dfrac{5}{8(m - 2)}$

    $= \dfrac{5}{8(m - 2)} \cdot \dfrac{3m}{3m}$

    $= \dfrac{15m}{24m^2 - 48m}$

13. $\dfrac{5}{x} - \dfrac{6}{x} = \dfrac{5-6}{x}$

$= \dfrac{-1}{x}$ or $-\dfrac{1}{x}$

14. $\dfrac{-3}{a+1} + \dfrac{5}{6a+6} = \dfrac{-3 \cdot 6}{6(a+1)} + \dfrac{5}{6(a+1)}$

$= \dfrac{-18+5}{6(a+1)}$

$= \dfrac{-13}{6(a+1)}$

15. $\dfrac{m^2}{m-3} + \dfrac{m+1}{3-m}$

$= \dfrac{m^2}{m-3} + \dfrac{-1(m+1)}{m-3}$

$= \dfrac{m^2 - m - 1}{m-3}$

16. $\dfrac{3}{2k^2+3k-2} - \dfrac{k}{k^2+3k+2}$

$= \dfrac{3}{(2k-1)(k+2)} - \dfrac{k}{(k+2)(k+1)}$

$= \dfrac{3(k+1)}{(2k-1)(k+2)(k+1)} -$

$\dfrac{(2k-1)(k)}{(2k-1)(k+2)(k+1)}$

$= \dfrac{(3k+3) - (2k^2-k)}{(2k-1)(k+2)(k+1)}$

$= \dfrac{3k+3-2k^2+k}{(2k-1)(k+2)(k+1)}$

$= \dfrac{-2k^2+4k+3}{(2k-1)(k+2)(k+1)}$

17. $\dfrac{\frac{2p}{k^2}}{\frac{3p^2}{k^3}} = \dfrac{2p}{k^2} \div \dfrac{3p^2}{k^3}$

$= \dfrac{2p}{k^2} \cdot \dfrac{k^3}{3p^2}$

$= \dfrac{2k^3 p}{3k^2 p^2}$

$= \dfrac{2k}{3p}$

18. $\dfrac{\frac{1}{p+4} - 2}{\frac{1}{p+4} + 2}$

$= \dfrac{(\frac{1}{p+4} - 2)(p+4)}{(\frac{1}{p+4} + 2)(p+4)}$

$= \dfrac{1 - 2(p+4)}{1 + 2(p+4)}$

$= \dfrac{1 - 2p - 8}{1 + 2p + 8}$

$= \dfrac{-2p - 7}{2p + 9}$

19. $\dfrac{3}{2p} + \dfrac{12}{5p} = \dfrac{13}{20}$

$20p\left(\dfrac{3}{2p} + \dfrac{12}{5p}\right) = 20p\left(\dfrac{13}{20}\right)$

$20p\left(\dfrac{3}{2p}\right) + 20p\left(\dfrac{12}{5p}\right) = 20p\left(\dfrac{13}{20}\right)$

$10 \cdot 3 + 4 \cdot 12 = 13p$

$30 + 48 = 13p$

$78 = 13p$

$6 = p$

20. $\dfrac{p}{p-2} = \dfrac{2}{p-2} + 3$

$(p-2)\left(\dfrac{p}{p-2}\right) = (p-2)\left(\dfrac{2}{p-2}\right) + 3(p-2)$

$p = 2 + 3p - 6$

$p = 3p - 4$

$4 = 2p$

$2 = p$

No solution since $p = 2$ makes the denominator zero.

21. $\dfrac{2}{z^2-2z-3} = \dfrac{3}{z-3} + \dfrac{2}{z+1}$

$\dfrac{2}{(z-3)(z+1)} = \dfrac{3}{z-3} + \dfrac{2}{z+1}$

$(z-3)(z+1)\left[\dfrac{2}{(z-3)(z+1)}\right]$

$= (z-3)(z+1)\left[\dfrac{3}{z-3}\right] +$

$(z-3)(z+1)\left[\dfrac{2}{z+1}\right]$

$$2 = 3(z + 1) + 2(z - 3)$$
$$2 = 3z + 3 + 2z - 6$$
$$2 = 5z - 3$$
$$5 = 5z$$
$$1 = z$$

22. Let x represent the number.

Four times a number	added to	the reciprocal of twice the number
↓	↓	↓
$4 \cdot x$	$+$	$\dfrac{1}{2 \cdot x}$

the result is   3.

↓   ↓

=   3

Solve the equation.

$$4x + \frac{1}{2x} = 3$$
$$2x(4x) + 2x\left(\frac{1}{2x}\right) = 2x(3)$$
$$8x^2 + 1 = 6x$$
$$8x^2 - 6x + 1 = 0$$
$$(4x - 1)(2x - 1) = 0$$
$$4x - 1 - 0 \quad \text{or} \quad 2x - 1 = 0$$
$$x = \frac{1}{4} \qquad\qquad x = \frac{1}{2}.$$

1/4 and 1/2 are solutions.

23. Let x represent the speed of the boat.

	d	r	t = d/r
Downstream	125	x + 5	$\dfrac{125}{x + 5}$
Upstream	75	x - 5	$\dfrac{75}{x - 5}$

The times are equal.
Solve the equation.

$$\frac{125}{x + 5} = \frac{75}{x - 5}$$

$$(x - 5)(x + 5)\left(\frac{125}{x + 5}\right)$$
$$= (x - 5)(x + 5)\left(\frac{75}{x - 5}\right)$$
$$125(x - 5) = 75(x + 5)$$
$$125x - 625 = 75x + 375$$
$$50x - 625 = 375$$
$$50x = 1000$$
$$x = 20$$

The speed of the boat in still water is 20 miles per hour.

24. Let x represent the time required for the couple to paint a room together. Then 1/x of the room can be painted in 1 hour. Alone, the man can paint 1/5 of the room and the woman 1/4.

$$\frac{1}{5} + \frac{1}{4} = \frac{1}{x}$$

Solve the equation.

$$20x\left(\frac{1}{5}\right) + 20x\left(\frac{1}{4}\right) = 20x\left(\frac{1}{x}\right)$$
$$4x + 5x = 20$$
$$9x = 20$$
$$x = \frac{20}{9}$$

It takes them $\frac{20}{9} = 2\frac{2}{9}$ hours working together.

25. $$x = ky$$
$$8 = k \cdot 12 \quad \textit{Let x = 8 and y = 12}$$
$$\frac{8}{12} = k$$
$$\frac{2}{3} = k$$

$x = ky$ becomes $x = \frac{2}{3}y$.

$$x = \frac{2}{3} \cdot 28 \quad \textit{Let y = 28}$$
$$x = \frac{56}{3}$$

CHAPTER 6 GRAPHING LINEAR EQUATIONS

Section 6.1 (page 255)

1. $x + y = 9$; (2, 7)

Substitute 2 for x and 7 for y in the equation.

$$2 + 7 = 9$$
$$9 = 9 \quad True$$

Therefore (2, 7) is a solution.

5. $4x - 3y = 6$: (1, 2)

Substitute 1 for x and 2 for y in the equation.

$$4(1) - 3(2) = 6$$
$$4 - 6 = 6$$
$$-2 = 6 \quad False$$

Therefore (1, 2) is not a solution.

9. $x = -6$; (-6, 8)

Substitute -6 for x and 8 for y in the equation.

$$x + 0y = -6$$
$$-6 + 0(8) = -6$$
$$-6 + 0 = -6$$
$$-6 = -6 \quad True$$

Therefore (-6, 8) is a solution.

13. The ordered pair (2,) means that x = 2 in y = 3x + 5.

$$y = 3(2) + 5 \quad Let \; x = 2$$
$$= 6 + 5$$
$$= 11$$

This gives the ordered pair (2, 11).

17. The ordered pair (-3,) means that x = -3 in y = 3x + 5.

$$y = 3(-3) + 5 \quad Let \; x = -3$$
$$= -9 + 5$$
$$= -4$$

This gives the ordered pair (-3, -4).

21. The ordered pairs (3,), (0,), and (-1,) mean that x = 3, x = 0, and x = -1 in y = 2x + 1.

$$y = 2(3) + 1 \qquad y = 2(0) + 1$$
$$= 6 + 1 \qquad\quad\; = 0 + 1$$
$$= 7 \qquad\qquad\;\; = 1$$

$$y = 2(-1) + 1$$
$$= -2 + 1$$
$$= -1$$

The ordered pairs are (3, 7), (0, 1), and (-1, -1).

25. The ordered pairs (0,), (3,), (12,) mean that a = 0, a = 3, and a = 12 in 2a + b = 9.

$$2(0) + b = 9 \qquad 2(3) + b = 9$$
$$b = 9 \qquad\qquad 6 + b = 9$$
$$b = 3$$

$$2(12) + b = 9$$
$$24 + b = 9$$
$$b = -15$$

The ordered pairs are (0, 9), (3, 3) and (12, -15).

29. The equation x + 9 = 0 can be written as x = -9. Therefore, x is -9 in (, 8), (, 3), and (, 0). The ordered pairs are (-9, 8), (-9, 3), and (-9, 0).

33. A(2, 5)

37. E(7, 3)

41. To plot the point (-4, -5), start-
     ing from the origin, go 4 units
     to the left, then down 5 units.

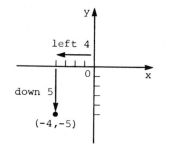

45. To plot (3, -5), go 3 units to
     the right, then down 5 units.

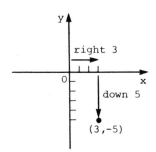

49. To graph (0, -5), do not go left
     or right, but go straight down
     from the origin.

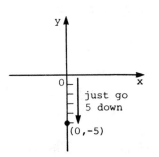

53. (-2, 3) Since x is negative and
     y positive, (-2, 3) is in Quad-
     rant II.

57. (-3, 6) Since x is negative and
     y positive, (-3, 6) is in Quad-
     rant II.

61. (0, 0) This point is located at
     the origin. Therefore it does
     not lie in a quadrant.

65. (0,) means that x = 0 in 3x + 5y =

$$3(0) + 5y = 15$$
$$5y = 15$$
$$y = 3.$$

     This gives the ordered pair (0, 3).
     Similarly for (10,)

$$3(10) + 5y = 15$$
$$30 + 5y = 15$$
$$5y = -15$$
$$y = -3.$$

     See the final graph in your text-
     book. The ordered pair is (10, -3).

     For (, 0)   3x + 5(0) = 15
                        $$3x = 15$$
                        $$x = 5.$$

     The ordered pair is (5, 0).

     And for (, 6) 3x + 5(6) = 15
                     $$3x + 30 = 15$$
                     $$3x = -15$$
                     $$x = -5.$$

     The ordered pair is (-5, 6).

69. The ordered pair (5,) means that
     x = 5 in the equation y + 2 = 0
     or y = -2. This gives the ordered
     pair (5, -2). See the graph in
     your textbook. The value of y is
     -2 for every ordered pair. Thus,
     the other ordered pairs are
     (0, -2), (-3, -2), and (-2, -2).

73. See answer graph in textbook. There appears to be a linear relationship.

77. 3 - y = 12

    -y = 9

    y = -9

81. 8 - q = -7

    -q = -15

    q = 15

Section 6.2 (page 265)

1. The ordered pair (0,) means that x = 0 in x + y = 5.

   $$0 + y = 5$$
   $$y = 5$$

   This gives the ordered pair (0, 5). The ordered pair (, 0) means that y = 0.

   $$x + 0 = 5$$
   $$x = 5$$

   This gives the ordered pair (5, 0). The ordered pair (2,) means that x = 2.

   $$2 + y = 5$$
   $$y = 3$$

   This gives the ordered pair (2, 3). The graph of the three points (0, 5), (5, 0), (2, 3) is shown in your textbook with the resulting line passing through the three points.

5. The ordered pair (0,) means that x = 0 in y = 3x - 6.

   $$y = 3(0) - 6$$
   $$= -6$$

   This gives the ordered pair (0, -6).

The ordered pair (, 0) means that y = 0.

   $$0 = 3x - 6$$
   $$6 = 3x$$
   $$x = 2$$

This gives the ordered pair (2, 0). Finally, (3,) means that x = 3.

   $$y = 3 \cdot 3 - 6 = 9 - 6 = 3$$

This gives (3, 3). See the final graph in your textbook.

9. The equation x + 5 = 0 becomes x = -5. Since the y-value of an ordered pair does not change for the equation x = -5, the ordered pairs are (-5, 2), (-5, 0), (-5, -3). The graph of these ordered pairs and the resulting line passing through is in your textbook.

13. 3x - 5y = 9

    To find the y-intercept, let x = 0.

    $$3(0) - 5y = 9$$
    $$-5y = 9$$
    $$y = -\frac{9}{5}$$

    Therefore the y-intercept -9/5. To find the x-intercept, let y = 0.

    $$3x - 5(0) = 9$$
    $$3x = 9$$
    $$x = 3$$

    Therefore the x-intercept is 3.

17. -2x = 8 simplifies to x = -4. For any value of y, x is always equal to -4. The graph of x = -4 is a vertical line going through the x-intercept -4. There is no y-intercept, since the line is parallel to the y-axis.

For Exercises 21-49 see the answer graphs in your textbook.

21. In the equation $y = x + 4$, let $x = 0$. Then

$$y = 0 + 4$$
$$= 4.$$

This gives the y-intercept 4. Let $y = 0$ to get

$$0 = x + 4$$
$$x = -4.$$

This gives the x-intercept -4. The graph is the line through $(0, 4)$ and $(-4, 0)$.

25. Let $x = 0$ in the equation $4x = 3y - 12$.

$$4(0) = 3y - 12$$
$$0 = 3y - 12$$
$$12 = 3y$$
$$y = 4$$

The y-intercept is 4.

$$4x = 3(0) - 12 \quad \textit{Let } y = 0$$
$$4x = -12$$
$$x = -3$$

The x-intercept is -3. The graph is the line through $(0, 4)$ and $(-3, 0)$.

29. In the equation $2x - 7y = 13$, let $x = 0$. Then

$$2(0) - 7y = 14$$
$$-7y = 14$$
$$y = -2.$$

This gives the ordered pair $(0, -2)$. Now let $y = 0$ to get

$$2x - 7(0) = 14$$
$$2x = 14$$
$$x = 7.$$

This gives the ordered pair $(7, 0)$.

The graph is the line through $(0, 2)$ and $(7, 0)$.

33. In the equation $y = 2x$, let $x = 0$. Then

$$y = 2(0) = 0.$$

This gives the point $(0, 0)$. Letting $y = 0$ will give $(0, 0)$ again, so choose another value of x, say $x = 1$. Then

$$y = 2(1) = 2,$$

giving the ordered pair $(1, 2)$. The graph is the line through $(0, 0)$ and $(1, 2)$.

37. The equation $x + 2 = 0$ becomes $x = -2$ and is of the form $x = k$, a vertical line passing through the x-axis at $(-2, 0)$.

41. $x = 0$ is of the form $x = k$, a vertical line passing through the x-axis at $(0, 0)$. This line is the y-axis.

45.

The y-value	is	twice	x-value	less	3.
↓	↓	↓		↓	↓
y	=	2x		−	3

Let $x = 0$, then

$$y = 2(0) - 3$$
$$= -3.$$

This gives the ordered pair $(0, -3)$. Let $y = 0$, then

$$0 = 2x - 3$$
$$3 = 2x$$
$$x = \frac{3}{2}.$$

This gives the ordered pair $(3/2, 0)$. The graph is the line through these points.

49. (a) Let r = 23 in

$$h = 73.5 + 3.9r$$
$$h = 73.5 + 3.9(23)$$
$$h = 163.2.$$

(b) Let r = 25,

$$h = 73.5 + 3.9(25)$$
$$h = 171.0.$$

(c) Let r = 20,

$$h = 73.5 + 3.9(20)$$
$$h = 151.5.$$

(d) Graph the ordered pairs

(23, 163.2), (25, 171.0), (20, 151.5)

and draw the line through them.

53. $\dfrac{4 - 2}{8 - 5} = \dfrac{2}{3}$

57. $\dfrac{-2 - (-5)}{-9 - 12} = \dfrac{3}{-21}$

$$= -\dfrac{1}{7}$$

61. $\dfrac{-2 - (-7)}{3 - 3} = \dfrac{5}{0}$ *Undefined*

Section 6.3 (page 273)

1. Using the designated points on the line, (-5, 2) and (5, -3), the x-values are -5 and 5, and the y-values are 2 and -3.

$$\text{Slope} = \dfrac{\text{difference in y-values}}{\text{difference in x-values}}$$

$$= \dfrac{2 - (-3)}{-5 - 5}$$

$$= \dfrac{5}{-10}$$

$$= \dfrac{-1}{2}$$

5. Using the designated points on the line, (-4, 3) and (2, 3), the x-values are -4 and 2, and the y-values are both 3.

$$\text{Slope} = \dfrac{\text{difference in y-values}}{\text{difference in x-values}}$$

$$= \dfrac{3 - 3}{-4 - 2}$$

$$= \dfrac{0}{-6}$$

$$= 0$$

Also note, the graph is a horizontal line and thus has slope 0.

9. For the points (-1, 2) and (-3, -7), the x-values are -1 and -3 and the y-values are 2 and -7. Using the definition for slope, then

$$\text{Slope} = \dfrac{\text{difference in y-values}}{\text{difference in x-values}}$$

$$= \dfrac{2 - (-7)}{-1 - (-3)}$$

$$= \dfrac{2 + 7}{-1 + 3}$$

$$= \dfrac{9}{2}$$

13. For the points (-1, 6) and (4, 6), the x-values are -1 and 4, and the y-values are both 6.

$$\text{Slope} = \dfrac{\text{difference of y-values}}{\text{difference of x-values}}$$

$$= \dfrac{6 - 6}{-1 - 4}$$

$$= \dfrac{0}{-5}$$

$$= 0$$

17. For the points (.03, 1.57) and (3.54, -2.01), the x-values are .03 and 3.54, and the y-values are 1.57 and -2.01.

$$\text{Slope} = \frac{1.57 - (-2.01)}{.03 - 3.54}$$

$$= \frac{3.58}{-3.51}$$

$$= -1.020$$

This answer is rounded.

21. $y = 6 - 5x$

The slope is given by the coefficient of x, which is -5.

25. $-6x + 4y = 1$

Solve the equation for y.

$4y = 6x + 1$ *Add 6x to both sides*

$y = \frac{6}{4}x + 1$ *Divide by 4*

$y = \frac{3}{2}x + 1$ *Simplify*

The coefficient of x is 3/2, so the slope is 3/2.

29. Solve $y + 4 = 0$ for y.

$$y + 4 = 0$$
$$y = -4$$

Since $y = -4$ is of the form $y = k$, the line is horizontal and the slope is 0.

33. Solve the equation $2x - 5y = 4$ for y.

$$-5y = 4 - 2x$$
$$y = \frac{2}{5}x - \frac{4}{5}$$

The slope is 2/5.
Solve $4x - 10y = 1$ for y.

$$-10y = -4x + 1$$
$$y = \frac{4}{10}x - \frac{1}{10}$$
$$y = \frac{2}{5}x - \frac{1}{10}$$

The slope is 2/5. The two lines have the same slope, so they are parallel.

37. Solve the equation $x - 4y = 2$ for y.

$$x - 4y = 2$$
$$-4y = -x + 2$$
$$y = \frac{x}{4} - \frac{2}{4}$$
$$y = \frac{1}{4}x - \frac{1}{2}$$

The slope of the line is 1/4.
Slove $2x + 4y = 1$ for y.

$$2x + 4y = 1$$
$$4y = -2x + 1$$
$$y = \frac{-2}{4}x + \frac{1}{4}$$
$$y = -\frac{1}{2}x + \frac{1}{4}$$

The slope of the line is -1/2.
The lines are neither parallel nor perpendicular.

41. Solve $2x - 5y = 11$ for y.

$$2x - 5y = 11$$
$$-5y = -2x + 11$$
$$y = \frac{-2}{-5}x + \frac{11}{-5}$$
$$y = \frac{2}{5}x - \frac{11}{5}$$

The slope is 2/5.
Solve for y in $4x + 5y = 2$.

$$4x + 5y = 2$$
$$5y = -4x + 2$$
$$y = -\frac{4}{5}x + \frac{2}{5}$$

The slope is -4/5.
The lines are neither parallel nor perpendicular.

45. $\frac{5}{4}x + \frac{1}{4}y = -3$

$\qquad \frac{1}{4}y = \frac{-5}{4}x - 3$ *Solve for y*

$\qquad 4\left(\frac{1}{4}y\right) = 4\left(\frac{-5}{4}x - 3\right)$

$\qquad\qquad y = -5x - 12$

The slope is -5.

49. Slope = $\frac{\text{change in } y}{\text{change in } x}$

$\qquad = \frac{120}{140}$

$\qquad = \frac{6}{7}$

53. $y - (-4) = -(x + 1)$

$\qquad y + 4 = -x - 1$ *Simplify*
$\qquad\qquad\qquad\qquad$ *each side*

$\qquad\qquad y = -x - 5$

57. $y = \left(-\frac{3}{5}\right) = -\frac{1}{2}[x - (-3)]$

$\qquad y + \frac{3}{5} = -\frac{1}{2}(x + 3)$ *Simplify*
$\qquad\qquad\qquad\qquad\quad$ *each side*

$\qquad y + \frac{3}{5} = -\frac{1}{2}x - \frac{3}{2}$ *Distribute*

$\qquad\qquad y = -\frac{1}{2}x - \frac{3}{2} - \frac{3}{5}$
$\qquad\qquad\qquad\qquad$ *Subtract 3/5*
$\qquad\qquad\qquad\qquad$ *from each side*

$\qquad\qquad y = -\frac{1}{2}x - \frac{21}{10}$

Section 6.4   (page 279)

1. With m = 3 and y-intercept b = 5, substitute into the slope-intercept form.

$\qquad\qquad y = mx + b$
$\qquad\qquad y = 3x + 5$

5. With m = 2/5 and b = -1/4, use slope-intercept form.

$\qquad\qquad y = mx + b$
$\qquad\qquad y = \frac{2}{5}x - \frac{1}{4}$

9. With m = 4.61 and b = -2.38, use slope-intercept form.

$\qquad\qquad y = mx + b$
$\qquad\qquad y = 4.16x - 2.38$

13. Starting at (0, 2), the slope 7/4 says to go up 7 then over 4 to the right. This path leads to another point through which the line is graphed.
See answer graph in textbook.

17. Start at (-4, 7). The slope -3 = -3/1 says to go down 3 and then right 1 to reach the point (-3, 4). Draw a line through this point and (-4, 7).
See answer graph in textbook.

21. The slope m = 0 means that the line through (1, 2) is a horizontal line.
See answer graph in textbook.

25. Use the values m = 2, x_1 = 5, and y_1 = 3 in the point-slope form.

$\qquad\qquad y - y_1 = m(x - x_1)$
$\qquad\qquad y - 3 = 2(x - 5)$
$\qquad\qquad y - 3 = 2x - 10$
$\qquad\quad -2x + y = -10 + 3$
$\qquad\quad -2x + y = -7$
$\qquad\quad\; 2x - y = 7$

29. Use the values m = $\frac{2}{3}$, x_1 = 3, and y_1 = 5 in the point-slope form.

$$y - y_1 = m(x - x_1)$$
$$y - 5 = \frac{2}{3}(x - 3)$$
$$3(y - 5) = 2(x - 3)$$
$$3y - 15 = 2x - 6$$
$$-2x + 3y = -6 + 15$$
$$-2x + 3y = 9$$
$$2x - 3y = -9$$

33. If the x-intercept is 6 then the point (6, 0) is on the line. Use $m = -\frac{8}{11}$, $x_1 = 6$, $y_1 = 0$ in the point-slope form.

$$y - y_1 = m(x - x_1)$$
$$y - 0 = \frac{-8}{11}(x - 6)$$
$$11y = -8(x - 6)$$

Multiply both sides by 11

$$11y = -8x + 48$$
$$8x + 11y = 48$$

37. (3, -4) and (-2, -1)

$$x = 3, \ y = -4, \ x_1 = -2, \ y_1 = 1$$

First find the slope of the line, using the definition of slope.

$$\begin{aligned} \text{slope} &= \frac{-4 - (-1)}{3 - (-2)} \\ &= \frac{-4 + 1}{3 + 2} \\ &= \frac{-3}{5} \end{aligned}$$

Now use either point and $m = -\frac{3}{5}$ in the point-slope form. If we use (-2, -1) we get

$$y - y_1 = m(x - x_1)$$
$$y - (-1) = \frac{-3}{5}[x - (-2)]$$
$$y + 1 = \frac{-3}{5}(x + 2)$$
$$5y + 5 = -3x - 6$$
$$5y = -3x - 11$$
$$3x + 5y = -11.$$

41. (2, -5) and (-4, 7)

$$x = 2, \ y = -5, \ x_1 = -4, \ y_1 = 7$$

Use the definition to find the slope.

$$\begin{aligned} m &= \frac{-5 - 7}{2 - (-4)} \\ &= \frac{-12}{6} \\ &= -2 \end{aligned}$$

Now use either point and $m = -2$ in the point-slope form. Using (-4, 7) we get

$$y - y_1 = m(x - x_1)$$
$$y - 7 = -2[x - (-4)]$$
$$y - 7 = -2(x + 4)$$
$$y - 7 = -2x - 8$$
$$2x + y = -1.$$

45. $(-1, \frac{5}{8})$ and $(\frac{1}{8}, 2)$

$$x = -1, \ y = \frac{5}{8}, \ x_1 = \frac{1}{8}, \ y_1 = 2$$

Use the definition to find the slope.

$$\begin{aligned} m &= \frac{\frac{5}{8} - 2}{-1 - \frac{1}{8}} \\ &= \frac{\frac{5}{8} - \frac{16}{8}}{-\frac{8}{8} - \frac{1}{8}} \\ &= \frac{\frac{-11}{8}}{\frac{-9}{8}} \\ m &= \frac{11}{9} \end{aligned}$$

Use one of the points, say $(\frac{1}{8}, 2)$, and $m = \frac{11}{9}$ in the point-slope form.

$$y - y_1 = m(x - x_1)$$

$$y - 2 = \frac{11}{9}(x - \frac{1}{8})$$

$$72(y - 2) = 72 \cdot \frac{11}{9}(x - \frac{1}{8})$$
Multiply by 72

$$72y - 144 = 88(x - \frac{1}{8})$$

$$72y - 144 = 88x - 11$$

$$72y = 88x + 133$$

$$-88x + 72y = 133$$

$$88x - 72y = -133$$

49. From Exercise 47, the cost equation is $y = 12x + 100$.

   (a) Let $x = 50$.

   $$y = 12(50) + 100$$
   $$y = 600 + 100 = 700$$

   The total cost is $700.

   (b) Let $x = 125$.

   $$y = 12(125) + 100$$
   $$y = 1500 + 100$$
   $$y = 1600$$

   The total cost is $1600.

53. $m + 3 < 10$

   $m + 3 - 3 < 10 - 3$ *Subtract 3 from both sides*

   $$m < 7$$

57. $6 - 2p < 12$

   $6 - 6 - 2p < 12 - 6$ *Subtract 6 from both sides*

   $$-2p < 6$$

   $\dfrac{-2p}{-2} > \dfrac{6}{-2}$ *Divide by -2 on both sides, reverse direction of inequality*

   $$p > -3$$

1. Use $(0, 0)$ as a test point.

   $x + y \le 4$
   $0 + 0 \le 4$ *Let $x = 0$, $y = 0$*
   $0 \le 4$ *True*

   Since this statement is true, shade the side of the graph containing $(0, 0)$.
   See answer graph in your textbook.

5. Use $(0, 0)$ as a test point.

   $-3x + 4y < 12$
   $-3(0) + 4(0) < 12$
   $0 + 0 < 12$
   $0 < 12$ *True*

   Therefore, shade the side of the graph containing $(0, 0)$.
   See answer graph in your textbook.

9. Use $(0, 0)$ as a test point.

   $x < 4$ *Let $x = 0$*
   $0 < 4$ *True*

   Since this statement is true, shade the side of the graph that contains $(0, 0)$.
   See answer graph in your textbook.

13. Graph $x + y = 8$.

   If $x = 0$, then $y = 8$, giving $(0, 8)$.
   If $y = 0$, then $x = 8$, giving $(8, 0)$.

   Graph these points and the line through them. The line is solid because of the $\le$ symbol.
   Since the statement $0 + 0 \le 8$ is true then shade the side of the graph containing $(0, 0)$.
   See answer graph in the textbook.

17.   Graph $x + 2y = 4$.

If $x = 0$, then

$$0 + 2y = 4$$
$$y = 2,$$

giving $(0, 2)$.

If $y = 0$, then

$$x + 2(0) = 4$$
$$x = 4,$$

giving $(4, 0)$.

Graph these points and the line through them. The line is solid because of the $\geq$ symbol.
Use $(0, 0)$ as a test point.

$$x + 2y \geq 4$$
$$0 + 2(0) \geq 4$$
$$0 \geq 4 \quad \textit{False}$$

Since the statement $0 \geq 4$ is false, shade the side that does not contain $(0, 0)$.
See answer graph in the textbook.

21.   Graph $3x - 4y = 12$.

If $x = 0$, then

$$3(0) - 4y = 12$$
$$-4y = 12$$
$$y = -3,$$

giving $(0, -3)$.

If $y = 0$, then

$$3x - 4(0) = 12$$
$$3x = 12$$
$$x = 4,$$

giving $(4, 0)$.

Graph these points and the line through them. The line is dashed because of the $<$ symbol.

Use $(0 , 0)$ as a test point.

$$3x - 4y < 12$$
$$3(0) - 4(0) < 12$$
$$0 < 12 \quad \textit{True}$$

Since the statement is true, shade the side containing $(0, 0)$.
See answer graph in your textbook.

25.   Graph the line $x = 4$. The graph is a vertical line through the x-axis at $x = 4$. The line is dashed because of the $<$ sign.
Use $(0, 0)$ as a test point.

$$x < 4$$
$$0 < 4 \quad \textit{Let } x = 0 \quad \text{True}$$

Since $0 < 4$, shade the side of the graph containing $(0, 0)$.
See answer graph in textbook.

29.   Graph $x = -2$

This is a vertical line through the x-axis at $x = -2$. The line is solid because of the $\geq$ symbol.
Use $(0, 0)$ as a test point.

$$x \geq -2$$
$$0 \geq -2 \quad \textit{True}$$

Since the statement is true, shade the side of the graph containing $(0, 0)$.
See answer graph in textbook.

33.   Graph the line $-4x = y$.
Some points to graph are $(0, 0)$, and $(1, -4)$. The line through them is solid because of the $\leq$ symbol.
Since $(0, 0)$ is on the line, use another point such as $(1, 1)$.

$$-4x \leq y$$
$$-4(1) \leq 1$$
$$-4 \leq 1 \quad \textit{True}$$

Since the statement is true, shade
the side of the graph containing
(1, 1).
See answer graph in textbook.

37. (a)
Graph the line x + y = 200 when
x ≥ 0 and y ≥ 0.
Let x = 0, then y = 200 giving
(0, 200).
Let y = 0, then x = 200 giving
(200, 0).
The line through them is solid
because of the ≤ symbol.
Use (0, 0) as a test point.

$$0 + 0 \le 200 \quad True$$

Shade the side of the graph containing (0, 0).
See answer graph in textbook.

(b)
Some values of x and y that satisfy the inequality are:

(0, 0)   0 + 0 ≤ 200   True
(100, 000) 100 + 100 ≤ 200   True
(50, 120)   50 + 120 ≤ 200   True

There are many other values that
will also satisfy the inequality.

41. Let x = 2 in $3x^2 - 2x + 5$.

$$3(2)^2 - 2(2) + 5$$
$$= 3(4) - 2(2) + 5$$
$$= 12 - 4 + 5$$
$$= 13$$

45. Let x = 3 in $2x^4 - x^2$.

$$2(3)^4 - (3)^2$$
$$= 2(81) - 9$$
$$= 162 - 9$$
$$= 153$$

Section 6.6 (page 292)

1. { (-4, 3), (-2, 1), (0, 5), (-2, -4) }

This relation is not a function
since one value of x, namely -2,
corresponds to two values of y,
namely 1 and -4.

5. This relation is not a function
since the x-value 4 corresponds
to two values of y, namely -2
and -1. Also, the x-value of 10
corresponds to two values of y,
namely -6 and -8.

9. This relation is not a function
since a vertical line can cross
the graph more than once.

13. The linear equation y = 5x - 1 can
be written y - 5x = -1. Since the
graph of this equation is not a
vertical line, the equation defines
a function.

17. $y = x^2 + 3$

Since every value chosen for x
corresponds to only one value
for x^2, each value of x corresponds to exactly one value of
y. Therefore $y = x^2 + 3$ is a
function.

21. 2x + y < 6 can be written y < -2x +
6. For any value of x, there are
an infinite number of values for
y that satisfy the inequality.
Therefore, 2x + y < 6 is not a
function.

25. $y = 2x + 5$

Any number can be used for x, so the domain is the set of all real numbers. Any number can be used for y, so the range is the set of all real numbers.

29. $y = x^2 - 3$

Since any number can be squared, any number can be used for x so the domain is all real numbers. However, since the square of a real number cannot be negative and $y = x^2 - 3$ the values of y cannot be less than -3, making the range the set of all real numbers greater than or equal to -3.

33. $f(x) = 3x + 2$

(a) $f(2) = 3(2) + 2 = 6 + 2 = 8$
(b) $f(0) = 3(0) + 2 = 0 + 2 = 2$
(c) $f(-3) = 3(-3) + 2 = -9 + 2 = -7$

37. $f(x) = -4 - 4x$

(a) $f(2) = 4 - 4(2) = -4 - 8 = -12$
(b) $f(0) = -4 - 4(0) = -4 - 0 = -4$
(c) $f(-3) = -4 - 4(-3) = -4 + 12 = 8$

41. $f(x) = (x - 3)^2$

(a) $f(2) = (2 - 3)^2 = (-1)^2 = 1$
(b) $f(0) = (0 - 3)^2 = (-3)^2 = 9$
(c) $f(-3) = (-3 - 3)^2 = (-6)^2 = 36$

45. $P(x) = x^2 + 2x$

(a) $P(0) = (0)^2 + 2(0) = 0 + 0 = 0$
(b) $P(-3) = (-3)^2 + 2(-3) = 9 - 6 = 3$
(c) $P(2) = (2)^2 + 2(2) = 4 + 4 = 8$

49. $P(x) = x^3 - 4x^2 + 1$

(a) $P(0) = (0)^3 - 4(0)^2 + 1$
$= 0 - 4(0) + 1$
$= 0 - 0 + 1 = 1$
(b) $P(-3) = (-3)^3 - 4(-3)^2 + 1$
$= -27 - 4(9) + 1$
$= -27 - 36 + 1$
(c) $P(2) = (2)^3 - 4(2)^2 + 1$
$= 8 - 4(4) + 1$
$= 8 - 16 + 1 = -7$

53.   Write $x = |y| - 3$ as $|y| = x + 3$.

Let $x = 0$. Then $|y| = 3$, and y can be 3 or -3 (since $|-3| = 3$ and $|3| = 3$). Since one x-value leads to more than one y-value, $x = |y| - 3$ is not a function.

57.   With $x = 0$, then $|x + y| = 2$ becomes $|0 + y| = 2$, or $|y| = 2$, and $y = 2$ or $y = -2$. Since one value of x leads to more than one y-value, then $|x + y| = 2$ is not a function.

61.
$$
\begin{array}{r}
9a - 5b \\
-9a + 7b \\
\hline
0 + 2b = 2b
\end{array}
$$

Chapter 6 Review Exercises   (page 295)

1. $x + y = 7$
$3 + 4 = 7$ *Let x = 3, y = 4*
$7 = 7$ *True*

(3, 4) is a solution.

5.
$3x - y = 4$
$3(1) - (-1) = 4$ *Let x = 1, y = -1*
$3 + 1 = 4$
$4 = 4$ *True*

(1, -1) is a solution.

9. The equation $x + 4 = 0$ can be written as $x = -4$. So x is -4 in (, -3), (, 0), and (, 5). Thus, the ordered pairs are $(-4, -3)$, $(-4, 0)$, and $(-4, 5)$.

13.
$$2x - y = 5$$
$$2(0) - y = 5 \quad \textit{Let x = 0}$$
$$y = -5$$

This gives the ordered pair $(0, -5)$.
$$2x - 0 = 5 \quad \textit{Let y = 0}$$
$$x = \frac{5}{2}$$

This gives the ordered pair $(\frac{5}{2}, 0)$.

The graph is the line through $(0, -5)$ and $(\frac{5}{2}, 0)$,

See answer graph in textbook.

17.
$$y = 2x - 5$$
$$0 = 2x - 5 \quad \textit{Let y = 0}$$
$$5 = 2x$$
$$x = \frac{5}{2} \qquad \textit{x-intercept}$$
$$y = 2(0) - 5 \quad \textit{Let x = 0}$$
$$y = -5 \qquad \textit{y-intercept}$$

21. $(0, 0)$ and $(-1, -2)$
$$m = \frac{0 - (-2)}{0 - (-1)}$$
$$= \frac{2}{1}$$
$$= 2$$

25. $x = 2$

The graph is a vertical line, so the slope is undefined.

29. Solve $4x + 3y = 10$ for y.
$$4x + 3y = 10$$
$$3y = 10 - 4x \quad \textit{Subtract 4x}$$
$$y = \frac{10}{3} - \frac{4}{3}x \quad \textit{Divide by 3}$$

The slope is $-\frac{4}{3}$.

Solve $3x - 4y = 12$ for y.
$$3x - 4y = 12$$
$$-4y = 12 - 3x$$
$$y = \frac{12}{-4} - \frac{3}{-4}x$$
$$y = -3 + \frac{3}{4}x$$

The slope is $\frac{3}{4}$.

The product of the slopes is $(-\frac{4}{3})(\frac{3}{4}) = -1$, so the lines are perpendicular.

33. Let $m = \frac{2}{3}$ and $b = 5$ in the slope-intercept form.
$$y = mx + b$$
$$y = \frac{2}{3}x + 5 \quad \textit{Substitute}$$
$$-\frac{2}{3}x + y = 5 \qquad \textit{Subtract } \frac{2}{3}x$$
$$2x - 3y = -15 \qquad \textit{Multiply by -3}$$

37. $(2, 1)$ and $(-2, 2)$

$x = 2$, $y = 1$, $x_1 = -2$, $y_1 = 2$

Use the definition of slope.
$$m = \frac{1 - 2}{2 - (-2)} = \frac{-1}{4}$$

Use $(-2, 2)$ and $m = \frac{-1}{4}$.

Substitute into point-slope form.
$$y - 2 = \frac{-1}{4}[x - (-2)]$$
$$y - 2 = \frac{-1}{4}(x + 2)$$
$$4y - 8 = -x - 2$$
$$x + 4y = 6$$

41.　　　$x + 2y \leq 6$
　　　　$0 + 2y = 6$　　　*Let x = 0*
　　　　　　$y = 3$

　　　$x + 2(0) = 6$　　*Let y = 0*
　　　　　　$x = 6$

Graph the solid line through
(0, 3) and (6, 0).
Use (0, 0) as the test point.

　　　　$x + 2y \leq 6$
　　　　$0 + 2(0) \leq 6$
　　　　　　$0 \leq 6$　　*True*

Shade the region that contains
(0, 0).
See answer graph in textbook.

45.　Since a vertical line will cross
the graph more than once, this
is not a function.

49.　$x - 5y < 10$

　　If $x = 0$, then

　　　　$0 - 5y < 10$
　　　　　$y > -2.$

So y could be many values, say
$-1\frac{1}{2}$, 0, 1, 2 for example. Since
one value of x leads to many
values of y, then $x - 5y < 10$
is not a function.

53.　　　$f(x) = 3x + 2$
　(a)　$f(2) = 3(2) + 2$
　　　　　　$= 6 + 2$
　　　　　　$= 8$

　(b)　$f(-1) = 3(-1) + 2$
　　　　　　$= -3 + 2$
　　　　　　$= -1$

57.　(4, -1) and (-2, -3)

　$x_1 = 4, \ y_1 = -1, \ x_2 = -2, \ y_2 = -3$

Use the definition of slope.

　$m = \dfrac{-3 - (-1)}{-2 - 4} = \dfrac{-2}{-6} = \dfrac{1}{3}$

Use (-2, -3) and $m = \dfrac{1}{3}$

Substitute into point-slope form.

　　$y - (-3) = \frac{1}{3}[x - (-2)]$

　　　$y + 3 = \frac{1}{3}(x + 2)$

　　$3y + 9 = x + 2$

　$-x + 3y = -7$

　　$x - 3y = 7$

　$0 - 3y = 7$　*Let x = 0*

　　　$y = \dfrac{7}{3}$

　$x - 3(0) = 7$

　　　$x = 7$　*Let y = 0*

The y-intercept is $\dfrac{-7}{3}$.

The x-intercept is 7.

61.　The ordered pairs (0,　), (　, 0),
and (-2,　) mean that x = 0 and
x = -2 and y = 0 in 4x + 3y = 9.
Let x = 0. Then

　　　$4(0) + 3y = 9$
　　　　　$3y = 9$
　　　　　　$y = 3$

Let x = -2. Then

　　　$4(-2) + 3y = 9$
　　　　$-8 + 3y = 9$
　　　　　$3y = 17$
　　　　　　$y = \dfrac{17}{3}$

Let y = 0. Then

　　　$4x + 3(0) = 9$
　　　　　$4x = 9$
　　　　　　$x = \dfrac{9}{4}$

The ordered pairs are $(0, 3)$, $(\frac{9}{4}, 0)$, and $(-2, \frac{17}{3})$.

65. Use the point-slope form with $(x_1, y_1) = (8, 6)$ and $m = -3$.

$$y - y_1 = m(x - x_1)$$
$$y - 6 = -3(x - 8)$$
$$y - 6 = -3x + 24$$
$$3x + y = 30$$

69. $y = 4x - 1$

   $y = 4(0) - 1$ *Let x = 0*

   $y = -1$

   This gives the ordered pair $(0, -1)$.

   $0 = 4x - 1$ *Let y = 0*

   $x = \frac{1}{4}$

   This gives the ordered pair $(\frac{1}{4}, 0)$.

   The graph is the line through $(0, -1)$ and $(\frac{1}{4}, 0)$.

   See the answer graph in textbook.

Chapter 6 Test   **(page 297)**

1. $y = 5x - 6$

   If $x = 0$, then
   $$y = 5(0) - 6$$
   $$= -6$$

   to give the ordered pair $(0, -6)$.

   If $x = -2$, then
   $$y = 5(-2) - 6$$
   $$= -10 - 6$$
   $$= -16$$

   to give the ordered pair $(-2, -16)$.

   If $y = 14$, then
   $$14 = 5x - 6$$
   $$20 = 5x$$
   $$4 = x.$$

   The ordered pair is $(4, 14)$.

2. $2x + 7y = 21$

   If $x = 0$, then
   $$2 \cdot 0 + 7y = 21$$
   $$7y = 21$$
   $$y = 3$$

   to give the ordered pair $(0, 3)$.

   If $y = 0$, then
   $$2x + 7 \cdot 0 = 21$$
   $$2x = 21$$
   $$x = \frac{21}{2}$$

   to give the ordered pair $(21/2, 0)$.

   If $x = 3$, then
   $$2 \cdot 3 + 7y = 21$$
   $$6 + 7y = 21$$
   $$7y = 15$$
   $$y = \frac{15}{7}$$

   to give the ordered pair $(3, 15/7)$.

   If $y = 2$, then
   $$2x + 7 \cdot 2 = 21$$
   $$2x + 14 = 21$$
   $$2x = 7$$
   $$x = \frac{7}{2}$$

   to give the ordered pair $(7/2, 2)$.

3. $x = 3y$

   If $x = 0$, then
   $$0 = 3y$$
   $$y = 0$$

   to give $(0, 0)$.

   If $y = 2$, then
   $$x = 3(2) = 6$$

   to give $(6, 2)$.

   If $x = 8$, then
   $$8 = 3y$$
   $$y = \frac{8}{3}$$

   to give $(8, 8/3)$.

If x = -12, then

$$-12 = 3y$$
$$y = -4$$

to give (-12, -4).

4. y - 2 = 0

If x = 5, then

$$y - 2 = 0$$
$$y = 2$$

giving (5, 2).

For all values of x, y = 2, so

if x = 4, then y = 2, giving (4, 2);

if x = 0, then y = 2, giving (0, 2);

if x = -3, then y = 2, giving (-3, 2).

See answer graphs in your textbook for problems 5-10.

5.   x + y = 4

If x = 0, then

$$0 + y = 4$$
$$y = 4$$

so the y-intercept is 4.

If y = 0,

$$x + 0 = 4$$
$$x = 4$$

so the x-intercept is 4.

The graph is the line through (0, 4) and (4, 0).

6.   2x + y = 6

If x = 0, then

$$2(0) + y = 6$$
$$y = 6$$

so the y-intercept is (0, 6). If y = 0, then

$$2x + 0 = 6$$
$$2x = 6$$
$$x = 3.$$

The x-intercept is (3, 0). The

graph is the line through (0, 6) and (3, 0).

7. 3x - 4y = 18

If x = 0, then

$$3(0) - 4y = 18$$
$$0 - 4y = 18$$
$$-4y = 18$$
$$y = \frac{-18}{4}$$
$$= -\frac{9}{2}.$$

The y-intercept is $(0, -\frac{9}{2})$.

If y = 0, then

$$3x - 4(0) = 18$$
$$3x - 0 = 18$$
$$3x = 18$$
$$x = 6.$$

The x-intercept is (6, 0).
The graph is the line through

$(0, -\frac{9}{2})$ and (6, 0).

8. 2x + y = 0

If x = 0, then

$$2(0) + y = 0$$
$$y = 0$$

The x-intercept is (0, 0) and the y-intercept is (0, 0).

To graph the equation we must find another point. Let x = 1, then

$$2(1) + y = 0$$
$$2 + y = 0$$
$$y = -2$$

Another point is (1, -2). The graph is the line through (0, 0) and (1, -2).

9. Write $x + 5 = 0$ as $x = -5$. The graph is a vertical line through the x-axis at the x-intercept -5. There is no y-intercept.

10. The graph of $y = 2$ is a horizontal line through the y-axis at the y-intercept 2. There is no x-intercept.

11. $(-2, 4)$ and $(5, 1)$

    $x = -2$, $y = 4$, $x_1 = 5$, $y_1 = 1$

    Use the definition of slope.

    $$m = \frac{4 - 1}{-2 - 5}$$
    $$= \frac{3}{-7}$$
    $$= -\frac{3}{7}$$

12. The equation $y = -\frac{3}{4}x + 6$ is in the slope-intercept form, $y = mx + b$. Thus $m = -\frac{3}{4}$.

13. $4x + 7y = 10$
    $$7y = -4x + 10$$
    $$y = -\frac{4}{7}x + \frac{10}{7}$$

    The slope is $-4/7$ (slope-intercept form).

14. $x - 5 = 0$
    $$x = 5$$

    This is a vertical line whose slope is undefined.

15. $(1, -3)$; $m = -4$

    Use the point-slope form with $x_1 = 1$, $y_1 = -3$, and $m = -4$.

    $$y - y_1 = m(x - x_1)$$
    $$y - (-3) = -4(x - 1)$$
    $$y + 3 = -4x + 4$$
    $$4x + y = 1$$

16. Use the slope-intercept form with $m = 3$ and $b = -1$.

    $$y = mx + b$$
    $$y = 3x - 1$$
    $$-3x + y = -1$$
    $$3x - y = 1$$

17. Use the slope-intercept form with $m = -\frac{3}{4}$ and $b = 2$.

    $$y = mx + b$$
    $$y = -\frac{3}{4} \text{ and } b = 2.$$
    $$4y = 4(-\frac{3}{4}x + 2)$$
    $$4y = -3x + 8$$
    $$3x + 4y = 8$$

18. $(-2, -6)$ and $(-1, 3)$

    $x = -2$, $y = -6$, $x_1 = -1$, $y_1 = 3$

    $$\text{slope} = \frac{-6 - 3}{-2 - (-1)}$$
    $$= \frac{-9}{-1}$$
    $$= 9$$

    Use the value $m = 9$ and one point, say $(-1, 3)$, in the point-slope form.

    $$y - y_1 = m(x - x_1)$$
    $$y - 3 = 9[x - (-1)]$$
    $$y - 3 = 9(x + 1)$$
    $$y - 3 = 9x + 9$$
    $$-9x + y = 12$$
    $$9x - y = -12$$

19. $2x + y \leq 8$

Graph the line $2x + y = 8$
Let $x = 0$, then

$$2(0) + y = 8$$
$$y = 8$$

Let $y = 0$, then

$$2x + 0 = 8$$
$$2x = 8$$
$$x = 4$$

Graph the solid line through
(0, 8) and (4, 0).
Use test point (0, 0).

$$2x + y \leq 8$$
$$2(0) + 0 \leq 8$$
$$0 \leq 8 \quad \textit{True}$$

Since the statement is true, the
region shaded should contain
(0, 0).
See answer graph in textbook.

20. $y < -3$

Graph the line $y = -3$.
The graph of $y = -3$ is a horizontal line through (0, -3). The
line is solid because of the $\leq$
sign.
Use (0, 0) as a test point.

$$y \leq -3$$
$$0 \leq -3 \quad \textit{False}$$

Since $0 \leq -3$ is false, shade the
region below the line, which does
not contain (0, 0).

21.   The vertical line test shows that
this graph is not a function; a
vertical line can cross the graph
twice.

22. $y = 3x + 5$

For any one value of x, there will
be only one value of y. This
equation is a function.

23. $x = y^2 - 1$

Let $x = 3$, then

$$3 = y^2 - 1$$
$$4 = y^2$$

But $y^2 = 4$ has two solutions, $y = 2$
and $y = -2$. Therefore $x = y^2 - 1$
is not a function.

24. $y = 2x^2 + 1$

Since any real number can be
squared, the domain is the set
of all real numbers. However,
since the square of a number is
always positive and $y = 2x^2 + 1$,
y is always greater than or equal
to 1. The range is then the set
of all real numbers greater than
or equal to 1.

25. $f(-3) = 6(-3) - 2$
$$= -18 - 2$$
$$= -20$$

$f(5) = 6(5) - 2$
$$= 30 - 2$$
$$= 28$$

CHAPTER 7   LINEAR SYSTEMS

Section 7.1   (page 304)

1. To decide whether or not (2, -5) is
    a solution for the system, substi-
    tute 2 for x and -5 for y in each
    equation.

$$3x + y = 1$$
$$3(2) + (-5) = 1$$
$$6 + (-5) = 1$$
$$1 = 1 \qquad True$$

$$2x + 3y = -11$$
$$2(2) + 3(-5) = -11$$
$$4 + (-15) = -11$$
$$11 = -11 \quad True$$

Since (2, -5) satisfies both
systems, then (2, -5) is a
solution of the system.

5. Substitute 2 for x and 0 for y in
    each equation.

$$3x + 5y = 6$$
$$3 \cdot 2 + 5 \cdot 0 = 6$$
$$6 + 0 = 6$$
$$6 = 6 \quad True$$

$$4x + 2y = 5$$
$$4 \cdot 2 + 2 \cdot 0 = 5$$
$$8 + 0 = 5$$
$$8 = 5 \quad False$$

Not a solution.

9. Substitute 6 for x and -8 for y
    in each equation.

$$x + 2y + 10 = 0$$
$$6 + 2(-8) + 10 = 0$$
$$6 + (-16) + 10 = 0$$
$$0 = 0 \qquad True$$

$$2x - 3y + 30 = 0$$
$$2(6) - 3(-8) + 30 = 0$$
$$12 + 24 + 30 = 0$$
$$66 = 0 \quad False$$

Since (6, -8) does not satisfy
the second equation, then it is
not a solution of the system.

13. To graph x + y = 6:
    Let x = 0, then y = 6, giving the
    ordered pair (0, 6).
    Let y = 0, then x = 6, giving the
    ordered pair (6, 0).
    Graph these two points and the
    line through them.

    To graph x - y = 2:
    Let x = 0, then y = -2, giving the
    ordered pair (0, -2).
    Let y = 0, then x = 2, giving the
    ordered pair (2, 0).
    Graph these two points and the
    line through them.
    The two lines intersect at the
    solution (4, 2).

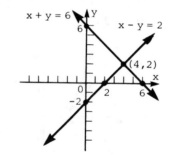

17. $4x + 5y = 3$

    Let x = 0, then y = $\frac{3}{5}$.

    Let y = 0, then x = $\frac{3}{4}$.

    Plot the points (0, $\frac{3}{5}$) and ($\frac{3}{4}$, 0),
    and draw the line through them.

    $2x - 5y = 9$

    Let x = 0, then y = $-\frac{9}{5}$.

    Let y = 0, then x = $\frac{9}{2}$.

    Plot the points (0, $-\frac{9}{5}$) and ($\frac{9}{2}$, 0),
    and draw the line through them.
    The two lines intersect at the
    solution (2, -1).

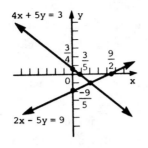

21. 3x - 4y = -24

Let x = 0, then y = 6.

Let y = 0, then x = -8.

Plot the points (0, 6) and (-8, 0), and draw the line through them.

5x + 2y = -14

Let x = 0, then y = -7.

Let y = 0, then x = $-\frac{14}{5}$.

Plot the points (0, -7) and $(-\frac{14}{5}, 0)$, and draw the line through them.

The lines intersect at the solution (-4, 3).

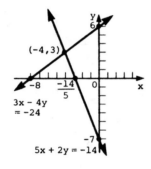

25. 2x + 3y = 3

Let x = 0, then y = 1, giving (0, 1).

Let y = 0, then x = $\frac{3}{2}$, giving $(\frac{3}{2}, 0)$.

Graph these two points and the line through them.

x + y = 3

Let x = 0, then y = 3, giving (0, 3).

Let y = 0, then x = 3, giving (3, 0).

Graph these two points and the line through them.

The intersection of these two lines is the solution (6, -3).

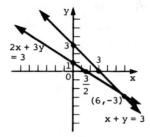

29. 2x + 5y - 20 = 0

        2x + 5y = 20

Let x = 0, then y = 4, (0, 4).

Let y = 0, then x = 10, (10, 0).

Graph these two points and the line through them.

x + y - 10 = 0

        x + y = 10

Let x = 0, then y = 10, (0, 10).

Let y = 0, then x = 10, (10, 0).

Graph these two points and the line through them.

The intersection of these two lines is the solution (10, 0).

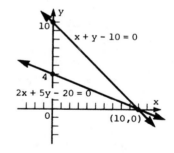

33. x = 5

The line x = 5 is a vertical line passing through the x-axis at (5, 0).

2x - y = 4

Let x = 0, then y = -4, (0, -4).

Let y = 0, then x = 2, (2, 0).

Graph these two points and the line through them.

The intersection of these lines
is the solution (5, 6).

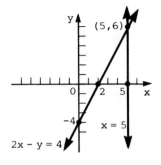

37.   4x + 1 = x

Let x = 0, then y = $-\frac{1}{4}$.

Let y = 0, then x = 1.
Graph the points (0, $-\frac{1}{4}$) and (1, 0)
and draw the line.

2x - 3 = 8y

Let x = 0, then y = $-\frac{3}{8}$.

Let y = 0, then x = $\frac{3}{2}$.

Graph the points (0, $-\frac{3}{8}$) and ($\frac{3}{2}$, 0)

and draw the line.
The lines are parallel so there
is no solution and the system
is inconsistent.

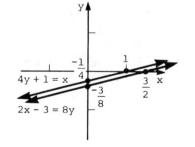

41. $\frac{3}{5}$x + $\frac{2}{5}$y = 2

Let x = 0, then y = 5.

Let y = 0, then x = $\frac{10}{3}$.

Graph the points (0, 5) and ($\frac{10}{3}$, 0)

and draw the line.

$2x - \frac{3}{2}y = -\frac{15}{2}$

Let x = 0, then y = 5.

Let y = 0, then x = $-\frac{15}{4}$.

Graph the points (0, 5) and ($-\frac{15}{4}$, 0)

and draw the line.
The lines intersect at the solution (0, 5).

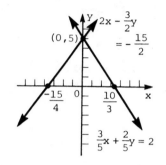

45.   x + 2y = 0
        4y = -2x

Write both equations in slope-
intercept form.

x + 2y = 0   4y = -2x

    2y = -x   y = $-\frac{1}{2}$x

    y = $-\frac{1}{2}$x

a.   Since the equations are iden-
      tical, they are dependent.
b.   The graph is one line.
c.   The system has an infinite
      number of solutions.

49.   5x + 4y = 7
        4y = -5x + 7
        y = $-\frac{5}{4}$x + $\frac{7}{4}$

      2x - 3y = 12
        -3y = -2x + 12
        y = $\frac{2}{3}$x - 4

a.   Since the equations have dif-
      ferent slopes and y-intercepts,
      the system is neither inconsis-

tent nor are the equations
dependent.

c. The system has one solution.

53. 6p + 2q
     4p + 5q
     ──────────
     10p + 7q *Add in columns*

57. 4a + 3b and -3b - 2a
      = 4a + (-2a) + 3b + (-3b)
      = 2a

Section 7.2 (page 312)

1.   x - y = 3
     x + y = -1
     ──────────────
     2x   = 2   *Add the two equations*
          x = 1   *Solve for x*

     1 - y = 3   *Let x = 1 in the
                   first equation*

        -y = 2
         y = -2

     The solution is (1, -2).

5.   2x + y = 14
     x - y = 4
     ──────────────
     3x   = 18 *Add the two
                   equations*
          x = 6   *Solve for x*

     2·6 + y = 14 *Let x = 6 in the
                    first equation*

     12 + y = 14
          y = 2

     The solution is (6, 2).

9.   6x - y = 1
     -6x + 5y = 7
     ──────────────
          4y = 8   *Add the two
                    equations*
           y = 2   *Solve for y*

6x - (2) = 1   *Let y = 2 in the
                first equation*

     6x = 3

      x = $\frac{3}{6}$

        = $\frac{1}{2}$

The solution is (1/2, 2).

13. 5x - y = 15
     7x + y = 21
     ──────────────
     12x   = 36   *Add the two
                    equations*

         x = 3   *Solve for x*

     5(3) - y = 15   *Let x = 3 in the
                      first equation*

     15 - y = 15
         -y = 0
          y = 0

The solution is (3, 0).

17. x + 3y = 16   *(1)*
     2x - y = 4   *(2)*

         x + 3y = 16 *(1)*
     3(2x - y) = 3 *(4) Multiply equation
                      (2) by 3*

       x + 3y = 16   *(1)*
      6x - 3y = 12   *(2) times 3*
     ──────────────
     7x   = 28   *Solve for x*
          x = 4

     (4) + 3y = 16   *Let x = 4 in (1)*
          3y = 12
           y = 4

The solution is (4, 4).

21. 3x - 2y = -6   *(1)*
     -5x + 4y = 16   *(2)*

     6x - 4y = -12   *Multiply (1) by 2*
     -5x + 4y = 16   *(2)*
     ──────────────
      x   = 4

$6 \cdot 4 - 4y = -12$ *Let x = 4 in (1)*

$24 - 4y = -12$

$-4y = -36$

$y = 9$

The solution is (4, 9).

25. $2x + y = 5$ *(1)*

$5x + 3y = 11$ *(2)*

$-6x - 3y = -15$ *Multiply (1) by -3*

$\underline{5x + 3y = 11}$ *(2)*

$-x \qquad = -4$

$x = 4$

$2(4) + y = 5$ *Let x = 4 in (1)*

$8 + y = 5$

$y = -3$

The solution is (4, -3).

29. $3x + 5y = 33$ *(1)*

$4x - 3y = 15$ *(2)*

$3(3x + 5y) = 3(33)$ *Multiply (1) by 3*

$5(4x - 3y) = 5(15)$ *Multiply (2) by 5*

$9x + 15y = 99$ *(1) times 3*

$\underline{20x - 15y = 75}$ *(2) times 5*

$29x \qquad = 174$

$x = 6$

$3(6) + 5y = 33$ *Let x = 6 in (1)*

$18 + 5y = 33$

$5y = 15$

$y = 3$

The solution is (6, 3).

33. $2x + 3y = -12$

$5x = 7y - 30$

Rewrite these equations.

$2x + 3y = -12$ *(1)*

$5x - 7y = -30$ *(2)*

$7(2x + 3y) = 7(-12)$

$3(5x - 7y) = 3(-30)$

$14x + 21y = -84$ *Add the equations*

$\underline{15x - 21y = -90}$

$29x \qquad = -174$

$x = -6$

$2(-6) + 3y = -12$ *Let x = -6 in (1)*

$-12 + 3y = -12$

$3y = 0$

$y = 0$

The solution is (-6, 0)

37. $5x - 2y = 6$ *(1)*

$10x - 4y = 10$ *(2)*

$-2(5x - 2y) = -2(6)$ *Multiply (1) by 2*

$-10x + 4y = -12$

$\underline{10x - 4y = 10}$ *(2)*

$0 = -2$ *False*

The system has no solution. The lines are parallel. The system is inconsistent.

41. $2x + 3y = 8$ *(1)*

$4x + 6y = 12$ *(2)*

$-2(2x + 3y) = -2(8)$ *Multiply (1) by -2*

$-4x - 6y = -16$ *(1) times -2*

$\underline{4x + 6y = 12}$ *(2)*

$0 = -4$ *False*

The graphs of the equations are parallel lines. The system is inconsistent and has no solutions.

45. $24x + 12y = 19$ *(1)*

$16x - 18y = -9$ *(2)*

$72x + 36y = 57$ *Multiply (1) by 3*

$\underline{32x - 36y = -18}$ *Multiply (2) by 2*

$104x \qquad = 39$

$x = \frac{39}{104}$

$x = \frac{3}{8}$ *Solve for x*

$$24\left(\frac{3}{8}\right) + 12y = 19 \quad \textit{Let } x = 3/8 \textit{ in (1)}$$

$$9 + 12y = 19$$

$$12y = 10$$

$$y = \frac{10}{12}$$

$$y = \frac{5}{6}$$

The solution is (3/8, 5/6).

49. $\quad \frac{6}{5}x + \frac{1}{5}y = \frac{33}{5}$

$$-x + \frac{3}{2}y = \frac{19}{2}$$

$$5\left(\frac{6}{5}x\right) + 5\left(\frac{1}{5}y\right) = 5\left(\frac{33}{5}\right)$$

$\qquad$ *Multiply both sides of each equation by the common denominator for that equation*

$$2(-x) + 2\left(\frac{3}{2}y\right) = 2\left(\frac{19}{2}\right)$$

$$6x + y = 33 \quad \textit{Multiply the second equation by 3}$$

$$-2x + 3y = 19$$

$$6x + y = 33 \quad \textit{Add the equations}$$
$$\underline{-6x + 9y = 57}$$
$$10y = 90$$
$$y = 9$$

$$-x + \frac{3}{2}(9) = \frac{19}{2} \quad \textit{Let } y = 9 \textit{ in the original second equation}$$

$$-x + \frac{27}{2} = \frac{19}{2}$$

$$-x = \frac{19}{2} - \frac{27}{2}$$

$$-x = -\frac{8}{2}$$

$$x = 4$$

The solution is (4, 9).

53. $\quad \frac{2}{3}x - y = 0$

$$\frac{4}{3}x + \frac{4}{3}y = 0$$

$$3\left(\frac{2}{3}x - y\right) = 3(0)$$

$$3\left(\frac{4}{3}x + \frac{4}{3}y\right) = 3(0) \quad \textit{Multiply both equations by 3}$$

$$2x - 3y = 0 \quad \textit{Multiply the first}$$
$$4x + 4y = 0 \quad \textit{equation by -2}$$

$$-4x + 6y = 0 \quad \textit{Add the equations}$$
$$\underline{4x + 4y = 0} \quad \textit{together and solve}$$
$$10y = 0 \quad \textit{for } y$$
$$y = 0$$

$$\frac{2}{3}x - 0 = 0 \quad \textit{Let } y = 0 \textit{ in the first original equation and solve for } x$$

$$\frac{2}{3}x = 0$$

$$x = 0$$

The solution is (0, 0).

57. $\quad .13x - .52y = -.39 \qquad (1)$

$$.39x + .08y = -2.81 \qquad (2)$$

$$-.39x + 1.56y = 1.17 \quad \textit{Multiply}$$
$$\underline{.39x + .08y = -2.81} \quad \begin{matrix}\textit{(1) by -3}\\ (2)\end{matrix}$$
$$1.64y = -1.64$$
$$y = -1 \quad \textit{Solve for } y$$

$$.13x - .52(-1) = -.39 \quad \begin{matrix}\textit{Let } y = -1\\ \textit{in (1)}\end{matrix}$$

$$.13x + .52 = -.39$$
$$.13x = -.91$$
$$x = -7$$

The solution is (-7, -1).

61. $\quad 2m - 3(4 - m) = 8$

$$2m - 12 + 3m = 8$$
$$5m - 12 = 8$$
$$5m = 20$$
$$m = 4$$

65. $a + 3(\dfrac{1 - a}{2}) = 5$

$2 \cdot a + 2 \cdot 3(\dfrac{1 - a}{2}) = 2 \cdot 5$

Multiply each term by the least common denominator 2

$2a + 3(1 - a) = 10$

$2a + 3 - 3a = 10$

$3 - a = 10$

$-a = 7$

$a = -7$

Section 7.3 (page 317)

1. $x + y = 6$ *(1)*

$y = 2x$ *(2) Notice that this equation is solved for y*

$x + (2x) = 6$ *Replace 2x for y in (1)*

$3x = 6$

$x = 2$ *Solve for x*

$y = 2(2)$ *Let x = 2 in (2)*

$y = 4$

The solution is (2, 4).

5. $x + 5y = 3$ *(1)*

$x = 2y + 10$ *(2)*

$2y + 10 + 5y = 3$ *Replace (2y + 10) for x in (1)*

$7y + 10 = 3$

$7y = -7$

$y = -1$ *Solve for y*

$x = 2(-1) + 10$ *Let y = -1*

$x = -2 + 10$

$x = 8$

The solution is (8, -1).

9. $3x - 2y = 14$ *(1)*

$2x + y = 0$ *(2)*

$y = -2x$ *Solve (2) for y*

$3x - 2(-2x) = 14$ *Replace y by -2x in (1)*

$3x + 4x = 14$

$7x = 14$

$x = 2$

$y = -2(2)$ *Let x = 2 in y = -2x*

$y = -4$

The solution is (2, -4).

13. $6x - 8y = 4$ *(1)*

$3x = 4y + 2$ *(2)*

$x = \dfrac{4y + 2}{3}$ *Solve (2) for x*

$6(\dfrac{4y + 2}{3}) - 8y = 4$ *Replace x by $(\dfrac{4y + 2}{3})$ in (1)*

$2(4y + 2) - 8y = 4$

$8y + 4 - 8y = 4$

$4 = 4$ *True*

The equations represent the same line so they are dependent and there is an infinite number of solutions.

17. $6x + 5y = 13$ *(1)*

$3x + 2y = 4$ *(2)*

$3x = 4 - 2y$

$x = \dfrac{4 - 2y}{3}$ *Solve (2) for x*

$6(\dfrac{4 - 2y}{3}) + 5y = 13$ *Replace x by $\dfrac{4 - 2y}{3}$ in (1)*

$2(4 - 2y) + 5y = 13$

$8 - 4y + 5y = 13$

$8 + y = 13$

$y = 5$

$x = \dfrac{4 - 2(5)}{3}$ *Let y = 5 in $x = \dfrac{4 - 2y}{3}$*

$x = \dfrac{4 - 10}{3}$

$x = \dfrac{-6}{3}$

$x = -2$

The solution is (-2, 5).

21. $5x + 2y = -19$ (1)

$y - 3 = 0$ (2)

$y = 3$ *Solve (2) for y*

$5x + 2 \cdot 3 = -19$ *Replace y by 3 in (1)*

$5x + 6 = -19$

$5x = -25$

$x = -5$ *Solve for y*

The solution is (-5, 3).

25.   Simplify the first equation.

$2x - 8y + 3y + 2 = 5y + 16$

$2x - 5y + 2 = 5y + 16$

$2x - 10y + 2 = 16$

$2x - 10y = 14$

Simplify the second equation.

$8x - 2y = 4x + 28$

$4x - 2y = 28$

The system to be solved is

$2x - 10y = 14$ (1)

$4x + 2y = 28.$ (2)

$2x = 10y + 14$

$x = 5y + 7$ *Solve (1) for x*

$4(5y + 7) + 2y = 28$ *Replace x by (5y + 7) in (2)*

$20y + 28 + 2y = 28$

$22y = 0$

$y = 0$

$x = 5(0) + 7$ *Let y = 0 in x = 5y + 7*

$x = 7$

The solution is (7, 0).

29.   Simplify the first equation.

$y + 9 = 3x - 2y + 6$

$-3x + 3y + 9 = 6$

$-3x + 3y = -3$

$x - y = 1$

Simplify the second equation.

$5 - 3x + 24 = -2x + 4y + 3$

$29 - 3x = -2x + 4y + 3$

$-x - 4y + 29 = 3$

$-x - 4y = -26$

$x + 4y = 26$

The system to be solved is

$x - y = 1$ (1)

$x + 4y = 26.$ (2)

$x = 1 + y$ *Solve (1) for x*

$1 + y + 4y = 26$ *Replace x by (1 + y) in (2)*

$1 + 5y = 26$

$5y = 25$

$y = 5$

$x = 1 + 5$ *Let y = 5 in x = 1 + y*

$x = 6$

The solution is (6, 5).

33.   Multiply the first equation by 6 to clear fractions.

$6\left(\frac{x}{6}\right) + 6\left(\frac{y}{6}\right) = 6(1)$

$x + y = 6$

Multiply the second equation by 6.

$6\left(-\frac{1}{2}x\right) - 6\left(\frac{1}{3}y\right) = 6(-5)$

$-3x - 2y = -30$

The system to be solved is

$x + y = 6$ (1)

$-3x - 2y = -30.$ (2)

$3x + 3y = 18$ *Multiply (1) by 3*

$\underline{-3x - 2y = -30}$ (2)

$y = -12$

$x - 12 = 6$ *Let y = -12 in (1)*

$x = 18$

The solution is (18, -12).

37. Multiply each side of the first equation by 6, the common denominator of 2, 3, and 6.

$$6\left(\frac{x}{2} + \frac{y}{3}\right) = 6\left(\frac{7}{6}\right)$$
$$3x + 2y = 7$$

Multiply the second equation by 4, the common denominator of 2 and 4.

$$4\left(\frac{x}{4} - \frac{3y}{2}\right) = 4\left(\frac{9}{4}\right)$$
$$x - 6y = 9$$

Solve the system

$$3x + 2y = 7 \quad (1)$$
$$x - 6y = 9. \quad (2)$$

$$\begin{array}{ll} 9x + 6y = 21 & \textit{Multiply (1) by 3} \\ \underline{x - 6y = 9} & \textit{(2)} \\ 10x = 30 & \\ x = 3 & \end{array}$$

$$\begin{array}{ll} 3(3) + 2y = 7 & \textit{Let } x = 3 \textit{ in (1)} \\ 9 + 2y = 7 & \\ 2y = -2 & \\ y = -1 & \end{array}$$

The solution is (3, -1).

41. Let x represent the number.

It three times a number	is added	to six,	the result is
↓	↓	↓	↓
3·x	+	6	= 69

$$3x + 6 = 69$$
$$3x = 63$$
$$x = 21$$

The number is 21.

45. Let x represent the number of twenties. Then x + 6 is the number of tens.

Number of twenties	plus	number of tens	is
↓	↓	↓	↓
x	+	(x + 6)	= 32

$$x + x + 6 = 32$$
$$2x + 6 = 32$$
$$2x = 26$$
$$x = 13$$

There are 13 twenties.

Section 7.4 (page 323)

1. Let x represent the larger number, and y the smaller number. Then from the problem we get the following two equations:

$$\begin{array}{ll} x + y = 52 & \textit{Sum is 52} \\ x - y = 34 & \textit{Difference is 34} \end{array}$$

Solve using the addition method.

$$\begin{array}{l} x + y = 52 \\ \underline{x - y = 34} \\ 2x = 86 \\ x = 43 \end{array}$$

$$43 + y = 52$$
$$y = 9$$

The two numbers are 43 and 9.

5. Let x represent the large angle and y the smaller angle.

$$\begin{array}{ll} x + y = 90 & \textit{Sum is 90} \\ x - y = 20 & \textit{Difference is 20} \end{array}$$

Solve by addition.

$$\begin{array}{l} x + y = 90 \\ \underline{x - y = 20} \\ 2x = 110 \\ x = 55 \end{array}$$

$$55 + y = 90$$
$$y = 35$$

The angles measure 55° and 35°.

9. Let x represent the number of 16¢
    candies and y the number of 20¢
    candies.

Kind of candy	Number of pieces	Cost of candy
16¢	x	.16x
20¢	y	.20y
Totals	170	31.04

$$.16x + .20y = 31.04$$
$$x + y = 170$$

Solve this system of equations by
the substitution method.

$$x = 170 - y$$
$$.16(170 - y) + .20y = 31.04$$
$$27.2 - .16y + .20y = 31.04$$
$$.04y = 3.84$$
$$y = 96$$

$$x = 170 - 96$$
$$x = 74$$

There are 74 16¢ candies and
96 20¢ candies.

13. Let x represent the number of
     large canvases and y represent
     the number of small canvases.

Size of canvas	Cost of canvas	Number bought	Price paid
Large	7	x	7x
Small	4	y	4y
Total		39	219

$$7x + 4y = 219$$
$$x + y = 39$$

Solve for y in the second equation.

$$y = 39 - x$$

Replace y with 39 - x in the
first equation and solve.

$$7x + 4(39 - x) = 219$$
$$7x + 156 - 4x = 219$$
$$3x + 156 = 219$$
$$3x = 63$$
$$x = 21$$

Replace x with 21 in y = 39 - x.

$$y = 39 - 21$$
$$y = 18$$

The artist bought 21 canvases at
$7 and 18 canvases at $4.

17. Let x represent the amount of 25%
     solution and y represent the
     amount of 55% solution.

Liters of solution	Percent	Liters of pure indicator
x	.25	.25x
y	.55	.55y
12	.45	12(.45)

Since there is a total of 12 liters.

$$x + y = 12.$$

The total amount of pure indicator
in the mixture is 45% of 12, which
is (.45)(12) = 5.4, so

$$.25x + .55y = 5.4$$
or $$25x + 55y = 540.$$

Solve the system by the addition
method.

$$x + y = 12 \quad (1)$$
$$25x + 55y = 540 \quad (2)$$

$-25x - 25y = -300$ *Multiply (1) by -25*

$\underline{25x + 55y = 540}$ *(2)*

$30y = 240$

$y = 8$

$x + 8 = 12$ *Let y = 8 in (1)*

$x = 4$

4 liters of 25% solution should be mixed with 8 liters of 55% solution.

21. Let x = the speed of the boat
     in still water
and y = the speed of the current.

	d	r	t
Downstream	36	x + y	3
Upstream	24	x - y	3

Since d = rt,

$36 = (x + y)3$

$24 = (x - y)3$

Use distributive property.

$36 = 3x + 3y$ *(1)*

$\underline{24 = 3x - 3y}$ *(2)*

$60 = 6x$ *Add the equation*

$10 = x$

$36 = 3(10) + 3y$ *Let x = 10 in (1)*

$36 = 30 + 3y$

$6 = 3y$

$2 = y$

The speed of the boat in still water is 10 miles per hour. The speed of the current is 2 miles per hour.

25. Let x be the amount invested at 10% and y the amount at 14%. Use I = prt to construct the following table. Since the time is one year, I = pr(1) = pr.

	Interest	Principal	Rate
	.10x	x	.10
	.14y	y	.14
Totals	1100	10,000	

Add the first and second columns to write the system of equations.

$.10x + .14y = 1100$ *(1)*

$x + y = 10,000$ *(2)*

$x = 10,000 - y$
Solve (2) for x

$.10(10,000 - y) + .14y = 1100$
Substitute for x in (1)

$1000 - .10y + .14y = 1100$

$.04y = 100$

$y = 2500$

$x = 10,000 - 2500$
Let y = 2500 in
x = 10,000 - y

She should invest $7500 at 10% and $2500 at 14%.

29. Let x represent the number of pounds of $6 per pound coffee and y represent the number of pounds of $3 per pound coffee.

Pounds of coffee	Cost per pound	Cost of coffee
x	6	6x
y	3	3y
90		90(4)

Use the first and third column to write the system.

$x + y = 90$ *(1)*

$6x + 3y = 360$ *(2)*

$-3x - 3y = -270$ *Multiply (1) by -3*

$\underline{6x + 3y = 360}$ *(2)*

$3x = 90$

$x = 30$

$30 + y = 90$ *Let x = 30 in (1)*

$y = 60$

The merchant needs 30 pounds of
$6 per pound coffee and 60
pounds of $3 per pound coffee.

33.   Let B represent the number of boys
and G represent the number of girls.
Since Janet cannot count herself
as one of the girls when talking
about her sisters and she has as
many brothers as sisters, then

$$B = G - 1$$

or $$G = B + 1.$$

In the same manner, Steve cannot
include himself as one of the
boys when talking about his
brothers. Since he has twice as
many sisters as brothers then,

$$2(B - 1) = G.$$

(Since there are twice as many
sisters, then we have to double
his number of brothers to get
the two equal, and thus get an
equation.) Our system is

$$G = B + 1 \quad (1)$$
$$2(B - 1) = G. \qquad (2)$$
$$2(B - 1) = B + 1 \quad \textit{Substitute}$$
$$\textit{B + 1 for G}$$
$$\textit{in (2)}$$
$$2B - 2 = B + 1$$
$$B - 2 = 1$$
$$B = 3$$
$$G = 3 + 1 \quad \textit{Let B = 3}$$
$$\textit{in (1)}$$
$$= 4$$

There are 3 boys and 4 girls.

37.   Graph $3x + 2y = 6$ as a dashed
line.
Check to see if the origin $(0, 0)$
satisfies the inequality

$$3x + 2y > 6$$
$$3 \cdot 0 + 2 \cdot 0 > 6$$
$$0 > 6 \quad \textit{False}$$

Shade all points on side of line
that does not include origin.
See the graph in your textbook.

Section 7.5 (page 329)

1.   <u>Step 1</u>: Graph $x + y = 6$ as a
solid line.
If $x = 0$, then $y = 6$, giving the
ordered pair $(0, 6)$.
If $y = 0$, then $x = 6$, giving the
ordered pair $(6, 0)$.
Graph these two points and the
solid line through them.

<u>Step 2</u>: Use $(0, 0)$ as a test point.

$$x + y \leq 6 \quad \textit{Original inequality}$$
$$0 + 0 \leq 6 \quad \textit{Substitute x = 0, y = 0}$$
$$0 \leq 6 \quad \textit{True}$$

<u>Step 3</u>: Since the inequality is
true for $(0, 0)$, shade the side
of the graph containing $(0, 0)$.
Go through the same steps above
for the second inequality.

<u>Step 1</u>: Graph the line $x - y = 1$
as a solid line.
If $x = 0$, then $-y = 1$ or $y = -1$,
giving the ordered pair $(0, -1)$.
If $y = 0$, then $x = 1$, giving the
ordered pair $(1, 0)$.
Graph these two points and the
solid line through them.

<u>Step 2</u>: Use $(0, 0)$ as a test point.

$$x - y \leq 1 \quad \textit{Original inequality}$$
$$0 - 0 \leq 1 \quad \textit{Substitute x = 0, y = 0}$$
$$0 \leq 1 \quad \textit{True}$$

Step 3: Since the inequality is true for (0, 0), shade the side of the graph containing (0, 0). The solution is where the two shaded regions overlap and the lines that border this region. See the answer graph in your textbook.

5. Graph $x + 4y = 8$ as a solid line. Use (0, 0) as a test point.

$$x + 4y \leq 8$$
$$0 + 4 \cdot 0 \leq 8$$
$$0 + 0 \leq 8$$
$$0 \leq 8 \quad \textit{True}$$

Shade the area on the side of the line containing (0, 0).

Graph the line $2x - y = 4$ as a solid line. Use (0, 0) for a test point.

$$2x - y \leq 4$$
$$2 \cdot 0 - 0 \leq 4$$
$$0 - 0 \leq 4$$
$$0 \leq 4 \quad \textit{True}$$

Shade the area on the side of this line containing (0, 0). The solution is the overlapped portion of the shaded areas. See the answer graph in your textbook.

9. Graph $x + 2y = 4$ as a solid line. Use (0, 0) as a test point. The inequality $x + 2y \leq 4$ is true at (0, 0). Shade the area on the side of the line containing (0, 0). Graph the line $x + 1 = y$ as a solid line. Use (0, 0) as a test point. The inequality $x + 1 \geq y$ is true at (0, 0).

Shade the area on the side of this line containing (0, 0). The solution is the overlapped portion of the shaded areas. See the graph in your textbook.

13. Graph $x - 2y = 6$ as a dashed line. Use (0, 0) for a test point. The inequality $x - 2y > 6$ is false at (0, 0). Shade the area on the side of the line that does not contain (0, 0). Graph the line $2x + y = 4$ as a dashed line. Use (0, 0) for a test point. The inequality $2x + y > 4$ is false at (0, 0). Shade the area on the side of this line that does not contain (0, 0). The solution is the overlapped portion of the shaded area. See graph in your textbook.

17. Graph $x - 3y = 6$ as a solid line. Use (0, 0) for a test point. The inequality $x - 3y \leq 6$ is true at (0, 0). Shade the area on the side of the line containing (0, 0). Graph the line $x = -1$ as a solid line. Use (0, 0) for a test point. The inequality $x \geq -1$ is true at (0, 0). Shade the area on the side of this line that contains (0, 0). The solution is the overlapped portion of the shaded areas. See the graph in your textbook.

21. Graph x = 2 as a solid line.
     Use (0, 0) as a test point.
     The inequality x ≥ 2 is false at
     (0, 0).
     Shade the area on the side of the
     line that does not contain (0, 0).

     Graph the line y = 3 as a solid
     line.
     Use (0, 0) as a test point.
     The inequality y ≤ 3 is true at
     (0, 0).
     Shade the area on the side of this
     line that contains (0, 0).
     The solution is the overlapped
     portion of the shaded areas.
     See the graph in your textbook.

25. $5^2 = 5 \cdot 5$
        $= 25$

29. $6^3 = 6 \cdot 6 \cdot 6$
        $= 216$

Chapter 7 Review Exercises   (page 330)

1.   Substitute 3 for x and 4 for y in
     each equation.

     $4x - 2y = 4$
     $4(3) - 2(4) = 4$
     $12 - 8 = 4$
     $4 = 4$ *True*

     $5x + y = 17$
     $5(3) + 4 = 17$
     $15 + 4 = 17$
     $19 = 17$ *False*

     (3, 4) is not a solution.

5.   Substitute -1 for x and -3 for y
     in each equation.

     $x + 2y = -7$
     $-1 + 2(-3) = -7$
     $-1 - 6 = -7$
     $-7 = -7$ *True*

     $-x + 3y = -8$
     $-(-1) + 3(-3) = -8$
     $1 - 9 = -8$
     $-8 = -8$ *True*

     (-1, -3) is a solution.

9. $2x + 3y = 1$
     Let x = 0, then y = $\frac{1}{3}$, giving
     $(0, \frac{1}{3})$.

     Let y = 0, then x = $\frac{1}{2}$, giving
     $(\frac{1}{2}, 0)$.

     Graph these two points and the
     line through them.

     $4x - y = 5$

     Let x = 0, then y = 5, giving
     (0, 5).

     Let y = 0, then x = $-\frac{5}{4}$, giving
     $(-\frac{5}{4}, 0)$.

     Graph these two points and the
     line through them. These two
     lines intersect at the solution
     point (-1, 1).

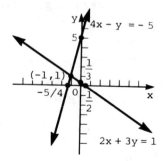

13. $x + y = 6$ *(1)*

   $2x + y = 8$ *(2)*

   $-x - y = -6$ *Multiply (1) by -1*

   $\underline{2x + y = 8}$ *(2)*

   $x = 2$ *Add*

   $2 + y = 6$ *Let x = 2 in (1)*

   $ y = 4$

   The solution is (2, 4).

17. $3x - 4y = 7$ *(1)*

   $6x - 8y = 14$ *(2)*

   $-6x + 8y = -14$ *Multiply (1) by -2*

   $\underline{6x - 8y = 14}$

   $ 0 = 0$ *True*

   The equations produce the same line, so there are an infinite number of solutions. The equations are dependent.

21. $3x - 4y = -1$ *(1)*

   $-6x + 8y = 2$ *(2)*

   $6x - 8y = -2$ *Multiply (1) by 2*

   $\underline{-6x + 8y = 2}$

   $ 0 = 0$ *True*

   The equations produce the same line, so there are an infinite number of solutions. The equations are dependent.

25. $4x + 5y = 35$ *(1)*

   $x = 2y - 1$ *(2)*

   $4(2y - 1) + 5y = 35$ *Let x = 2y - 1 in (1)*

   $8y - 4 + 5y = 35$

   $13y - 4 = 35$

   $13y = 39$

   $y = 3$

$x = 2(3) - 1$ *Let y = 3 in x = 2y - 1*

$x = 6 - 1$

$x = 5$

29.   Let L represent the length of the rectangle and W the width. Since the perimeter is 40,

$$2L + 2W = 40.$$

$$L = 1\tfrac{1}{2}W$$

Replace L by $1\tfrac{1}{2}W$ in the first equation and solve for W.

$$2(1\tfrac{1}{2}W) + 2W = 40$$

$$3W + 2W = 40$$

$$5W = 40$$

$$W = 8$$

To find L, let W = 8 in the second equation.

$$L = (1\tfrac{1}{2})(8)$$

$$L = 12$$

The length is 12 meters and the width is 8 meters.

33.   Let x represent the number of liters of 40% solution and y the number of liters of 70% solution.

Liters of Solution	Percent	Liters of Antifreeze
x	.40	.40x
y	.70	.70y
60	.50	.60(.50)

$$x + y = 60 \quad (1)$$

The amount of antifreeze in the 40% solution is .40x, and the amount of antifreeze in the 70% solution is .70y. The amount of 50% solution in the total 60 liters is (.50)(60) = 30 liters.

$$.40x + .70y = 30 \qquad (2)$$

$$x = 60 - y \quad \textit{Solve (1) for x}$$

$$.40(60 - y) + .70y = 30 \quad \textit{Subsitute} \\ \textit{60 - y for} \\ \textit{x in (2)}$$

$$24 - .40y + .70y = 30$$

$$.30y = 6$$

$$y = 20$$

$$x = 60 - 20 \quad \textit{Let y = 20 in x = 60}$$

$$x = 40$$

40 liters of 40% solution and 20 liters of 70% solution will be needed.

37. Graph the y = 3x as a solid line. Since this line passes through (0, 0), use (1, 1) for a test point. y $\geq$ 3x is false at (1, 1), so shade the region on the side of the line that does not contain (1, 1).
Next, graph 2x + 3y = 4 as a solid line. Use (0, 0) as a test point. 2x + 3y $\leq$ 4 is true at (0, 0), so shade the region on the side of the line containing (0, 0).
The solution is the overlapping portion of the two regions.
See the answer graph in your textbook. Only the solution regions are shaded in the text-book.

41. $$5x + 4y = 3 \qquad (1)$$
$$7x + 5y = 3 \qquad (2)$$

$$-25x - 20y = -15 \quad \textit{Multiply (1) by -5}$$
$$\underline{28x + 20y = 12} \quad \textit{Multiply (2) by 4}$$
$$3x = -3$$
$$x = -1$$

$$5(-1) + 4y = 3 \quad \textit{Let x = -1 in (1)}$$
$$-5 + 4y = 3$$
$$4y = 8$$
$$y = 2$$

The solution is (-1, 2).

45. To clear fractions, multiply the first equation by 10.

$$\frac{2x}{5} - \frac{y}{2} = \frac{7}{10}$$

$$10\left(\frac{2x}{5}\right) - 10\left(\frac{y}{2}\right) = 10\left(\frac{7}{10}\right)$$

$$4x - 5y = 7 \quad (1)$$

Multiply the second equation by 3.

$$\frac{x}{3} + y = 2$$

$$3\left(\frac{x}{3}\right) + 3y = 3(2)$$

$$x + 3y = 6 \qquad (2)$$

$$x = 6 - 3y \quad \textit{Solve (2)} \\ \textit{for x}$$

$$4(6 - 3y) - 5y = 7 \quad \textit{Substitute} \\ \textit{6 - 3y for} \\ \textit{x in (1)}$$

$$24 - 12y - 5y = 7$$

$$-17y = -17$$

$$y = 1$$

$$x = 6 - 3(1) \quad \textit{Let y - 1 in x = 6 - 3y}$$
$$x = 6 - 3$$
$$x = 3$$

The solution is (3, 1).

49. Clear fractions by multiplying the first equation by 6.

$$6\left(\frac{x}{2}\right) + 6\left(\frac{y}{3}\right) = 6\left(\frac{-8}{3}\right)$$

$$3x + 2y = -16 \quad (1)$$

Multiply the second equation by 4.

$$4\left(\frac{x}{4}\right) + 4(2y) = 4\left(\frac{1}{2}\right)$$

$$x + 8y = 2 \qquad (2)$$

$$x = 2 - 8y$$
$$\textit{Solve (2)} \\ \textit{for x}$$

$3(2 - 8y) + 2y = -16$ *Substitute*
$\qquad\qquad\qquad\qquad$ *2 - 8y for*
$\qquad\qquad\qquad\qquad$ *x in (1)*

$6 - 24y + 2y = -16$

$\qquad\quad -22y = -22$

$\qquad\qquad\quad y = 1$

$x = 2 - 8(1)$ *Let y = 1 in x = 2 - 8y*

$x = 2 - 8$

$x = -6$

The solution is (-6, 1).

Chapter 7 Test (page 332)

1. $2x + y = 5$

    Let x = 0, then y = 5, giving the point (0, 5).

    Let y = 0, then $x = \dfrac{5}{2}$, giving the point $(\dfrac{5}{2}, 0)$. Plot these two points and draw the line through them.

    Graph the line $3x - y = 15$.
    Let x = 0, then y = -15, giving the y-intercept (0, -15).
    Let y = 0, then x = 5, giving the x-intercept (5, 0).
    Graph the points (0, -15) and (5, 0) and draw a line through them.
    The two lines intersect at the solution (4, -3).

    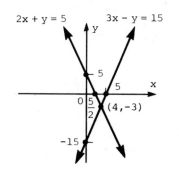

2. Graph the line $3x + 2y = 8$ by finding the intercepts, (0, 4) and $(2\dfrac{2}{3}, 0)$, and drawing the line through them.

Graph the line $5x + 4y = 10$ by finding the intercepts, $(0, 2\dfrac{1}{2})$ and (2, 0), and drawing the line through them.
The two lines intersect at the solution (6, -5).

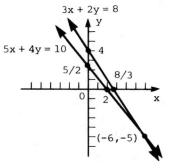

3. Graph the line $x + 2y = 6$ by finding the intercepts, (0, 3) and (6, 0), and drawing the line through them.
    Graph the line $2x - y = 7$ by finding the intercepts, (0, -7) and $(3\dfrac{1}{2}, 0)$, and drawing the line through them.
    The two lines intersect at the solution (4, 1).

    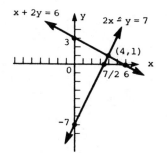

4. $2x - 5y = -13$ *(1)*

    $\underline{3x + 5y = 43}$ *(2)*

    $5x \qquad\quad = 30$ *Add the equations*

    $\qquad x = 6$ *Solve for x*

    $2(6) - 5y = -13$ *Let x = 6 in (1)*

    $\quad 12 - 5y = -13$

    $\qquad\quad -5y = -25$

    $\qquad\qquad y = 5$

    The solution is (6, 5).

5. $4x + 3y = 25$ *(1)*
   $5x + 4y = 32$ *(2)*

   $-16x - 12y = -100$ *Multiply (1) by -4*
   $\underline{15x + 12y = 96}$ *Multiply (2) by 3*
     $-x = -4$
        $x = 4$

   $4\cdot 4 + 3y = 25$ *Let x = 4 in 1*
    $16 + 3y = 25$
       $3y = 9$
       $y = 3$

   The solution is (4, 3).

6. $6x + 5y = -13$ *(1)*
  $-3x - \dfrac{5y}{2} = \dfrac{13}{2}$ *(2)*

  $2(-3x) - 2\left(\dfrac{5y}{2}\right) = 2\left(\dfrac{13}{2}\right)$ *Multiply 2 by the common denominator*

  $-6x - 5y = 13$ *(2) times 2*
  $\underline{6x + 5y = -13}$ *(1)*
       $0 = 0$ *True*

The equations represent the same line. They are dependent. There are an infinite number of solutions.

7. $2x - y = 5$ *(1)*
  $4x + 3y = 0$ *(2)*

  $6x - 3y = 15$ *Multiply (1) by 3*
  $\underline{4x + 3y = 0}$ *(2)*
  $10x = 15$
      $x = \dfrac{3}{2}$

  $2\left(\dfrac{3}{2}\right) - y = 5$ *Let x = 3/2 in (1)*
   $3 - y = 5$
    $-y = 2$
     $y = -2$

The solution is (3/2, -2).

8. $4x + 5y = 8$ *(1)*
 $-8x - 10y = -6$ *(2)*

  $8x + 10y = 16$ *Multiply (1) by 2*
  $\underline{-8x - 10y = -6}$ *(2)*
      $0 = 10$ *False*

Since $0 \ne 10$, there is no solution. The equations represent parallel lines. The system is inconsistent.

9. Multiply the first equation by 5 to clear fractions.

$$\frac{6}{5}x - y = \frac{1}{5}$$

$$5\left(\frac{6x}{5}\right) - 5(y) = 5\left(\frac{1}{5}\right)$$

$$6x - 5y = 1 \quad (1)$$

Multiply the second equation by 6.

$$-\frac{2}{3}x + \frac{1}{6}y = \frac{1}{3}$$

$$6\left(-\frac{2x}{3}\right) + 6\left(\frac{y}{6}\right) = 6\left(\frac{1}{3}\right)$$

$$-4x + y = 2 \quad (2)$$

  $6x - 5y = 1$ *(1)*
 $\underline{-20x + 5y = 10}$ *Multiply (2) by 5*
 $-14x = 11$
      $x = -\dfrac{11}{14}$

  $6\left(-\dfrac{11}{14}\right) - 5y = 1$ *Let x = -11/14 in (1)*

    $-\dfrac{66}{14} - 5y = 1$

 $14\left(-\dfrac{66}{14}\right) - 14(5y) = 14(1)$ *Multiply by 14*

    $-66 - 70y = 14$
      $-70y = 80$
        $y = -\dfrac{8}{7}$

The solution is $\left(-\dfrac{11}{14}, -\dfrac{8}{7}\right)$.

10. $2x + y = 1$ *(1)*

   $x = 8 + y$ *(2)*

   $2(8 + y) + y = 1$ *Let x = 8 + 4 in (1)*

   $16 + 2y + y = 1$

   $16 + 3y = 1$

   $3y = -15$

   $y = -5$

   $x = 8 + (-5) = 3$ *Let y = -5 in (2)*

   The solution is $(3, -5)$.

11. $4x + 3y = 0$ *(1)*

   $2x + y = -4$ *(2)*

   $y = -2x - 4$ *Solve 2 for y*

   $4x + 3(-2x - 4) = 0$ *Let y = -2x - 4 in (1)*

   $4x - 6x - 12 = 0$

   $-2x = 12$

   $x = -6$

   $y = -2(-6) - 4$ *Let x = -6 in y = -2x - 4*

   $y = 12 - 4$

   $y = 8$

   The solution is $(-6, 8)$

12.   Simplify the first equation.

   $8 + 3x - 4y = 14 - 3y$

   $3x - y = 6$ *(1)*

   Simplify the second equation.

   $3x + y + 12 = 9x - y$

   $-6x + 2y = -12$ *(2)*

   $6x - 2y = 12$ *Multiply (1) by 2*

   $\underline{-6x + 2y = -12}$ *(2)*

   $0 = 0$ *True*

   The two equations produce the same line, so there are an infinite number of solutions, and the equations are dependent.

13. $\dfrac{x}{2} - \dfrac{y}{4} = -4$

   $\dfrac{2x}{3} + \dfrac{5y}{4} = 1$

   Multiply the first equation by 4 to clear the fractions.

   $4\left(\dfrac{x}{2} - \dfrac{y}{4}\right) = 4(-4)$

   $2x - y = -16$

   Multiply the second equation by 12 to clear the fractions.

   $12\left(\dfrac{2x}{3} + \dfrac{5y}{4}\right) = 12(1)$

   $8x + 15y = 12$

   The simplified system is

   $2x - y = -16$ *(1)*

   $8x + 15y = 12.$ *(2)*

   $-8x + 4y = 64$ *Multiply (1) by -4*

   $\underline{8x + 15y = 12}$ *(2)*

   $19y = 76$

   $y = 4$

   $2x - (4) = -16$ *Let y = 4 in (1)*

   $2x = -12$

   $x = -6$

   The solution is $(-6, 4)$.

14.   Let x represent the smaller number, and y the larger. The sum of both numbers is 39, so

   $x + y = 39.$ *(1)*

   Also, if the smaller number is doubled, it is 3 less than the larger, so

   $2x = y - 3$

   or $2x - y = -3.$ *(2)*

   Solve the system.

   $x + y = 39$ *(1)*

   $\underline{2x - y = -3}$ *(2)*

   $3x = 36$

   $x = 12$

12 + y = 39   *Let x = 12 in (1)*

     y = 27

The two numbers are 12 and 27.

15. Let x represent the number of $5 records and y the number of $7.50 records.

Number of records	Price per record	Cost of records
x	5	5x
y	7.50	7.50y
Total 6		40

Use the first and third column to write the system.

$$x + y = 6$$
$$5x + 7.50y = 40$$

Solve using substitution.

$$x = 6 - y$$
$$5(6 - y) + 7.50y = 40$$

$$30 - 5y + 7.50y = 40$$
$$2.50y = 10$$
$$y = 4$$
$$x + 4 = 6$$
$$x = 2$$

He can buy 2 of the $5 records and 4 of the $7.50 records.

16. Let x represent the amount of 40% solution and y represent the amount of 60% solution.

Liters of Solution	Percent	Liters of Acid
x	.40	.40x
y	.60	.60y
100	.45	.45(100)

Use the first and third columns to write the system.

$$x + y = 100 \quad (1)$$
$$.40x + .60y = .45(100)$$
$$.4x + .6y = 45 \quad \textit{Simplify}$$
$$4x + 6y = 450 \quad (2)$$

$$-4x - 4y = -400 \quad \textit{Multiply (1) by -4}$$
$$\underline{4x + 6y = 450} \quad (2)$$
$$2y = 50$$
$$y = 25$$

Let y = 25 in equation (1) to find x.

$$x + 25 = 100 \quad \textit{Let y = 25 in (1)}$$
$$x = 75$$

75 liters of the 40% solution should be mixed with 25 liters of the 60% solution.

17. Let x be the speed of the faster car and y the speed of the slower car. Use d = rt in constructing the table.

	d	r	t
Faster car	3x	x	3
Slower car	3y	y	3

The faster car travels $1\frac{1}{3}$ times as fast as the other car, so

$$x = 1\frac{1}{3}y$$
$$x = \frac{4}{3}y. \quad (1)$$

After 3 hours, they are 45 miles apart. That is, the difference of their distances is 45.

$$3x - 3y = 45$$
$$3\left(\frac{4}{3}y\right) - 3y = 45 \quad \textit{Let } x = \frac{4}{3}y \textit{ in (2)}$$
$$4y - 3y = 45$$
$$y = 45$$
$$x = \frac{4}{3}(45) \quad \textit{Let y = 45 in (1)}$$
$$x = 60$$

The speed of the faster car is 60 miles per hour and the speed of the slower car is 45 miles per hour.

For Exercises 18-20 see the answer graphs in your textbook.

18. Graph $2x + 7y = 14$ as a solid line. Use $(0, 0)$ for a test point. $2x + 7y \leq 14$ is true at $(0, 0)$, so shade the region on the side of the line that contains $(0, 0)$. Next, graph $x - y = 1$ as a solid line. Use $(0, 0)$ for a test point. $x - y \geq 1$ is false at $(0, 0)$, so shade the region on the side of this line that does not contain $(0, 0)$.
The solution is the overlapped portion of the shaded regions.

19. Graph $2x - y = 6$ as a solid line. Use $(0, 0)$ for a test point. $2x - y \leq 6$ is true at $(0, 0)$, so shade the region on the side of the line that contains $(0, 0)$. Next, graph $4y + 12 = -3x$ as a solid line. Use $(0, 0)$ for a test point. $4y + 12 \geq -3x$ is true at $(0, 0)$, so shade the region on the side of this line that contains $(0, 0)$.
The solution is the overlapped portion of the shaded regions.

20. Graph $3x - 5y = 15$ as a dashed line. Use $(0, 0)$ as a test point. The inequality $3x - 5y < 15$ is true at $(0, 0)$, so shade the region on the side of the graph containing $(0, 0)$.
Graph $y = 2$ as a dashed horizontal line passing through the y-axis at $(0, 2)$. Use $(0, 0)$ as a test point. The inequality $y < 2$ is true at $(0, 0)$, so shade the region on the side of the graph containing $(0, 0)$.
The solution is the overlapping portion of the two shaded regions.

CHAPTER 8 ROOTS AND RADICALS
Section 8.1   (page 339)

1. Since $3^2 = 9$ and $(-3)^2 = 9$, then the square roots of 9 are 3 and -3.

5. Since $20^2 = 400$ and $(-20)^2 = 400$, then the square roots of 400 are 20 and -20.
    Also $9^2 = 81$ and $(-9)^2 = 81$, hence the square roots of 81 are 9 and -9. Thus, the square roots of 400/81 are 20/9 and -20/9.

9. Since $39^2 = 1521$ and $(-39)^2 = 1521$, then the square roots of 1521 are 39 and -39.

13. $\sqrt{4} = 2$ only since the radical sign indicates the positive square root.

17. Since $\sqrt{64} = 8$, then $-\sqrt{64} = -8$.

21. Since $\sqrt{\dfrac{49}{9}} = \dfrac{7}{3}$,
    then $-\sqrt{\dfrac{49}{9}} = -\dfrac{7}{3}$

25. $\sqrt{16}$ is a rational because $\sqrt{16} = 4$.

29. $\sqrt{47}$ is irrational; from Table 3, $\sqrt{47} \approx 6.856$.

33. $-\sqrt{121}$ is rational since $\sqrt{121} = 11$.
    $-\sqrt{121} = -11$

37. $\sqrt{400}$ is rational because $\sqrt{400} = 20$.

41. $\sqrt{571} \approx 23.896$ *By a calculator*

45. $\sqrt{3.94} \approx 1.985$ *By a calculator*

49. Use $c^2 = a^2 + b^2$.
    $$c^2 = (6)^2 + (8)^2$$
    $$c^2 = 36 + 64$$
    $$c^2 = 100$$
    $$c = 10$$

53. Use $c^2 = a^2 + b^2$.
    $$c^2 = (10)^2 + (8)^2$$
    $$c^2 = 100 + 64$$
    $$c^2 = 164$$
    $$c = \sqrt{164} \approx 12.806$$

57. $\sqrt[3]{1000} = 10$ since $10^3 = 1000$.

61. $-\sqrt[3]{8} = -2$ since $\sqrt[3]{8} = 2$.

65. $\sqrt[4]{1} = 1$ since $1^4 = 1$.

69. $-\sqrt[4]{81} = -3$ since $3^4 = 81$.

73. $-\sqrt[4]{32} = -\sqrt{\sqrt{32}} \approx -\sqrt{5.657} \approx -2.378$

77. $\sqrt[4]{1.42} = \sqrt{\sqrt{1.42}} \approx \sqrt{1.192} \approx 1.092$

81. $-\sqrt{16.81} = -4.1$ since $(4.1)^2 = 16.81$.

85. $\sqrt{.0049} = .07$ since $(.07)^2 = .0049$.

89. Use $c^2 = a^2 + b^2$
    $$9^2 = 3^2 + b^2$$
    $$81 = 9 + b^2$$
    $$72 = b^2$$
    $$\sqrt{72} = b$$
    $$8.485 \approx b$$

93. The positive integer factors of
300 are

1, 2, 3, 4, 5, 6, 10, 12, 15, 20,
25, 30, 50, 60, 75, 100, 150, 300.

97. The positive integer factors of
150 are

1, 2, 3, 5, 6, 10, 15, 25, 30, 50,
75, 150.

Section 8.2   (page 343)

1. $\sqrt{8} \cdot \sqrt{2} = \sqrt{8 \cdot 2}$ *Product rule*
$$= \sqrt{16}$$
$$= 4$$

5. $\sqrt{21} \cdot \sqrt{21}$

$= \sqrt{3 \cdot 7} \cdot \sqrt{3 \cdot 7}$

$= \sqrt{3} \cdot \sqrt{7} \cdot \sqrt{3} \cdot \sqrt{7}$ *Product rule*

$= \sqrt{3} \cdot \sqrt{3} \cdot \sqrt{7} \cdot \sqrt{7}$ *Rearrange factors*

$= \sqrt{9} \cdot \sqrt{49}$ *Multiply*

$= 3 \cdot 7$ $\sqrt{9} = 3; \sqrt{49} = 7$

$= 21$

9. $\sqrt{27} = \sqrt{9 \cdot 3}$ *9 is a perfect square*
$= \sqrt{9} \cdot \sqrt{3}$ *Product rule*
$= 3\sqrt{3}$ $\sqrt{9} = 3$

13. $\sqrt{48} = \sqrt{16 \cdot 3}$ *16 is a perfect square*
$= \sqrt{16} \cdot \sqrt{3}$ *Product rule*
$= 4\sqrt{3}$ $\sqrt{16} = 4$

17. $10 \cdot \sqrt{27}$
$= 10 \cdot \sqrt{9 \cdot 3}$ *9 is a perfect square*
$= 10 \cdot \sqrt{9} \cdot \sqrt{3}$ *Product rule*
$= 10 \cdot 3 \cdot \sqrt{3}$ $\sqrt{9} = 3$
$= 30\sqrt{3}$ *Multiply*

21. $\sqrt{27} \cdot \sqrt{48}$
$= \sqrt{9 \cdot 3} \cdot \sqrt{16 \cdot 3}$ *9 and 19 are perfect squares*
$= \sqrt{9} \cdot \sqrt{3} \cdot \sqrt{16} \cdot \sqrt{3}$ *Product rule*
$= 3\sqrt{3} \cdot 4\sqrt{3}$ $\sqrt{9} = 3; \sqrt{16} = 4$
$= 3 \cdot 4 \cdot \sqrt{3} \cdot \sqrt{3}$ *Rearrange the factors*
$= 12\sqrt{9}$ *Multiply*
$= 12 \cdot 3$ $\sqrt{9} = 3$
$= 36$

25. $\sqrt{80} \cdot \sqrt{15} = \sqrt{16} \cdot \sqrt{5} \cdot \sqrt{15}$
$= 4 \cdot \sqrt{75}$
$= 4 \cdot \sqrt{25} \cdot \sqrt{3}$
$= 4 \cdot 5 \cdot \sqrt{3}$
$= 20\sqrt{3}$

29. $\sqrt{\dfrac{100}{9}} = \dfrac{\sqrt{100}}{\sqrt{9}}$ *Quotient rule*
$= \dfrac{10}{3}$ $\sqrt{100} = 10$
$\sqrt{9} = 3$

33. $\sqrt{\dfrac{1}{5}} \cdot \sqrt{\dfrac{4}{5}} = \dfrac{\sqrt{1} \cdot \sqrt{4}}{\sqrt{5} \cdot \sqrt{5}}$ *Quotient rule*
$= \dfrac{\sqrt{1 \cdot 4}}{\sqrt{5 \cdot 5}}$ *Product rule*
$= \dfrac{\sqrt{4}}{\sqrt{25}}$ *Multiply*
$= \dfrac{2}{5}$ $\sqrt{4} = 2$
$\sqrt{25} = 5$

37. $\dfrac{\sqrt{75}}{\sqrt{3}} = \sqrt{\dfrac{75}{3}}$ *Quotient rule*
$= \sqrt{25}$ *Divide*
$= 5$ $\sqrt{25} = 5$

41. $\dfrac{15\sqrt{10}}{5\sqrt{2}} = \dfrac{15}{5} \cdot \sqrt{\dfrac{10}{2}}$ *Quotient rule*
$= 3\sqrt{5}$ *Divide*

45. $\sqrt{y} \cdot \sqrt{y} = \sqrt{y^2}$ *Product rule*

$\qquad = y \qquad \sqrt{y^2} = y \ since$

$\qquad\qquad\qquad y \cdot y = y^2$

49. $\sqrt{x^2} = x$

53. $\sqrt{x^2 y^4} = \sqrt{x^2} \cdot \sqrt{y^4}$ *Product rule*

$\qquad = xy^2$

57. $\sqrt{\dfrac{16}{x^2}} = \dfrac{\sqrt{16}}{\sqrt{x^2}}$ *Quotient rule*

$\qquad = \dfrac{4}{x}$

61. $\sqrt{28m^3} = \sqrt{4 \cdot 7}\sqrt{m^2 - m}$

$\qquad = \sqrt{4}\sqrt{7}\sqrt{m^2}\sqrt{m}$

$\qquad = 2 \cdot \sqrt{7} \cdot m \cdot \sqrt{m}$

$\qquad = 2 \cdot m \cdot \sqrt{7} \cdot \sqrt{m}$

$\qquad = 2m\sqrt{7m}$

65. $\sqrt[3]{40} = \sqrt[3]{8 \cdot 5}$ *8 is a perfect cube*

$\qquad\qquad\qquad\qquad since \ 2^3 = 8$

$\qquad = \sqrt[3]{8} \cdot \sqrt[3]{5}$ *Product rule*

$\qquad = 2\sqrt[3]{5}$

69. $\sqrt[3]{128} = \sqrt[3]{64 \cdot 2}$ *64 is a perfect*

$\qquad\qquad\qquad\qquad cube \ since \ 4^3 = 64$

$\qquad = \sqrt[3]{64} \cdot \sqrt[3]{2}$ *Product rule*

$\qquad = 4\sqrt[3]{2}$

73. $\sqrt[3]{\dfrac{8}{27}} = \dfrac{\sqrt[3]{8}}{\sqrt[3]{27}}$

$\qquad = \dfrac{2}{3}$

77. $\sqrt[3]{2} \cdot \sqrt[3]{4} = \sqrt[3]{2 \cdot 4}$

$\qquad = \sqrt[3]{8}$

$\qquad = 2$

81. $\sqrt[3]{4x} \cdot \sqrt[3]{8x^2} = \sqrt[3]{4x} \cdot \sqrt[3]{8} \cdot \sqrt[3]{x^2}$

$\qquad = \sqrt[3]{4x} \cdot 2 \cdot \sqrt[3]{x^2}$

$\qquad = 2\sqrt[3]{4x} \cdot \sqrt[3]{x^2}$

$\qquad = 2\sqrt[3]{4x^3}$

$\qquad = 2\sqrt[3]{4}\sqrt[3]{x^3}$

$\qquad = 2\sqrt[3]{4}x$

$\qquad = 2x\sqrt[3]{4}$

85. Use $V = s^3$. Since the volume of the cube is 216

$\qquad 216 = s^3$

$\qquad \sqrt[3]{216} = s$

$\qquad\quad 6 = s$

The depth is 6 centimeters.

89. $\dfrac{2}{3} = \dfrac{}{15}$

$\dfrac{2}{3} \cdot \dfrac{5}{5} = \dfrac{10}{15}$

93. $\dfrac{5}{\sqrt{3}} = \dfrac{}{2\sqrt{3}}$

$\dfrac{5}{\sqrt{3}} \cdot \dfrac{2}{2} = \dfrac{10}{2\sqrt{3}}$

Section 8.3   (page 347)

1. $2\sqrt{3} + 5\sqrt{3} = (2 + 5)\sqrt{3}$

$\qquad = 7\sqrt{3}$

5. $\sqrt{6} + \sqrt{6} = 1\sqrt{6} + 1\sqrt{6}$

$\qquad = (1 + 1)\sqrt{6}$

$\qquad = 2\sqrt{6}$

9. $5\sqrt{7} - \sqrt{7} = 5\sqrt{7} - 1\sqrt{7}$

$\qquad = (5 - 1)\sqrt{7}$

$\qquad = 4\sqrt{7}$

13. $-\sqrt{12} + \sqrt{75} = -\sqrt{4}\cdot\sqrt{3} + \sqrt{25}\cdot\sqrt{3}$

$$= -2\sqrt{3} + 5\sqrt{3}$$
$$= (-2 + 5)\sqrt{3}$$
$$= 3\sqrt{3}$$

17. $5\sqrt{7} - 2\sqrt{28} + 6\sqrt{63}$

$$= 5\sqrt{7} - 2\sqrt{4\cdot 7} + 6\sqrt{9\cdot 7}$$
$$= 5\sqrt{7} - 2(\sqrt{4}\cdot\sqrt{7}) + 6(\sqrt{9}\cdot\sqrt{7})$$
$$= 5\sqrt{7} - 2(2\sqrt{7}) + 6(3\sqrt{7})$$
$$= 5\sqrt{7} - 4\sqrt{7} + 18\sqrt{7}$$
$$= (5 - 4 + 18)\sqrt{7}$$
$$= 19\sqrt{7}$$

21. $5\sqrt{72} - 3\sqrt{48} - 4\sqrt{128}$

$$= 5(\sqrt{36}\cdot\sqrt{2}) - 3(\sqrt{16}\cdot\sqrt{3})$$
$$\quad - 4(\sqrt{64}\cdot\sqrt{2})$$
$$= 5(6\sqrt{2}) - 3(4\sqrt{3}) - 4(8\sqrt{2})$$
$$= 30\sqrt{2} - 12\sqrt{3} - 32\sqrt{2}$$
$$= -2\sqrt{2} - 12\sqrt{3}$$

25. $\frac{3}{5}\sqrt{75} - \frac{2}{3}\sqrt{45}$

$$= \frac{3}{5}\sqrt{25}\cdot\sqrt{3} - \frac{2}{3}\sqrt{9}\cdot\sqrt{5}$$
$$= \frac{3}{5}\cdot 5\sqrt{3} - \frac{2}{3}\cdot 3\sqrt{5}$$
$$= 3\sqrt{3} - 2\sqrt{5}$$

29. $\sqrt{6}\cdot\sqrt{2} + 3\sqrt{3} = \sqrt{12} + 3\sqrt{3}$

$$= \sqrt{4}\cdot\sqrt{3} + 3\sqrt{3}$$
$$= 2\sqrt{3} + 3\sqrt{3}$$
$$= (2 + 3)\sqrt{3}$$
$$= 5\sqrt{3}$$

33. $3\sqrt[3]{24} + 6\sqrt[3]{81}$

$$= 3\sqrt[3]{8}\cdot\sqrt[3]{3} + 6\sqrt[3]{27}\cdot\sqrt[3]{3}$$
$$= 3\cdot 2\sqrt[3]{3} + 6\cdot 3\sqrt[3]{3}$$
$$= 6\sqrt[3]{3} + 18\sqrt[3]{3}$$
$$= (6 + 18)\sqrt[3]{3}$$
$$= 24\sqrt[3]{3}$$

37. $\sqrt{9x} + \sqrt{49x} - \sqrt{16x}$

$$= \sqrt{9}\sqrt{x} + \sqrt{49}\sqrt{x} - \sqrt{16}\sqrt{x}$$
$$= 3\sqrt{x} + 7\sqrt{x} - 4\sqrt{x}$$
$$= (3 + 7 - 4)\sqrt{x}$$
$$= 6\sqrt{x}$$

41. $\sqrt{75x^2} + x\sqrt{300}$

$$= \sqrt{25}\cdot\sqrt{x^2}\cdot\sqrt{3} + x\cdot\sqrt{100}\cdot\sqrt{3}$$
$$= 5x\sqrt{3} + 10x\sqrt{3}$$
$$= (5x + 10x)\sqrt{3}$$
$$= 15x\sqrt{3}$$

45. $5\sqrt{75p^2} - 4\sqrt{27p^2}$

$$= 5\sqrt{25}\cdot\sqrt{3}\cdot\sqrt{p^2} - 4\sqrt{9}\cdot\sqrt{3}\cdot\sqrt{p^2}$$
$$= 5\cdot 5\cdot\sqrt{3}\,p - 4\cdot 3\cdot\sqrt{3}\cdot p$$
$$= 25p\sqrt{3} - 12p\sqrt{3}$$
$$= (25p - 12p)\sqrt{3}$$
$$= 13p\sqrt{3}$$

49. $3k\sqrt{24k^2h^2} + 9h\sqrt{54k^3}$

$$= 3k\cdot\sqrt{4}\cdot\sqrt{6}\cdot\sqrt{k^2}\cdot\sqrt{h^2} +$$
$$\quad 9h\cdot\sqrt{9}\cdot\sqrt{6}\cdot\sqrt{k^2}\cdot\sqrt{k}$$
$$= 3k\cdot 2\cdot\sqrt{6}\cdot k\cdot h + 9h\cdot 3\cdot\sqrt{6}\cdot k\cdot\sqrt{k}$$
$$= 6k^2h\sqrt{6} + 27hk\sqrt{6}$$

53. $5\sqrt[4]{m^4} + 3\sqrt[4]{81m^4}$

$= 5\cdot m + 3\cdot\sqrt[4]{81}\cdot\sqrt[4]{m^4}$

$= 5m + 3\cdot 3\cdot m$

$= 5m + 9m$

$= 14m$

57. $10\sqrt[3]{4m^4} - 3m\sqrt[3]{32m}$

$= 10\cdot\sqrt[3]{4}\cdot\sqrt[3]{m^3}\cdot\sqrt[3]{m} - 3m\sqrt[3]{8}\cdot\sqrt[3]{4}\sqrt[3]{m}$

$= 10\cdot\sqrt[3]{4}\cdot m\cdot\sqrt[3]{m} - 3m\cdot 2\cdot\sqrt[3]{4}\cdot\sqrt[3]{m}$

$= 10m\sqrt[3]{4m} - 6m\sqrt[3]{4m}$

$= (10m - 6m)\sqrt[3]{4m}$

$= 4m\sqrt[3]{4m}$

61. $(p - 2)(p + 7) = p^2 + 7p - 2p - 14$

$\qquad\qquad\qquad\quad = p^2 + 5p - 14$

65. $(2y + 5)^2 = 4y^2 + 2(10y) + 25$

$\qquad\qquad\quad = 4y^2 + 20y + 25$

Section 8.4   (page 350)

1. $\dfrac{6}{\sqrt{5}} = \dfrac{6\cdot\sqrt{5}}{\sqrt{5}\cdot\sqrt{5}}$

$\quad = \dfrac{6\sqrt{5}}{5} \qquad \sqrt{5}\cdot\sqrt{5} = \sqrt{25} = 5$

5. $\dfrac{3}{\sqrt{7}} = \dfrac{3\cdot\sqrt{7}}{\sqrt{7}\cdot\sqrt{7}}$

$\quad = \dfrac{3\sqrt{7}}{7} \qquad \sqrt{7}\cdot\sqrt{7} = \sqrt{49} = 7$

9. $\dfrac{12\sqrt{10}}{8\sqrt{3}} = \dfrac{12\sqrt{10}\cdot\sqrt{3}}{8\sqrt{3}\cdot\sqrt{3}}$

$\quad = \dfrac{12\sqrt{30}}{8\cdot 3} \qquad \sqrt{10}\cdot\sqrt{3} = \sqrt{30}$

$\qquad\qquad\qquad\qquad \sqrt{3}\cdot\sqrt{3} = 3$

$\quad = \dfrac{12\sqrt{30}}{24}$

$\quad = \dfrac{\sqrt{30}}{2} \qquad\quad Lowest\ terms$

13. $\dfrac{3}{\sqrt{50}} = \dfrac{3\sqrt{2}}{\sqrt{50}\cdot\sqrt{2}}$ *Multiply by $\sqrt{2}$ since* $\sqrt{50}\cdot\sqrt{2} = \sqrt{100} = 10$

$\quad = \dfrac{3\sqrt{2}}{\sqrt{100}}$

$\quad = \dfrac{3\sqrt{2}}{10}$

17. $\dfrac{\sqrt{10}}{\sqrt{5}} = \sqrt{\dfrac{10}{5}}$ *Quotient rule*

$\quad = \sqrt{2}$

21. $\sqrt{\dfrac{1}{2}} = \dfrac{\sqrt{1}}{\sqrt{2}}$ *Quotient rule*

$\quad = \dfrac{1}{\sqrt{2}} \qquad \sqrt{1} = 1$

$\quad = \dfrac{1\cdot\sqrt{2}}{\sqrt{2}\cdot\sqrt{2}}$ *Rationalize the denominator*

$\quad = \dfrac{\sqrt{2}}{2} \qquad \sqrt{2}\cdot\sqrt{2} = 2$

25. $\sqrt{\dfrac{3}{4}}\cdot\sqrt{\dfrac{1}{5}} = \sqrt{\dfrac{3\cdot 1}{4\cdot 5}}$ *Product rule*

$\quad = \sqrt{\dfrac{3}{20}}$ *Multiply*

$\quad = \dfrac{\sqrt{3}}{\sqrt{20}}$ *Quotient rule*

$\quad = \dfrac{\sqrt{3}\cdot\sqrt{5}}{\sqrt{20}\cdot\sqrt{5}}$

$\quad = \dfrac{\sqrt{15}}{\sqrt{100}}$

$\quad = \dfrac{\sqrt{15}}{10}$

29. $\sqrt{\dfrac{2}{5}}\cdot\sqrt{\dfrac{3}{10}} = \sqrt{\dfrac{2\cdot 3}{5\cdot 10}}$ *Product rule*

$\quad = \sqrt{\dfrac{6}{50}}$ *Multiply*

$\quad = \sqrt{\dfrac{3}{25}} \qquad \dfrac{6}{50} = \dfrac{3}{25}$

$\quad = \dfrac{\sqrt{3}}{\sqrt{25}}$ *Quotient rule*

$\quad = \dfrac{\sqrt{3}}{5} \qquad \sqrt{25} = 5$

33. $\sqrt{\dfrac{6}{p}} = \dfrac{\sqrt{6}}{\sqrt{p}}$ *Quotient rule*

$\quad = \dfrac{\sqrt{6}\cdot\sqrt{p}}{\sqrt{p}\cdot\sqrt{p}}$ *Rationalize denominator*

$\quad = \dfrac{\sqrt{6p}}{p}$ *Product rule*

37. $\sqrt{\dfrac{16}{m}} = \dfrac{\sqrt{16}}{\sqrt{m}}$ *Quotient rule*

$\quad = \dfrac{4}{\sqrt{m}}$ $\sqrt{16} = 4$

$\quad = \dfrac{4\cdot\sqrt{m}}{\sqrt{m}\cdot\sqrt{m}}$ *Rationalize denominator*

$\quad = \dfrac{4\sqrt{m}}{m}$ $\sqrt{m}\cdot\sqrt{m} = m$

41. $\sqrt{\dfrac{7x^3}{y}} = \dfrac{\sqrt{7x^3}}{\sqrt{y}}$ *Quotient rule*

$\quad = \dfrac{\sqrt{7x}\sqrt{x^2}\cdot\sqrt{y}}{\sqrt{y}\cdot\sqrt{y}}$ *Rationalize denominator*

$\quad = \dfrac{x\sqrt{7xy}}{y}$ *Product rule and* $\sqrt{y}\cdot\sqrt{y} = y$

45. $\sqrt{\dfrac{x^2}{4y}} = \dfrac{\sqrt{x^2}}{\sqrt{4}\sqrt{y}}$ *Quotient rule and product rule*

$\quad = \dfrac{x}{2\sqrt{y}}$ $\sqrt{x^2} = x$

$\quad = \dfrac{x\cdot\sqrt{y}}{2\sqrt{y}\cdot\sqrt{y}}$ *Rationalize the denominator*

$\quad = \dfrac{x\sqrt{y}}{2y}$ $\sqrt{y}\cdot\sqrt{y} = y$

49. $\sqrt[3]{\dfrac{1}{2}} = \dfrac{\sqrt[3]{1}}{\sqrt[3]{2}}$ *Quotient rule*

$\quad = \dfrac{1\cdot\sqrt[3]{4}}{\sqrt[3]{2}\cdot\sqrt[3]{4}}$ *Get the denominator to the perfect cube 8 by multiplying numerator and denominator by* $\sqrt[3]{4}$

$\quad = \dfrac{\sqrt[3]{4}}{\sqrt[3]{8}}$

$\quad = \dfrac{\sqrt[3]{4}}{2}$ $\sqrt[3]{8} = 2$ *since* $2^3 = 8$

53. $\sqrt[3]{\dfrac{1}{11}} = \dfrac{\sqrt[3]{1}}{\sqrt[3]{11}}$ *Quotient rule*

$\quad = \dfrac{1\sqrt[3]{121}}{\sqrt[3]{11}\cdot\sqrt[3]{121}}$ *Denominator becomes perfect cube 11^3 by multiplying numerator and denominator by* $\sqrt[3]{121}$

$\quad = \dfrac{\sqrt[3]{121}}{11}$

57. $\sqrt[3]{\dfrac{3}{4y^2}} = \dfrac{\sqrt[3]{3}}{\sqrt[3]{4y^2}}$ *Quotient rule*

$\quad = \dfrac{\sqrt[3]{3}\cdot\sqrt[3]{2y}}{\sqrt[3]{4y^2}\cdot\sqrt[3]{2y}}$ *Since* $\sqrt[3]{4y^2}\cdot\sqrt[3]{2y}$ $= \sqrt[3]{8y^3} = 2y$

$\quad = \dfrac{\sqrt[3]{6y}}{2y}$

61. $p = k\sqrt{\dfrac{L}{g}}$ Let $k = 6$, $L = 289$, $g = 32$

$\quad p = 6\sqrt{\dfrac{289}{32}} = 6\dfrac{\sqrt{289}}{\sqrt{32}}$ *Quotient rule*

$\qquad = \dfrac{6\cdot 17}{\sqrt{16}\cdot\sqrt{2}}$ *Product rule*

$\qquad = \dfrac{102}{4\sqrt{2}}$

$\qquad = \dfrac{102\cdot\sqrt{2}}{4\sqrt{2}\cdot\sqrt{2}}$ *Rationalize denominator*

$\qquad = \dfrac{102\sqrt{2}}{4\cdot 2}$

$\qquad = \dfrac{102\sqrt{2}}{8}$

$\qquad = \dfrac{51\sqrt{2}}{4}$

65. $m + 2 - 3m - 5$

$\quad = m - 3m + 2 - 5$

$\quad = -2m - 3$

Section 8.5   (page 356)

1. $3\sqrt{5} + 8\sqrt{45} = 3\sqrt{5} + 8\cdot\sqrt{9}\cdot\sqrt{5}$

$\qquad\qquad\qquad = 3\sqrt{5} + 8\cdot3\cdot\sqrt{5}$

$\qquad\qquad\qquad = 3\sqrt{5} + 24\sqrt{5}$

$\qquad\qquad\qquad = (3 + 24)\sqrt{5}$

$\qquad\qquad\qquad = 27\sqrt{5}$

5. $2(\sqrt{8} - \sqrt{32}) = \sqrt{2}\cdot\sqrt{8} - \sqrt{2}\cdot\sqrt{32}$

$\qquad\qquad\qquad\quad = \sqrt{16} - \sqrt{64}$

$\qquad\qquad\qquad\quad = 4 - 8$

$\qquad\qquad\qquad\quad = -4$

9. $2\sqrt{5}(\sqrt{2} + \sqrt{5})$

$\qquad = 2\sqrt{5}\cdot\sqrt{2} + 2\sqrt{5}\cdot\sqrt{5}$

$\qquad = 2\sqrt{10} + 2\cdot5 \qquad \sqrt{5}\cdot\sqrt{5} = 5$

$\qquad = 2\sqrt{10} + 10$

13. $(2\sqrt{6} + 3)(3\sqrt{6} - 5)$

$\qquad = (2\sqrt{6})(3\sqrt{6}) + (2\sqrt{6})(-5) +$
$\qquad\quad (3)(3\sqrt{6}) + (3)(-5)$

$\qquad = 6\cdot6 - 10\sqrt{6} + 9\sqrt{6} - 15$

$\qquad = 36 - 15 - 10\sqrt{6} + 9\sqrt{6}$

$\qquad = 21 - 1\sqrt{6} \;\; \text{or} \;\; 21 - \sqrt{6}$

17. $(3\sqrt{2} + 4)(3\sqrt{2} + 4)$

$\qquad = (3\sqrt{2})(3\sqrt{2}) + (3\sqrt{2})(4) +$
$\qquad\quad 4(3\sqrt{2}) + 4(4)$

$\qquad = 9\cdot2 + 12\sqrt{2} + 12\sqrt{2} + 16$

$\qquad = 18 + 16 + 12\sqrt{2} + 12\sqrt{2}$

$\qquad = 34 + 24\sqrt{2}$

21. $(\sqrt{2} + \sqrt{3})^2$

$\qquad = (\sqrt{2})^2 + 2\cdot\sqrt{2}\cdot\sqrt{3} + (\sqrt{3})^2$

$\qquad = 2 + 2\sqrt{6} + 3$

$\qquad = 5 + 2\sqrt{6}$

25. $(2 + \sqrt{8})(2 - \sqrt{8})$

$\qquad = 2\cdot2 - 2\sqrt{8} + 2\sqrt{8} - \sqrt{8}\cdot\sqrt{8}$

$\qquad = 4 - 8$

$\qquad = -4$

29. $(\sqrt{8} - \sqrt{2})(\sqrt{2} + \sqrt{4})$

$\qquad = \sqrt{8}\cdot\sqrt{2} + \sqrt{8}\cdot\sqrt{4} - \sqrt{2}\cdot\sqrt{2} - \sqrt{4}\cdot\sqrt{2}$

$\qquad = \sqrt{16} + \sqrt{32} - 2 - 2\sqrt{2}$

$\qquad = 4 + \sqrt{16}\cdot\sqrt{2} - 2 - 2\sqrt{2}$

$\qquad = 4 - 2 + 4\sqrt{2} - 2\sqrt{2}$

$\qquad = 2 + 2\sqrt{2}$

33. $(3\sqrt{t} + \sqrt{7})(2\sqrt{t} - \sqrt{14})$

$\qquad = 3\sqrt{t}\cdot2\sqrt{t} - 3\sqrt{t}\cdot\sqrt{14} + 2\sqrt{t}\cdot\sqrt{7} -$
$\qquad\quad \sqrt{7}\cdot\sqrt{14}$

$\qquad = 3\sqrt{2}\cdot\sqrt{t}\cdot\sqrt{t} = 3\sqrt{14t} + 2\sqrt{7t} - \sqrt{98}$

$\qquad = 6t - 3\sqrt{14t} + 2\sqrt{7t} - \sqrt{49}\cdot\sqrt{2}$

$\qquad = 6t - 3\sqrt{14t} + 2\sqrt{7t} - 7\sqrt{2}$

37. $\dfrac{5\sqrt{7} - 10}{5} = \dfrac{5(\sqrt{7} - 2)}{5}$ *Factor numerator*

$\qquad\qquad\quad = \sqrt{7} - 2$ *Fundamental property*

$\qquad\qquad\qquad \text{or} \; -2 + \sqrt{7}$

41. $\dfrac{12 - 2\sqrt{10}}{4} = \dfrac{2(6 - \sqrt{10})}{2\cdot2}$ *Factor*

$\qquad\qquad\quad = \dfrac{6 - \sqrt{10}}{2}$ *Fundamental property*

45. $\dfrac{5}{2 + \sqrt{5}}$

$\qquad = \dfrac{5(2 - \sqrt{5})}{(2 + \sqrt{5})(2 - \sqrt{5})}$

$\qquad\qquad$ *Multiply numerator and denominator by conjugate*

$\qquad = \dfrac{5(2 - \sqrt{5})}{(2)^2 - (\sqrt{5})^2}$

$\qquad = \dfrac{5(2 - \sqrt{5})}{4 - 5}$

$\qquad = \dfrac{10 - 5\sqrt{5}}{-1}$

$= -(10 - 5\sqrt{5})$

$= -10 + 5\sqrt{5}$

49. $\dfrac{\sqrt{12}}{\sqrt{3} + 1}$

$= \dfrac{\sqrt{12}(\sqrt{3} - 1)}{(\sqrt{3} + 1)(\sqrt{3} - 1)}$ *Multiply by the conjugate*

$= \dfrac{\sqrt{12}(\sqrt{3} - 1)}{(\sqrt{3})^2 - (1)^2}$

$= \dfrac{\sqrt{12}(\sqrt{3} - 1)}{3 - 1}$

$= \dfrac{\sqrt{36} - \sqrt{12}}{2}$

$= \dfrac{6 - 2\sqrt{3}}{2}$

$= \dfrac{2(3 - \sqrt{3})}{2}$ *Factor the numerator*

$= 3 - \sqrt{3}$ *Fundamental property*

53. $\dfrac{\sqrt{2} + 3}{\sqrt{3} - 1}$

$= \dfrac{(\sqrt{2} + 3)(\sqrt{3} + 1)}{(\sqrt{3} - 1)(\sqrt{3} + 1)}$ *Multiply by the conjugate*

$= \dfrac{(\sqrt{2})(\sqrt{3}) + \sqrt{2}(1) + 3\sqrt{3} + 3(1)}{(\sqrt{3})^2 - (1)^2}$

$= \dfrac{\sqrt{6} + \sqrt{2} + 3\sqrt{3} + 3}{3 - 1}$

$= \dfrac{\sqrt{6} + \sqrt{2} + 3\sqrt{3} + 3}{2}$

57. $\dfrac{2\sqrt{6} + 1}{\sqrt{2} + 5}$

$= \dfrac{(2\sqrt{6} + 1)(\sqrt{2} - 5)}{(\sqrt{2} + 5)(\sqrt{2} - 5)}$ *Multiply by the conjugate*

$= \dfrac{2\sqrt{12} - 10\sqrt{6} + \sqrt{2} - 5}{(\sqrt{2})^2 - (5)^2}$

$= \dfrac{2 \cdot 2\sqrt{3} - 10\sqrt{6} + \sqrt{2} - 5}{2 - 25}$

$= \dfrac{4\sqrt{3} - 10\sqrt{6} + \sqrt{2} - 5}{-23}$

$= \dfrac{-(4\sqrt{3} - 10\sqrt{6} + \sqrt{2} - 5)}{23}$

$= \dfrac{10\sqrt{6} - 4\sqrt{3} - \sqrt{2} + 5}{23}$

61. $\dfrac{3 + \sqrt{3}}{\sqrt{2}}$

$= \dfrac{(3 + \sqrt{3}) \cdot \sqrt{2}}{\sqrt{2} \cdot \sqrt{2}}$ *Rationalize denominator*

$= \dfrac{3\sqrt{2} + \sqrt{6}}{2}$

65. $\dfrac{\sqrt{8} + \sqrt{3}}{\sqrt{2}}$

$= \dfrac{(\sqrt{8} + \sqrt{3}) \cdot \sqrt{2}}{\sqrt{2} \cdot \sqrt{2}}$

$= \dfrac{\sqrt{16} + \sqrt{6}}{2}$

$= \dfrac{4 + \sqrt{6}}{2}$

69. $2\sqrt[4]{2}(3\sqrt[4]{8} + 5\sqrt[4]{4})$

$= 2 \cdot 3 \cdot \sqrt[4]{2} \cdot \sqrt[4]{8} + 2 \cdot 5 \cdot \sqrt[4]{2} \cdot \sqrt[4]{4}$ *Distributive property*

$= 6\sqrt[4]{16} + 10\sqrt[4]{8}$ *Product rule*

$= 6 \cdot 2 + 10\sqrt[4]{8}$

$= 12 + 10\sqrt[4]{8}$

73. $(\sqrt[3]{5} - \sqrt[3]{4})(\sqrt[3]{25} + \sqrt[3]{20} + \sqrt[3]{16})$

$= \sqrt[3]{5} \cdot \sqrt[3]{25} + \sqrt[3]{5} \cdot \sqrt[3]{20} + \sqrt[3]{5} \cdot \sqrt[3]{16} - \sqrt[3]{4} \cdot \sqrt[3]{25} - \sqrt[3]{4} \cdot \sqrt[3]{20} - \sqrt[3]{4} \cdot \sqrt[3]{16}$ *Distributive property*

$= \sqrt[3]{125} + \sqrt[3]{100} + \sqrt[3]{80} - \sqrt[3]{100} - \sqrt[3]{80} - \sqrt[3]{64}$ *Product rule*

$= \sqrt[3]{125} - \sqrt[3]{64}$

$= 5 - 4$

$= 1$

77. $y^2 - 4y + 3 = 0$

$(y - 3)(y - 1) = 0$ *Factor*

$y - 3 = 0$ or $y - 1 = 0$

$y = 3$ or $y = 1$

81. $k - 1 = (1 - 1)^2$

$\qquad k - 1 = k^2 - 2(k) + 1$

$\qquad\quad 0 = k^2 - 2k - k + 1 + 1$

$\qquad\quad 0 = k^2 - 3k + 2$

$\qquad\quad 0 = (k - 2)(k - 1)$

$\quad k - 2 = 0 \quad\text{or}\quad k - 1 = 0$

$\qquad\quad k = 2 \quad\text{or}\qquad k = 1$

Section 8.6 (page 363)

In Exercises 1-43, the student should check all proposed solutions in the original equation. Only checks that determine false solutions are shown there.

1. $\sqrt{x} = 2$

$\quad (\sqrt{x})^2 = (2)^2$ *Square both sides*

$\qquad\quad x = 4$

5. $\sqrt{t - 3} = 2$

$\quad (\sqrt{t - 3})^2 = (2)^2$ *Square both sides*

$\qquad t - 3 = 4$

$\qquad\qquad t = 7$

9. $\sqrt{m + 5} = 0$

$\quad (\sqrt{m + 5})^2 = (0)^2$ *Square both sides*

$\qquad m + 5 = 0$ *Solve for m*

$\qquad\qquad m = -5$

13. $\sqrt{k} - 2 = 5$

$\qquad\quad \sqrt{k} = 7$ *Get $\sqrt{k}$ alone on one side*

$\quad (\sqrt{k})^2 = (7)^2$ *Square both sides*

$\qquad\quad k = 49$

17. $\sqrt{5t - 9} = 2\sqrt{t}$

$\quad (\sqrt{5t - 9})^2 = (2\sqrt{t})^2$ *Square both sides*

$\qquad 5t - 9 = 4t$

$\qquad\qquad t = 9$

21. $\sqrt{5y - 5} = \sqrt{4y + 1}$

$\quad (\sqrt{5y - 5})^2 = (\sqrt{4y + 1})^2$ *Square both sides*

$\qquad 5y - 5 = 4y + 1$ *Solve for y*

$\qquad\quad y - 5 = 1$

$\qquad\qquad y = 6$

25. $p = \sqrt{p^2 - 3p - 12}$

$\quad (p)^2 = (\sqrt{p^2 - 3p - 12})^2$ *Square both sides*

$\qquad p^2 = p^2 - 3p - 12$

$\qquad 0 = -3p - 12$

$\qquad 3p = -12$

$\qquad p = -4$

Check:

$-4 = \sqrt{(-4)^2 - 3(-4) - 12}$

$-4 = \sqrt{16 + 12 - 12}$

$-4 = \sqrt{16}$ *False*

No solution exists since -4 does not check.

29. $\sqrt{2x + 1} = x - 7$

$\quad (\sqrt{2x + 1})^2 = (x - 7)^2$ *Square both sides*

$\qquad 2x + 1 = x^2 - 14x + 49$

$\qquad\quad 0 = x^2 - 16x + 48$

$\qquad\quad 0 = (x - 12)(x - 4)$ *Factor*

$x - 12 = 0 \quad\text{or}\quad x - 4 = 0$

$\quad x = 12 \quad\text{or}\qquad x = 4$

Check for $x = 4$:

$\sqrt{2(4) + 1} = 4 - 7$

$\sqrt{8 + 1} = -3$

$\sqrt{9} = -3$ *False*

The only solution is 12 since 4 does not check.

33. $\sqrt{x + 1} - 1 = x$

    $\sqrt{x + 1} = x + 1$ *Get $\sqrt{x + 1}$ alone on one side*

    $(\sqrt{x + 1})^2 = (x + 1)^2$ *Square both sides*

    $x + 1 = x^2 + 2x + 1$

    $0 = x^2 + x$ *Get 0 alone on one side*

    $0 = x(x + 1)$ *Factor*

    $x = 0$ or $x + 1 = 0$ *Set each factor equal to 0 and solve*
          or $x = -1$

    The solutions are 0 and -1 since both solutions check in the original equation.

37. $3\sqrt{x + 13} = x + 9$

    $(3\sqrt{x + 13})^2 = (x + 9)^2$ *Square both sides*

    $9(x + 13) = x^2 + 18x + 81$

    $9x + 117 = x^2 + 18x + 81$

    $0 = x^2 + 9x - 36$ *Get 0 alone on one side*

    $0 = (x + 12)(x - 3)$ *Factor*

    $x + 12 = 0$ or $x - 3 = 0$ *Set each factor equal to 0 and solve*
    $x = -12$ or $x = 3$

    Check for $x = -12$:

    $3\sqrt{-12 + 13} = -12 + 9$

    $3\sqrt{1} = -3$

    $3 = -3$ *False*

    The only solution is 3 since -12 does not check.

41. $\sqrt{3x} - 4 = x - 10$

    $\sqrt{3x} = x - 6$ *Get $\sqrt{3x}$ alone*

    $(\sqrt{3x})^2 = (x - 6)^2$ *Square both sides*

    $3x = x^2 - 12x + 36$

    $0 = x^2 - 15x + 36$

    $0 = (x - 12)(x - 3)$ *Factor*

    $x - 12 = 0$ or $x - 3 = 0$
    $x = 12$ or $x = 3$

    Check for $x = 3$:

    $\sqrt{3(3)} - 4 = 3 - 10$

    $\sqrt{9} - 4 = -7$

    $3 - 4 = -7$

    $-1 = -7$ *False*

    The only solution is 12 since 3 does not check.

45. Let x represent the number.

    $\sqrt{x + 4} = 5$

    $x + 4 = 25$ *Square both sides*

    $x = 25 - 4$

    $x = 21$

    The number is 21.

49. (a) Use $s = 30\sqrt{\dfrac{a}{p}}$ with $a = 900$ and $p = 100$.

    $s = 30\sqrt{\dfrac{900}{100}}$

    $= 30\sqrt{9}$

    $= 30 \cdot 3$

    $= 90$

    The speed is 90 miles per hour.

    (b) $a = 400$ and $p = 25$

    $s = 30\sqrt{\dfrac{400}{25}}$

    $= 30\sqrt{16}$

    $= 30 \cdot 4$

    $= 120$

The speed is 120 miles per hour.

(c) $a = 80$ and $p = 20$

$$s = 30\sqrt{\dfrac{80}{20}}$$

$$= 30\sqrt{4}$$

$$= 30 \cdot 2$$

$$= 60$$

The speed is 60 miles per hour.

(d) $a = 120$ and $p = 30$

$$s = 30\sqrt{\dfrac{120}{30}}$$

$$= 30\sqrt{4}$$

$$= 30 \cdot 2$$

$$= 60$$

The speed is 60 miles per hour.

53. $(2x^3)^{-1} = \dfrac{1}{2x^3}$

Section 8.7 (page 367)

1. $16^{1/2} = \sqrt{16} = 4$

5. $8^{1/3} = \sqrt[3]{8} = 2$

9. $16^{1/4} = \sqrt[4]{16} = 2$

13. $4^{3/2} = (4^{1/2})^3 = (\sqrt{4})^3 = 2^3 = 8$

17. $16^{3/4} = (16^{1/4})^3 = (\sqrt[4]{16})^3 = 2^3 = 8$

21. $(-8)^{2/3} = ((-8)^{1/3})^2$

$$= (\sqrt[3]{-8})^2$$

$$= (-2)^2$$

$$= 4$$

25. $2^{1/2} \cdot 2^{5/2} = 2^{1/2+5/2}$

$$= 2^{6/2}$$

$$= 2^3$$

29. $\dfrac{15^{3/4}}{15^{5/4}} = 15^{3/4-5/4}$

$$= 15^{-2/4}$$

$$= 15^{-1/2}$$

$$= \dfrac{1}{15^{1/2}}$$

33. $(8^{3/2})^2 = 8^{(3/2)(2)} = 8^3$

37. $(9^{1/4})^{3/2} = 9^{(1/4)(3/2)}$

$$= 9^{(1/2)(1/2)(3/2)}$$

$$= (\sqrt{9})^{(1/2)(3/2)}$$

$$= 3^{3/4}$$

41. $\left(\dfrac{8}{27}\right)^{2/3} = \dfrac{8^{2/3}}{27^{2/3}}$

$$= \dfrac{(8^{1/3})^2}{(27^{1/3})^2}$$

$$= \dfrac{(\sqrt[3]{8})^2}{(\sqrt[3]{27})^2}$$

$$= \dfrac{2^2}{3^2}$$

$$= \dfrac{4}{9}$$

45. $\dfrac{6^{-2/9}}{6^{1/9} \cdot 6^{-5/9}} = \dfrac{6^{-2/9}}{6^{1/9+(-5/9)}}$

$$= \dfrac{6^{-2/9}}{6^{-4/9}}$$

$$= 6^{-2/9-(-4/9)}$$

$$= 6^{2/9}$$

49. $\dfrac{z^{2/3}}{z^{-1/3}} = z^{2/3-(-1/3)}$

$\qquad = z^{3/3}$

$\qquad = z$

53. $(x^{1/2}y^{2/3})^{3/4}$

$\qquad = (x^{1/2})^{3/4}(y^{2/3})^{3/4}$

$\qquad = x^{3/8}y^{1/2}$

57. $\dfrac{c^{2/3}\cdot c^{-1/3}}{c^{5/3}} = c^{2/3+(-1/3)-5/3}$

$\qquad = c^{-4/3}$

$\qquad = \dfrac{1}{c^{4/3}}$

61. $\sqrt[6]{4^3} = 4^{3/6} = 4^{1/2} = 2$

65. $\sqrt[4]{a^2} = a^{2/4} = a^{1/2} = \sqrt{a}$

69. $d = 1.22x^{1/2}$

(a) Let $x = 20,000$

Then $d = 1.22(20,000)^{1/2}$

$\qquad d = 1.22\sqrt{20000}$

$\qquad d = 1.22\cdot\sqrt{10000}\cdot\sqrt{2}$

$\qquad d = 1.22(100)\cdot\sqrt{2}$

$\qquad d = 122\sqrt{2}$ miles
or approximately 172.5 miles.

(b) Let $x = 30,000$

Then $d = 1.22(30,000)^{1/2}$

$\qquad d = 1.22\sqrt{30000}$

$\qquad d = 1.22\sqrt{10000}\cdot\sqrt{3}$

$\qquad d = 1.22(100)\cdot\sqrt{3}$

$\qquad d = 122\sqrt{3}$ miles
or approximately 211.3 miles.

73. The square roots of 14 are $\sqrt{14}$ and $-\sqrt{14}$, or, from Table 3, approximately 3.742 and -3.742.

77. $80 = 16\cdot 5 = 4^2\cdot 5$ so the square roots of 80 are $4\sqrt{5}$ and $-4\sqrt{5}$, or, approximately 8.944 and -8.944.

Chapter 8 Review Exercises (page 369)

1. Since $(7)^2 = 49$ and $(-7)^2 = 49$, the square roots of 49 are 7 and -7.

5. $\sqrt{16} = 4$ since $4^2 = 16$.

9. $\sqrt[4]{16} = 2$ becomes $2^4 = 16$.

13. $-\sqrt{169}$ is rational because $-\sqrt{169} = -13$.

17. $\sqrt{98}\cdot\sqrt{50} = (\sqrt{49\cdot 2})(\sqrt{25\cdot 2})$

$\qquad = (\sqrt{49}\cdot\sqrt{2})(\sqrt{25}\cdot\sqrt{2})$

$\qquad = (7\sqrt{2})(5\sqrt{2})$

$\qquad = 35(2)$

$\qquad = 70$

21. $\sqrt{p}\cdot\sqrt{p} = \sqrt{p^2} = p$

25. $\sqrt[3]{\dfrac{6}{125}} = \dfrac{\sqrt[3]{6}}{\sqrt[3]{125}} = \dfrac{\sqrt[3]{6}}{5}$

29. $\dfrac{2}{5}\sqrt{75} - \dfrac{3}{4}\sqrt{160}$

$\qquad = \dfrac{2}{5}\sqrt{25\cdot 3} - \dfrac{3}{4}\sqrt{16\cdot 10}$

$\qquad = \dfrac{2}{5}\sqrt{25}\cdot\sqrt{3} - \dfrac{3}{4}\sqrt{16}\cdot\sqrt{10}$

$\qquad = \dfrac{2}{5}(5)\sqrt{3} - \dfrac{3}{4}(4)\sqrt{10}$

$\qquad = 2\sqrt{3} - 3\sqrt{10}$

33. $\sqrt{16p} + 3\sqrt{p} - \sqrt{49p}$

$= \sqrt{16}\cdot\sqrt{p} + 3\sqrt{p} - \sqrt{49}\cdot\sqrt{p}$

$= 4\sqrt{p} + 3\sqrt{p} - 7\sqrt{p}$

$= (4 + 3 - 7)\sqrt{p}$

$= 0\cdot\sqrt{p} = 0$

37. $\dfrac{3\sqrt{2}}{\sqrt{5}} = \dfrac{3\sqrt{2}\cdot\sqrt{5}}{\sqrt{5}\cdot\sqrt{5}} = \dfrac{3\sqrt{2\cdot5}}{5} = \dfrac{3\sqrt{10}}{5}$

41. $\sqrt[3]{\dfrac{5}{4}} = \dfrac{\sqrt[3]{5}}{\sqrt[3]{4}} = \dfrac{\sqrt[3]{5}\cdot\sqrt[3]{2}}{\sqrt[3]{4}\cdot\sqrt[3]{2}} = \dfrac{\sqrt[3]{10}}{\sqrt[3]{8}} = \dfrac{\sqrt[3]{10}}{2}$

45. $3\sqrt{2}(\sqrt{3} + 2\sqrt{2}) = 3\sqrt{2}(\sqrt{3}) + 3\sqrt{2}(2\sqrt{2})$

$= 3\sqrt{6} + 6(2)$

$= 3\sqrt{6} + 12$

49. $\dfrac{\sqrt{3}}{1 + \sqrt{3}}$

$= \dfrac{\sqrt{3}(1 - \sqrt{3})}{(1 + \sqrt{3})(1 - \sqrt{3})}$

   Multiply numerator and denominator by the conjugate

$= \dfrac{\sqrt{3} - 3}{1 - 3}$

$= \dfrac{\sqrt{3} - 3}{-2}$

$= \dfrac{-\sqrt{3} + 3}{2}$ *Multiply numerator and denominator by -1*

53. $\sqrt{k + 1} = 10$

$k + 1 = 100$ *Square both sides*

$k = 99$ *Subtract 1*

57. $81^{1/2} = \sqrt{81} = 9$

61. $\dfrac{x^{1/4}\cdot x^{5/4}}{x^{3/4}} = x^{1/4+5/4-3/4}$

$= x^{3/4}$

65. $\sqrt{\dfrac{36}{p^2}} = \dfrac{\sqrt{36}}{\sqrt{p^2}} = \dfrac{6}{p}$

69. $\sqrt[12]{125} = 125^{4/12} = 125^{1/3}$

$= \sqrt[3]{125} = 5$

73. $3\sqrt{75} + 2\sqrt{27}$

$= 3\sqrt{25}\cdot\sqrt{3} + 2\sqrt{9}\cdot\sqrt{3}$

$= 3(5)\sqrt{3} + 2(3)\sqrt{3}$

$= 15\sqrt{3} + 6\sqrt{3} = 21\sqrt{3}$

77. $\sqrt{48} - \sqrt{16\cdot3} = \sqrt{16}\cdot\sqrt{3} = 4\sqrt{3}$

Chapter 8 Test   (page 371)

1. $\sqrt{100} = 10$ since $10^2 = 100$.

2. $\sqrt{77} \approx 8.775$ from Table 3 or a calculator.

3. $-\sqrt{190} \approx -13.784$ from Table 3.

4. $\sqrt[3]{-27} = -3$ since $(-3)^3 = -27$.

5. $\sqrt[4]{625} = 5$ since $5^4 = 625$.

6. $\sqrt{27} = \sqrt{9\cdot3}$

$= \sqrt{9}\cdot\sqrt{3}$

$= 3\sqrt{3}$

7. $\sqrt{128} = \sqrt{64\cdot2}$

$= \sqrt{64}\cdot\sqrt{2}$

$= 8\sqrt{2}$

8. $\sqrt[3]{-32} = \sqrt[3]{-8\cdot4}$

$= \sqrt[3]{-8}\cdot\sqrt[3]{4}$

$= -2\sqrt[3]{4}$

9. $3\sqrt{6} + \sqrt{14}$ cannot be simplified further because 6 and 14 have no perfect squares as factors, and $3\sqrt{6}$ and $\sqrt{14}$ are not multiples of the same root of the same number.

10. $3\sqrt{28} + \sqrt{63}$

$$= 3\cdot\sqrt{4}\cdot\sqrt{7} + \sqrt{9}\cdot\sqrt{7}$$
$$= 3\cdot2\cdot\sqrt{7} + 3\cdot\sqrt{7}$$
$$= 6\sqrt{7} + 3\sqrt{7}$$
$$= 9\sqrt{7}$$

11. $m\sqrt{20} - m\sqrt{45} = m\sqrt{4\cdot5} - m\sqrt{9\cdot5}$

$$= m\sqrt{4}\cdot\sqrt{5} - m\sqrt{9}\cdot\sqrt{5}$$
$$= 2m\sqrt{5} - 3m\sqrt{5}$$
$$= (2m - 3m)\sqrt{5}$$
$$= -m\sqrt{5}$$

12. $3\sqrt{27x} - 4\sqrt{48x} + 2\sqrt{3x}$

$$= 3\sqrt{9\cdot3x} - 4\sqrt{16\cdot3x} + 2\sqrt{3x}$$
$$= 3\sqrt{9}\cdot\sqrt{3x} - 4\sqrt{16}\cdot\sqrt{3x} + 2\sqrt{3x}$$
$$= 3\cdot3\sqrt{3x} - 4\cdot4\sqrt{3x} + 2\sqrt{3x}$$
$$= 9\sqrt{3x} - 16\sqrt{3x} + 2\sqrt{3x}$$
$$= (9 - 16 + 2)\sqrt{3x}$$
$$= -5\sqrt{3x}$$

13. $\sqrt[3]{32x^2y^3} = \sqrt[3]{8\cdot4}\sqrt[3]{x^2}\sqrt[3]{y^3}$

$$= \sqrt[3]{8}\sqrt[3]{4}\sqrt[3]{x^2}y$$
$$= 2y\sqrt[3]{4x^2}$$

14. $\sqrt[4]{32m^3n^4p^6}$

$$= \sqrt[4]{16\cdot2}\sqrt[4]{m^3}\sqrt[4]{n^4}\sqrt[4]{p^4\cdot p^2}$$
$$= \sqrt[4]{16}\sqrt[4]{2}\sqrt[4]{m^3}n\sqrt[4]{p^4}\sqrt[4]{p^2}$$
$$= 2\sqrt[4]{2m^3}\cdot n\cdot p\cdot\sqrt[4]{p^2}$$
$$= 2np\sqrt[4]{2m^3p^2}$$

15. Use the formula $(a - b)(a + b) = a^2 - b^2$.

$$(6 - \sqrt{5})(6 + \sqrt{5}) = (6)^2 - (\sqrt{5})^2$$
$$= 36 - 5$$
$$= 31$$

16. Use the FOIL method to multiply.

$$(2 - \sqrt{7})(3\sqrt{2} + 1)$$
$$= 2(3\sqrt{2}) + 2(1) - \sqrt{7}(3\sqrt{2}) - \sqrt{7}$$
$$= 6\sqrt{2} + 2 - 3\sqrt{14} - \sqrt{7}$$

17. Use the formula $(a + b) = a^2 + 2ab + b^2$.

$$(\sqrt{5} + \sqrt{6})^2$$
$$= (\sqrt{5})^2 + 2(\sqrt{5})(\sqrt{6}) + (\sqrt{6})^2$$
$$= 5 + 2\sqrt{30} + 6$$
$$= 11 + 2\sqrt{30}$$

18. $\dfrac{3\sqrt{2}}{6}$

$$= 3\sqrt{\frac{2}{6}} = 3\sqrt{\frac{1}{3}} = \frac{3\sqrt{1}}{\sqrt{3}}$$
$$= \frac{3\sqrt{3}}{\sqrt{3}\cdot\sqrt{3}} = \frac{3\sqrt{3}}{3} = \sqrt{3}$$

19. $\dfrac{4p}{\sqrt{k}} = \dfrac{4p\sqrt{k}}{\sqrt{k}\cdot\sqrt{k}}$

$$= \frac{4p\sqrt{k}}{k}$$

20. $\sqrt[3]{\dfrac{5}{9}} = \dfrac{\sqrt[3]{5}}{\sqrt[3]{9}}$

$$= \frac{\sqrt[3]{5}\cdot\sqrt[3]{3}}{\sqrt[3]{9}\cdot\sqrt[3]{3}}$$
$$= \frac{\sqrt[3]{15}}{\sqrt[3]{27}}$$
$$= \frac{\sqrt[3]{15}}{3}$$

21.

$$\frac{-3}{4 - \sqrt{3}} = \frac{-3(4 + \sqrt{3})}{(4 - \sqrt{3})(4 + \sqrt{3})}$$

$$= \frac{-3(4 + \sqrt{3})}{(4)^2 - (\sqrt{3})^2}$$

$$= \frac{-3(4 + \sqrt{3})}{16 - 3}$$

$$= \frac{-3(4 + \sqrt{3})}{13}$$

$$= \frac{-12 - 3\sqrt{3}}{13}$$

22.

$$\frac{\sqrt{2} + 1}{3 - \sqrt{7}}$$

$$= \frac{(\sqrt{2} + 1)(3 + \sqrt{7})}{(3 - \sqrt{7})(3 + \sqrt{7})}$$

$$= \frac{3\sqrt{2} + \sqrt{2}(\sqrt{7}) + 3 + \sqrt{7}}{(3)^2 - (\sqrt{7})^2}$$

$$= \frac{3\sqrt{2} + \sqrt{14} + 3 + \sqrt{7}}{9 - 7}$$

$$= \frac{3\sqrt{2} + \sqrt{14} + 3 + \sqrt{7}}{2}$$

23.

$$\sqrt{k + 2} + 3 = -2$$

$$\sqrt{k + 2} = -5$$

$$(\sqrt{k + 2})^2 = (-5)^2$$

$$k + 2 = 25$$

$$k = 23$$

Check:

$$\sqrt{23 + 2} + 3 = -2$$

$$\sqrt{25} + 3 = -2$$

$$5 + 3 = -2 \quad False$$

No solution exists since 23 does not check.

24.

$$\sqrt{2y + 8} = 2\sqrt{y}$$

$$(\sqrt{2y + 8})^2 = (2\sqrt{y}) \quad \textit{Square both sides}$$

$$2y + 8 = 4y$$

$$8 = 2y$$

$$4 = y$$

25.

$$6\sqrt{k} - 3 = k + 2$$

$$6\sqrt{k} = k + 5 \quad \textit{Get } 6\sqrt{k} \textit{ alone}$$

$$(6\sqrt{k})^2 = (k + 5)^2 \quad \textit{Square both sides}$$

$$36k = k^2 + 10k + 25$$

$$0 = k^2 - 26k + 25$$

$$0 = (k - 25)(k - 1) \quad \textit{Factor}$$

$$k - 25 = 0 \quad \text{or} \quad k - 1 = 0$$

$$k = 25 \quad \text{or} \quad k = 1$$

25 and 1 both satisfy the original equation, so they are both solutions.

26.

$$\sqrt{y + 3} = \sqrt{y} + 1$$

$$(\sqrt{y + 3})^2 = (\sqrt{y} + 1)^2 \quad \textit{Square both sides}$$

$$y + 3 = (\sqrt{y})^2 + 2(\sqrt{x})(1) + (1)^2$$

$$y + 3 = y + 2\sqrt{y} + 1$$

$$y - y + 3 - 1 = y - y + 2\sqrt{y} + 1 - 1$$

$$\textit{Get } 2\sqrt{y} \textit{ alone}$$

$$2 = 2\sqrt{y}$$

$$(2)^2 = (2\sqrt{y})^2 \quad \textit{Square both sides}$$

$$4 = 4y$$

$$1 = y$$

27.

$$8^{4/3} = (8^{1/3})^4 = 2^4 = 16$$

28.

$$5^{3/4} \cdot 5^{7/4} = 5^{3/4 + 7/4} = 5^{10/4} = 5^{5/2}$$

29.

$$\frac{(3^{1/4})^3}{3^{7/4}} = \frac{3^{3/4}}{3^{7/4}}$$

$$= 3^{3/4 - 7/4} = 3^{-4/4}$$

$$= 3^{-1} = 1/3$$

30.

$$\frac{m^{2/3} \cdot m^{5/6}}{m^{4/3}} = m^{2/3 + 5/6 - 4/3}$$

$$= m^{4/6 + 5/6 - 8/6}$$

$$= m^{1/6}$$

CHAPTER 9   QUADRATIC EQUATIONS
Section 9.1   (page 375)

1. $x^2 = 25$, so, by the square root property, $x = \sqrt{25} = 5$ or $x = -\sqrt{25} = -5$.

5. $m^2 = 13$, so $m = \sqrt{13}$ or $m = -\sqrt{13}$.

9. $3p^2 = 6$

$p^2 = 2$ *Divide by 3*

$p = \sqrt{2}$ or $p = -\sqrt{2}$ *Square root property*

13. $3x^2 - 8 = 64$

$3x^2 = 72$

$x^2 = 24$ *Square root property*

$x = \sqrt{24}$ or $x = -\sqrt{24}$

$x = \sqrt{4 \cdot 6}$ $= -\sqrt{4 \cdot 6}$

$x = 2\sqrt{6}$ or $x = -2\sqrt{6}$

17. $k^2 = 2.56$

$k = \sqrt{2.56}$ or $k = -\sqrt{2.56}$

$k = 1.6$ or $k = -1.6$

21. $(x - 2)^2 = 16$

$x - 2 = \sqrt{16}$ or $x - 2 = -\sqrt{16}$

$x - 2 = 4$ $x - 2 = -4$

$x = 4 + 2$ $x = -4 + 2$

$x = 6$ or $x = -2$

25. $(m - 1)^2 = -4$

The square root of -4 is not a real number. There is no real number solution.

29. $(2m - 1)^2 = 9$

$2m - 1 = \sqrt{9}$ or $2m - 1 = -\sqrt{9}$

$2m - 1 = 3$ $2m - 1 = -3$

$2m = 4$ $2m = -2$

$m = 2$ or $m = -1$

33. $(2a - 5)^2 = 30$

$2a - 5 = \sqrt{30}$

$2a = 5 + \sqrt{30}$

$a = \dfrac{5 + \sqrt{30}}{2}$

or

$2a - 5 = -\sqrt{30}$

$2a = 5 - \sqrt{30}$

$a = \dfrac{5 - \sqrt{30}}{2}$

37. $(2k - 5)^2 = 98$

$2k - 5 = \sqrt{98}$

$2k - 5 = \sqrt{49 \cdot 2}$

$2k - 5 = 7\sqrt{2}$

$2k = 5 + 7\sqrt{2}$

$k = \dfrac{5 + 7\sqrt{2}}{2}$

or

$2k - 5 = -\sqrt{98}$

$2k - 5 = -\sqrt{49 \cdot 2}$

$2k - 5 = -7\sqrt{2}$

$2k = 5 - 7\sqrt{2}$

$k = \dfrac{5 - 7\sqrt{2}}{2}$

41. $(2.11p + 3.42)^2 = 9.58$

$2.11p + 3.42 = \sqrt{9.58}$ *Square root property*

$2.11p + 3.42 \approx 3.095$

$2.11p \approx -.325$

$p \approx -.15$

or

$2.11p + 3.42 = -\sqrt{9.58}$ *Take square root of each side*

$2.11p + 3.42 \approx -3.095$

$2.11p \approx -6.515$

$p \approx -3.09$

The solutions are approximately −.15 and −3.09.

45. Use $A = P(1 + r)^2$ with $P = 1$ and $A = 1.21$.

$$1.21 = 1(1 + r)^2$$
$$\sqrt{1.21} = 1 + r \quad \text{or} \quad -\sqrt{1.21} = 1 + r$$
$$1.1 = 1 + r \qquad\qquad -1.1 = 1 + r$$
$$.1 = r \quad \text{or} \quad -2.1 = r$$

Since interest rate cannot be negative in this problem, the rate is 10%.

49. $6 + \sqrt{\dfrac{2}{3}} = 6 + \dfrac{\sqrt{2}}{\sqrt{3}}$

$$= 6 + \frac{\sqrt{2}\cdot\sqrt{3}}{\sqrt{3}\cdot\sqrt{3}} \quad \textit{Rationalize denominator}$$

$$= 6 + \frac{\sqrt{6}}{3}$$

$$= \frac{18}{3} + \frac{\sqrt{6}}{3} \quad \textit{Common denominator}$$

$$= \frac{18 + \sqrt{6}}{3}$$

53. $p^2 - 5p + \dfrac{25}{4} = \left(p - \dfrac{5}{2}\right)\left(p - \dfrac{5}{2}\right)$

$$= \left(p - \frac{5}{2}\right)^2$$

Section 9.2   (page 381)

1. In $x^2 + 2x$, the coefficient of x is 2.

Take one-half of 2: $\dfrac{1}{2}(2) = 1$.

Square this last result: $(1)^2 = 1$.

To make $x^2 + 2x$ a perfect square trinomial, add 1.

5. In $z^2 + 9z$, the coefficient of z is 9.

One-half of 9 is $\dfrac{1}{2}(9) = \dfrac{9}{2}$.

Square this: $\left(\dfrac{9}{2}\right)^2 = \dfrac{81}{4}$.

To make $z^2 + 9z$ a perfect square trinomial, add 81/4.

9. $x^2 + 4x = -3$

Take one-half the coefficient of x:

$$\frac{1}{2}(4) = 2.$$

Square 2: $2^2 = 4$.

$$x^2 + 4x + 4 = -3 + 4 \quad \textit{Add 4 to each side}$$

$$(x + 2)^2 = 1 \qquad \textit{Factor}$$
$$x + 2 = \sqrt{1} \quad \text{or} \quad x + 2 = -\sqrt{1}$$
$$\textit{Square root property}$$
$$x + 2 = 1 \quad \text{or} \quad x + 2 = -1$$
$$x = -1 \quad \text{or} \qquad x = -3$$

The solutions are −1 and −3.

13. $z^2 + 6z = -8$

Take one-half the coefficient of z and square it.

$$\frac{1}{2}(6) = 3$$
$$3^2 = 9$$

$$z^2 + 6z + 9 = -8 + 9 \quad \textit{Add 9 to both sides}$$

$$(z + 3)^2 = 1$$
$$z + 3 = 1 \quad \text{or} \quad z + 3 = -1$$
$$z = -2 \quad \text{or} \qquad z = -4$$

The solutions are −2 and −4.

17. $c^2 + 3c = 2$

Take one-half the coefficient of c and square it.

$$\frac{1}{2}(3) = \frac{3}{2}$$

$$\left(\frac{3}{2}\right)^2 = \frac{9}{4}$$

$$c^2 + 3c + \frac{9}{4} = 2 + \frac{9}{4} \quad \textit{Add 9/4 to each side}$$

$$\left(c + \frac{3}{2}\right)^2 = \frac{8}{4} + \frac{9}{4}$$

$$\left(c + \frac{3}{2}\right)^2 = \frac{17}{4}$$

$$c + \frac{3}{2} = \sqrt{\frac{17}{4}}$$

$$c + \frac{3}{2} = \frac{\sqrt{17}}{2}$$

$$c = \frac{-3}{2} + \frac{\sqrt{17}}{2}$$

$$c = \frac{-3 + \sqrt{17}}{2}$$

or

$$c + \frac{3}{2} = -\sqrt{\frac{17}{4}}$$

$$c + \frac{3}{2} = \frac{-\sqrt{17}}{2} \quad \textit{Simplify the radical}$$

$$c = \frac{-3}{2} + \frac{-\sqrt{17}}{2}$$

$$c = \frac{-3 - \sqrt{17}}{2}$$

The solutions are $\frac{-3 + \sqrt{17}}{2}$ and $\frac{-3 - \sqrt{17}}{2}$.

21. $6q^2 - 8q + 3 = 0$

$$q^2 - \frac{8}{6}q + \frac{3}{6} = 0 \quad \textit{Divide each term by 6 to get the coefficient of } q^2 \textit{ equal to 1}$$

$$q^2 - \frac{4}{3}q = -\frac{1}{2}$$

Take one-half of the coefficient of q:

$$\frac{1}{2}\left(-\frac{4}{3}\right) = -\frac{2}{3}.$$

Square $-2/3$:

$$\left(-\frac{2}{3}\right)^2 = \frac{4}{9}$$

$$q^2 - \frac{4}{3}q + \frac{4}{9} = -\frac{1}{2} + \frac{4}{9} \quad \textit{Add 4/9 to each side}$$

$$\left(q - \frac{2}{3}\right)^2 = \frac{-9}{18} + \frac{8}{18} \quad \textit{Factor and simplify}$$

$$\left(q - \frac{2}{3}\right)^2 = -\frac{1}{18}$$

Since $\left(q - \frac{2}{3}\right)^2$ must be a positive number and here it is $-\frac{1}{18}$, there is no real number solution.

25. $3x^2 - 2x = 1$

$$x^2 - \frac{2}{3}x = \frac{1}{3} \quad \textit{Divide both sides by 3}$$

Take 1/2 the coefficient of x and square the result.

$$\frac{1}{2}\left(-\frac{2}{3}\right) = -\frac{1}{3}$$

$$\left(-\frac{1}{3}\right)^2 = \frac{1}{9}$$

$$x^2 - \frac{2}{3}x + \frac{1}{9} = \frac{1}{3} + \frac{1}{9} \quad \textit{Add 1/9 to both sides}$$

$$\left(x - \frac{1}{3}\right)^2 = \frac{3}{9} + \frac{1}{9} \quad \textit{Factor}$$

$$\left(x - \frac{1}{3}\right)^2 = \frac{4}{9} \quad \textit{Simplify}$$

$$x - \frac{1}{3} = \sqrt{\frac{4}{9}} \quad \text{or} \quad x - \frac{1}{3} = -\sqrt{\frac{4}{9}}$$

$$x - \frac{1}{3} = \frac{2}{3} \qquad\qquad x - \frac{1}{3} = -\frac{2}{3}$$

$$x = \frac{3}{3}$$

$$x = 1 \quad \text{or} \qquad x = -\frac{1}{3}$$

The solutions are 1 and -1/3.

29. $$3r^2 - 2 = 6r + 3$$

$$3r^2 - 6r = 5$$

$$r^2 - 2r = \frac{5}{3}$$

Take $\frac{1}{2}$ the coefficient of r and square it.

$$\frac{1}{2}(-2) = -1$$

$$(-1)^2 = 1$$

$r^2 - 2r + 1 = \frac{5}{3} + 1$ *Add 1 to both sides*

$(r - 1)^2 = \frac{5}{3} + \frac{3}{3}$ *Factor*

$(r - 1)^2 = \frac{8}{3}$ *Simplify*

$r - 1 = \sqrt{\frac{8}{3}}$ or $r - 1 = -\sqrt{\frac{8}{3}}$

$r - 1 = \sqrt{2.6667}$ $r - 1 = -\sqrt{2.6667}$

$r - 1 = 1.633$ $r - 1 = -1.633$

$r = 2.633$ or $r = -.633$

The solutions are approximately 2.6333 and -.633.

33. $$\left(\frac{d - 4}{4}\right)^2 = 9$$

$\frac{d - 4}{4} = \sqrt{9}$ or $\frac{d - 4}{4} = -\sqrt{9}$

Square root property

$\frac{d - 4}{4} = 3$ or $\frac{d - 4}{4} = -3$

$d - 4 = 12$ or $d - 4 = -12$

$d = 16$ or $d = -8$

Since d represents the diameter, d = -8 is not a reasonable answer. The required diameter is 16 feet.

37. $\frac{2 + 2\sqrt{3}}{2}$

$= \frac{2 \cdot (1 + \sqrt{3})}{2}$ *Factor the highest common factor (2)*

$= 1 + \sqrt{3}$ *Simplify*

41. $\frac{8 + 6\sqrt{3}}{4}$

$= \frac{2 \cdot (4 + 3\sqrt{3})}{4}$ *Factor*

$= \frac{4 + 3\sqrt{3}}{2}$ *Simplify*

Section 9.3   (page 386)

1. $3x^2 + 4x - 8 = 0$ matches the general form $ax^2 + bx + c = 0$ so a = 3, b = 4, and c = -8.

5.   Write $2x^2 = 3x - 2$ as $2x^2 - 3x + 2 = 0$ to match the general form $ax^2 + bx + c = 0$.   Then a = 2, b = -3, and c = 2.

9.   Write $3x^2 - 8x = 0$ as $3x^2 - 8x + 0 = 0$.   Now a = 3, b = -8, and c = 0.

13. $9(x - 1)(x + 2) = 8$

$9(x^2 + x - 2) = 8$ *Multiply*

$9x^2 + 9x - 18 = 8$

$9x^2 + 9x - 26 = 0$

Now a = 9, b = 9, and c = -26.

17.   Write $y^2 + 4y + 4 = 0$ as $1 \cdot y^2 + 4y + 4 = 0$.   Now a = 1, b = 4, and c = 4.

Substitute using the quadratic formula.

$$y = \frac{-b \pm \sqrt{b^2 - 4ac}}{2a}$$

$$= \frac{-4 \pm \sqrt{4^2 - 4(1)(4)}}{2 \cdot 1}$$

$$= \frac{-4 \pm \sqrt{16 - 16}}{2}$$

$$= \frac{-4 \pm 0}{2}$$

$$= \frac{-4}{2}$$

$$= -2$$

The only solution is -2.

21. $4p^2 - 12p + 9 = 0$

a = 4, b = -12, c = 9

$$p = \frac{-b \pm \sqrt{b^2 - 4ac}}{2a}$$

$$= \frac{-(-12) \pm \sqrt{(-12)^2 - 4(4)(9)}}{2 \cdot 4}$$

$$= \frac{12 \pm \sqrt{144 - 144}}{8}$$

$$= \frac{12 \pm 0}{8}$$

$$= \frac{12}{8}$$

$$= \frac{3}{2}$$

The solution is 3/2.

25. $$2z^2 = 3z + 5$$

$$2z^2 - 3z - 5 = 0$$

a = 2, b = -3, c = -5

$$z = \frac{-b \pm \sqrt{b^2 - 4ac}}{2a}$$

$$z = \frac{-(-3) \pm \sqrt{(-3)^2 - 4(2)(-5)}}{2(2)}$$

$$= \frac{3 \pm \sqrt{9 + 40}}{4}$$

$$= \frac{3 \pm \sqrt{49}}{4}$$

$$= \frac{3 \pm 7}{4}$$

The solutions are $\frac{3 + 7}{4} = \frac{10}{4} = \frac{5}{2}$

and $\frac{3 - 7}{4} = \frac{-4}{4} = -1$.

29. $2w^2 + 12w + 5 = 0$ already matches the general form.

a = 2, b = 12, c = 5

$$w = \frac{-b \pm \sqrt{b^2 - 4ac}}{2a}$$

$$= \frac{-12 \pm \sqrt{(12)^2 - 4(2)(5)}}{2(2)}$$

$$= \frac{-12 \pm \sqrt{144 - 40}}{4}$$

$$= \frac{-12 \pm \sqrt{104}}{4} = \frac{-12 \pm \sqrt{4 \cdot 26}}{4}$$

$$= \frac{-12 \pm 2\sqrt{26}}{4}$$

$$= \frac{2(-6 \pm \sqrt{26})}{4} \quad \textit{Factor out 2}$$

$$= \frac{-6 \pm \sqrt{26}}{2}$$

The solutions are $\frac{-6 + \sqrt{26}}{2}$ and

$\frac{-6 - \sqrt{26}}{2}$.

33. $$6p^2 = 10p$$

$$6p^2 - 10p + 0 = 0$$

a = 6, b = -10, c = 0

$$p = \frac{-(-10) \pm \sqrt{(-10)^2 - 4(6)(0)}}{2(6)}$$

$\textit{Quadratic}$
$\textit{formula}$

$$= \frac{10 \pm \sqrt{100}}{12}$$

$$= \frac{10 \pm 10}{12}$$

The solutions are $\frac{10 + 10}{12} = \frac{20}{12} = \frac{5}{3}$

and $\frac{10 - 10}{12} = \frac{0}{12} = 0$.

37.
$$9r^2 - 16 = 0$$

$$9r^2 + 0r - 16 = 0$$

$$a = 9, \; b = 0, \; c = -16$$

$$r = \frac{-0 \pm \sqrt{(0)^2 - 4(9)(-16)}}{2(9)} \quad \textit{Quadratic formula}$$

$$= \frac{\pm\sqrt{576}}{18}$$

$$= \pm\frac{24}{18} = \pm\frac{4}{3}$$

The solutions are $\frac{4}{3}$ and $-\frac{4}{3}$.

41.
$$2x^2 + x + 7 = 0$$

$$2x^2 + 1 \cdot x + 7 = 0$$

$$a = 2, \; b = 1, \; c = 7$$

$$x = \frac{-1 \pm \sqrt{1^2 - 4(2)(7)}}{2 \cdot 2}$$

$$= \frac{-1 \pm \sqrt{1 - 56}}{4}$$

$$= \frac{-1 \pm \sqrt{-55}}{4}$$

Since $\sqrt{-55}$ is not a real number, there are no real number solutions.

45.
$$x^2 = 1 + x$$

$$1 \cdot x^2 - x - 1 = 0$$

$$a = 1, \; b = -1, \; c = -1$$

$$x = \frac{-(-1) \pm \sqrt{(-1)^2 - 4(1)(-1)}}{2 \cdot 1}$$

$$= \frac{1 \pm \sqrt{1 + 4}}{2}$$

$$= \frac{1 \pm \sqrt{5}}{2}$$

Now find a decimal approximation. Since $\sqrt{5} \approx 2.236$,

$$x = \frac{1 \pm 2.236}{2}$$

The solutions are

$$\frac{1 + 2.236}{2} = \frac{3.236}{2} = 1.618$$

and $\frac{1 - 2.236}{2} = \frac{-1.236}{2} = -.618.$

49.
$$\frac{1}{2}x^2 = 1 - \frac{1}{6}x$$

$$6\left(\frac{1}{2}x^2\right) = 6(1) - 6\left(\frac{1}{6}x\right)$$

$$\textit{Eliminate denominators}$$

$$3x^2 = 6 - x$$

$$3x^2 + x - 6 = 0 \quad \textit{General quadratic equation form}$$

$$a = 3, \; b = 1, \; c = -6$$

$$x = \frac{-1 \pm \sqrt{(1)^2 - 4(3)(-6)}}{2(3)} \quad \textit{Quadratic formula}$$

$$x = \frac{-1 \pm \sqrt{1 + 72}}{6}$$

$$x = \frac{-1 \pm \sqrt{73}}{6}$$

The solutions are $\frac{-1 + \sqrt{73}}{6}$ and $\frac{-1 - \sqrt{73}}{6}.$

53.
$$\frac{r^2}{2} = r + \frac{1}{2}$$

$$2\left(\frac{r^2}{2}\right) = 2(r) + 2\left(\frac{1}{2}\right)$$

$$\textit{Eliminate denominators}$$

$$r^2 = 2r + 1$$

$$r^2 - 2r - 1 = 0 \quad \textit{General quadratic equation form}$$

$$a = 1, \; b = -2, \; c = -1$$

$$r = \frac{-b \pm \sqrt{b^2 - 4ac}}{2a}$$

$$r = \frac{(-2) \pm \sqrt{(-2)^2 - 4(1)(-1)}}{2(1)} \quad \textit{Quadratic formula}$$

$$= \frac{2 \pm \sqrt{4 + 4}}{2}$$

$$= \frac{2 \pm \sqrt{8}}{2} = \frac{2 \pm \sqrt{4} \cdot \sqrt{2}}{2}$$

$$= \frac{2 \pm 2\sqrt{2}}{2} = \frac{2(1 \pm \sqrt{2})}{2}$$

$$r = 1 \pm \sqrt{2}$$

The solutions are $1 + \sqrt{2}$ and $1 - \sqrt{2}$.

57.
$$\frac{m^2}{2} = \frac{m}{2} - 1$$

$$2(\frac{m^2}{2}) = 2(\frac{m}{2}) - 2(1)$$
Eliminate denominators

$$m^2 = m - 2$$

$m^2 - m + 2 = 0$ *General quadratic equation form*

$a = 1$, $b = -1$, $c = 2$

$$m = \frac{-(-1) \pm \sqrt{(-1)^2 - 4(1)(2)}}{2(1)}$$
Quadratic formula

$$= \frac{1 \pm \sqrt{1 - 8}}{2}$$

$$m = \frac{1 \pm \sqrt{-7}}{2}$$

Since $\sqrt{-7}$ is not a real number, there are no real number solutions.

61. The distance traveled is 14 feet.
Use $d = 2t^2 - 5t + 2$ with $d = 14$.

$$14 = 2t^2 - 5t + 2$$

$$0 = 2t^2 - 5t - 12$$ *In general form*

$a = 2$, $b = -5$, $c = -12$

$$t = \frac{-b \pm \sqrt{b^2 - 4ac}}{2a}$$

$$= \frac{-(-5) \pm \sqrt{(-5)^2 - 4(2)(-12)}}{2(2)}$$

$$= \frac{5 \pm \sqrt{25 + 96}}{4}$$

$$= \frac{5 \pm \sqrt{121}}{4}$$

$$= \frac{5 \pm 11}{4}$$

$$t = \frac{5 + 11}{4} \text{ or } t = \frac{5 - 11}{4}$$

$$t = \frac{16}{4} \qquad t = \frac{-6}{4}$$

$$t = 4 \qquad \text{or } t = \frac{-3}{2}$$

Since t represents the time in seconds, t must be a positive number.
It will take the projectile 4 seconds to travel 14 feet.

65. $\sqrt{48} = \sqrt{16 \cdot 3}$
$$= \sqrt{16} \cdot \sqrt{3}$$
$$= 4\sqrt{3}$$

69. $\sqrt{288} = \sqrt{144 \cdot 2}$
$$= \sqrt{144} \cdot \sqrt{2}$$
$$= 12\sqrt{2}$$

Supplementary Quadratic Equations (page 387)

1. $y^2 + 3y + 1 = 0$
The equation does not factor.
Use the quadratic formula.
$a = 1$, $b = 3$, $c = 1$

$$y = \frac{-b \pm \sqrt{b^2 - 4ac}}{2a}$$

$$= \frac{-3 \pm \sqrt{3^2 - 4(1)(1)}}{2 \cdot 1}$$

$$= \frac{-3 \pm \sqrt{9 - 4}}{2}$$

$$= \frac{-3 \pm \sqrt{5}}{2}$$

The solutions are $\frac{-3 + \sqrt{5}}{2}$ and $\frac{-3 - \sqrt{5}}{2}$.

5.
$$8m^2 = 2m + 15$$

$$8m^2 - 2m - 15 = 0$$

Use the method of factoring.

$$(4m + 5)(2m - 3) = 0$$

$4m + 5 = 0$ or $2m - 3 = 0$

$\quad\quad 4m = -5 \quad\quad\quad\quad 2m = 3$

$\quad\quad\quad m = -\dfrac{5}{4}$ or $m = \dfrac{3}{2}$

The solutions are 3/2 and -5/4.

9.
$$5k^2 + 8 = 22k$$

$$5k^2 - 22k + 8 = 0$$

$(5k - 2)(k - 4) = 0$ *Factor*

$5k - 2 = 0$ or $k - 4 = 0$ *Solve*
$\quad\quad 5k = 2$ $\quad\quad\quad\quad\quad$ *each*
$\quad\quad\quad$ *for k*
$\quad\quad\quad k = \dfrac{2}{5}$ or $k = 4$

The solutions are 2/5 and 4.

13. $(2q + 9)^2 = 48$

$2q + 9 = \sqrt{48}$
$2q + 9 = 4\sqrt{3}$
$\quad\quad 2q = -9 + 4\sqrt{3}$
$\quad\quad\quad q = \dfrac{-9 + 4\sqrt{3}}{2}$

or

$2q + 9 = -\sqrt{48}$
$2q + 9 = -4\sqrt{3}$
$\quad\quad 2q = -9 - 4\sqrt{3}$
$\quad\quad\quad q = \dfrac{-9 - 4\sqrt{3}}{2}$

The solutions are $\dfrac{-9 + 4\sqrt{3}}{2}$ and
$\dfrac{-9 - 4\sqrt{3}}{2}$.

17.   The left side of $p^2 + 5p + 5 = 0$
does not factor, so use the
quadratic formula with a = 1, b = 5,
and c = 5.

$$p = \dfrac{-b \pm \sqrt{b^2 - 4ac}}{2a}$$

$$p = \dfrac{-5 \pm \sqrt{5^2 - 4(1)(5)}}{2(1)}$$

$$= \dfrac{-5 \pm \sqrt{25 - 20}}{2}$$

$$= \dfrac{-5 \pm \sqrt{5}}{2}$$

The solutions are $\dfrac{-5 + \sqrt{5}}{2}$ and
$\dfrac{-5 - \sqrt{5}}{2}$.

21.   The left side of the equation
$2x^2 - 5x + 1 = 0$ does not
factor, so use the quadratic
formula with a = 2, b = -5,
and c = 1.

$$x = \dfrac{-b \pm \sqrt{b^2 - 4ac}}{2a}$$

$$x = \dfrac{-(-5) \pm \sqrt{(-5)^2 - 4(2)(1)}}{2(2)}$$

$$= \dfrac{5 \pm \sqrt{25 - 8}}{4}$$

$$= \dfrac{5 \pm \sqrt{17}}{4}$$

The solutions are $\dfrac{5 + \sqrt{17}}{4}$ and
$\dfrac{5 - \sqrt{17}}{4}$.

25. $(3p - 1)(p + 2) = -3$

$\quad 3p^2 + 5p - 2 = -3$ *Multiply*
$\quad\quad\quad\quad\quad\quad\quad$ *binomials*

$\quad 3p^2 + 5p + 1 = 0$ *General*
$\quad\quad\quad\quad\quad\quad\quad$ *quadratic*
$\quad\quad\quad\quad\quad\quad\quad$ *equation*
$\quad\quad\quad\quad\quad\quad\quad$ *form*

This cannot be factored, so use quadratic formula.

$a = 3$, $b = 5$, $c = 1$

$$p = \frac{-b \pm \sqrt{b^2 - 4ac}}{2a}$$

$$= \frac{-5 \pm \sqrt{(5)^2 - 4(3)(1)}}{2(3)}$$

$$= \frac{-5 \pm \sqrt{25 - 12}}{6}$$

$$p = \frac{-5 \pm \sqrt{13}}{6}$$

The solutions are $\dfrac{-5 + \sqrt{13}}{6}$ and $\dfrac{-5 - \sqrt{13}}{6}$.

29. $(2x + 1)(x - 1) = 5$

    $2x^2 - x - 1 = 5$ *Multiply binomials*

    $2x^2 - x - 6 = 0$ *General quadratic equation form*

  $(2x + 3)(x - 2) = 0$ *Factor*

  $2x + 3 = 0$ or $x - 2 = 0$

                Set factors equal to zero

      $2x = -3$

       $x = -\dfrac{3}{2}$ or $x = 2$ *Solve*

The solutions are $-3/2$ and 2.

Section 9.4 (page 393)

1. $\sqrt{-9} = \sqrt{(9)(-1)}$

        $= \sqrt{9} \cdot \sqrt{-1}$ $\sqrt{-1} = i$

        $= 3i$

5. $\sqrt{-36} = \sqrt{36(-1)}$

         $= \sqrt{36}\sqrt{-1}$ $\sqrt{-1} = i$

         $= 6i$

9. $(2 + 8i) + (3 - 5i)$

    $= (2 + 3) + (8 - 5)i$

    $= 5 + 3i$

13. $(3 - 4i) + (6 - i) - (3 + 2i)$

    $= 3 - 4i + 6 - i - 3 - 2i$

    $= (3 + 6 - 3) + (-4 - 1 - 2)i$

    $= 6 - 7i$

17. $(5 - 4i)(3 - 2i)$

    $= 15 - 22i + 8i^2$ *Multiply by Foil*

    $= 15 - 22i + 8(-1)$ $i^2 = -1$

    $= 15 - 22i - 8$

    $= 7 - 22i$ *Simplify*

21. $\dfrac{-2 + i}{1 - i}$

    $= \dfrac{-2 + i}{1 - i} \cdot \dfrac{1 + i}{1 + i}$ *Multiply numerator and denominator by $1 + i$*

    $= \dfrac{-2 - i + i^2}{1 - i^2}$ *Multiply by FOIL*

    $= \dfrac{-2 - i - 1}{1 - (-1)}$ $i^2 = -1$

    $= \dfrac{-3 - i}{2}$ *Simplify*

    $= -\dfrac{3}{2} - \dfrac{1}{2}i$ *Write in $a + bi$ form*

25. $\dfrac{4 - 3i}{i} = \dfrac{4 - 3i}{0 + i}$

    $= \dfrac{4 - 3i}{0 + i} \cdot \dfrac{0 - i}{0 - i}$ *Multiply by $0 - i$*

    $= \dfrac{-4i + 3i^2}{-i^2}$

    $= \dfrac{-4i + 3(-1)}{-(-1)}$ $i^2 = -1$

    $= \dfrac{-4i - 3}{1}$

    $= -3 - 4i$ *Write in $a + bi$ form*

29. $(k - 3)^2 = -5$

    $k - 3 = \pm\sqrt{-5}$ *Square root property*

    $k - 3 = \sqrt{-5}$

    $k - 3 = \sqrt{-1} \cdot \sqrt{5}$

    $k - 3 = i\sqrt{5}$

       $k = 3 + i\sqrt{5}$

or

$k - 3 = -\sqrt{-5}$

$k - 3 = -\sqrt{-1} \cdot \sqrt{5}$

$k - 3 = -i\sqrt{5}$

$k = 3 - i\sqrt{5}$

33. $m^2 - 2m + 2 = 0$

$a = 1, \ b = -2, \ c = 2$

$m = \dfrac{-b \pm \sqrt{b^2 - 4ac}}{2a}$

$m = \dfrac{-(-2) \pm \sqrt{(-2)^2 - 4(1)(2)}}{2(1)}$

$\ = \dfrac{2 \pm \sqrt{4 - 8}}{2}$

$\ = \dfrac{2 \pm \sqrt{-4}}{2}$

$\ = \dfrac{2 \pm \sqrt{4}\sqrt{-1}}{2}$

$\ = \dfrac{2 \pm 2i}{2}$

$\ = \dfrac{2(1 \pm i)}{2}$

$m = 1 \pm i$

The solutions are $1 + i$ and $1 - i$.

37. $p^2 - 3p + 4 = 0$

$a = 1, \ b = -3, \ c = 4$

$p = \dfrac{-(-3) \pm \sqrt{(-3)^2 - 4(1)(4)}}{2(1)}$

$\ = \dfrac{3 \pm \sqrt{9 - 16}}{2}$

$\ = \dfrac{3 \pm \sqrt{-7}}{2}$

$\ = \dfrac{3 \pm \sqrt{-1}\sqrt{7}}{2}$

$\ = \dfrac{3 \pm i\sqrt{7}}{2}$

$\ = \dfrac{3}{2} \pm \dfrac{\sqrt{7}}{2}i$

The solutions are $\dfrac{3}{2} + \dfrac{\sqrt{7}}{2}i$ and

$\dfrac{3}{2} - \dfrac{\sqrt{7}}{2}i$.

41. $2m^2 + 7 = -2m$

$2m^2 + 2m + 7 = 0$ *General quadratic*
equation form

$a = 2, \ b = 2, \ c = 7$

$m = \dfrac{-2 \pm \sqrt{(2)^2 - 4(2)(7)}}{2(2)}$

$\ = \dfrac{-2 \pm \sqrt{4 - 56}}{4}$

$\ = \dfrac{-2 \pm \sqrt{-52}}{4}$

$\ = \dfrac{-2 \pm \sqrt{-1}\sqrt{4}\sqrt{13}}{4}$

$\ = \dfrac{-2 \pm 2i\sqrt{13}}{4}$

$\ = \dfrac{2(-1 \pm i\sqrt{13})}{4}$

$\ = \dfrac{-1 \pm i\sqrt{13}}{2}$

The solutions are $\dfrac{-1}{2} + \dfrac{\sqrt{13}}{2}i$ and

$-\dfrac{1}{2} - \dfrac{\sqrt{13}}{2}i$.

45. $2x - 3y = 6$

Let $x = 0$, then $y = -2$, giving
(0, -2).
Let $y = 0$, then $x = 3$, giving
(3, 0).
Let $y = 2$, then $x = 6$, giving
(6, 2).
Let $x = -3$, then $y = -4$, giving
(-3, -4).
Plot the ordered pairs.
See answer graph in your textbook.

49. $y - 2x = 0$

Let $x = 0$, then $y = 0$, giving
(0, 0).
Let $x = 3$, then $y = 6$, giving
(3, 6).
Let $y = 5$, then $x = 5/2$, giving
(5/2, 5).
Let $y = 2$, then $x = 1$, giving
(1, 2).

Plot the ordered pairs.

See answer graph in your textbook.

Section 9.5 (page 400)

1. $y = 2x^2$

    If $x = 0$, then $y = 2(0)^2 = 0$ giving the ordered pair $(0, 0)$. Other ordered pairs are $(-3, 18)$, $(-2, 8)$, $(-1, 2)$, $(1, 2)$, $(2, 8)$, $(3, 18)$. Plot these points and draw smooth graph through them, as shown in your textbook. The vertex is at the low point $(0, 0)$.

5. $y = -(x + 1)^2$

    If $x = 0$, then $y = -(0 + 1)^2 = -1$, giving $(0, -1)$. Other ordered pairs are $(1, -4)$, $(2, -9)$, $(-1, 0)$, $(-2, -1)$. The vertex is $(-1, 0)$. Plot these points and draw smooth graph through them as shown in your textbook.

9. $y = 2 - x^2$

    If $x = 0$, then $y = 2 - 0^2 = 2$, giving $(0, 2)$. Other ordered pairs are $(1, 1)$, $(-1, 1)$, $(2, -2)$, $(-2, -2)$. The vertex is $(0, 2)$. Plot these points and draw smooth graph through them as shown in the graph in your textbook.

13. $y = (x + 1)^2 + 2$

    If $x = 0$, then $y = (0 + 1)^2 + 2 = 3$, giving $(0, 3)$. Other ordered pairs are $(1, 6)$, $(-1, 2)$, $(-2, 3)$, $(-3, 6)$. Rewrite the equation in the form

$$y = a(x - h)^2 + k.$$
$$y = 1[x - (-1)]^2 + 2$$

Thus, $a = 1$, $h = -1$, $k = 2$, so the vertex is $(-1, 2)$. Plot these points and the parabola through them.

See answer graph in your textbook.

17. $y = x^2 - 6x + 5$

    Let $y = 0 = x^2 - 6x + 5$ to find the x-intercepts.

$$0 = (x - 5)(x - 1) \quad \textit{Factor}$$
$$x - 5 = 0 \quad \text{or} \quad x - 1 = 0$$
$$x = 5 \quad \text{or} \qquad x = 1$$

These are the x-intercepts.

Let $x = 0$, then $y = 5$.

This is the y-intercept.

Rewrite the equation in

$$y = a(x - h)^2 + k$$

by completing the square.

$$y = (x^2 - 6x + 9) + 5 - 9$$
$$y = 1 \cdot (x - 3)^2 - 4$$

Now $a = 1$, $h = 3$, and $k = -4$.

The vertex is $(3, -4)$. The parabola opens upward since $1 > 0$.

See answer graph in your textbook.

21. $y = x^2 + 3x + 2$

    To find the x-intercepts, let $y = 0$.

$$0 = x^2 + 3x + 2$$
$$0 = (x + 2)(x + 1) \quad \textit{Factor}$$
$$x + 2 = 0 \quad \text{or} \quad x + 1 = 0$$
$$x = -2 \quad \text{or} \qquad x = -1$$
$$\textit{x-intercepts}$$

Let $x = 0$, then $y = 2$. This is the y-intercept.

To find the vertex (h, k) change to the form

$$y = a(x - h)^2 + k$$
$$y = 1 \cdot (x^2 + 3x\ ) + 2$$
$$y = 1 \cdot (x^2 + 3x + \frac{9}{4}) + 2 - \frac{9}{4}$$
$$y = 1 \cdot (x + \frac{3}{2})^2 - \frac{1}{4}$$
$$y = 1 \cdot (x - (-\frac{3}{2}))^2 - \frac{1}{4}$$

The vertex is (3/2, -1/4) and the parabola opens upward since 1 > 0. See answer graph in your textbook.

25.   The graph crosses the x-axis in two places, so the corresponding equation has two real solutions. Estimating from the graph, the solutions are 2 and -2.

29.   The function is defined for all possible values of x so the domain is all real numbers. The range is the possible values for y. From the graph it appears that y is never less than 0, so the range is all real numbers greater than or equal to zero.

33.   The function is defined for all possible values of x. The domain is all real numbers. The possible values for y appear to be only those greater than 1. Therefore the range is all real numbers greater than or equal to 1.

37. $f(x) = 2x^2 - 5x + 3$
$$f(-2) = 2(-2)^2 - 5(-2) + 3$$
$$= 2(4) + 10 + 3$$
$$= 8 + 10 + 3$$
$$f(-2) = 21$$

1. $y^2 = 49$
$$y = \sqrt{49} \quad \text{or} \quad y = -\sqrt{49}$$
$$y = 7 \quad \text{or} \quad y = -7$$

5. $(r - 3)^2 = 7$
$$r - 3 = \sqrt{7} \qquad \text{or} \quad r - 3 = -\sqrt{7}$$
$$r = 3 + \sqrt{7} \quad \text{or} \qquad r = 3 - \sqrt{7}$$

9. $m^2 + 6m + 5 = 0$
$$m^2 + 6m = -5 \quad \textit{Subtract 5}$$

Square half the coefficient of m.
$$\frac{1}{2}(6) = 3$$
$$(3)^2 = 9$$

Add 9 to each side of the equation.
$$m^2 + 6m + 9 = -5 + 9$$
$$m^2 + 6m + 9 = 4$$
$$(m + 3)^2 = 4 \quad \textit{Factor}$$
$$m + 3 = \sqrt{4} \quad \text{or} \quad m + 3 = -\sqrt{4}$$
$$m + 3 = 2 \qquad\qquad m + 3 = -2$$
$$m = -1 \quad \text{or} \qquad m = -5$$

13. $5k^2 - 3k - 2 = 0$
$$k^2 - \frac{3}{5}k - \frac{2}{5} = 0 \quad \begin{array}{l}\textit{Multiply} \\ \textit{by 1/5}\end{array}$$
$$k^2 - \frac{3}{5}k = \frac{2}{5} \quad \textit{Add 2/5}$$
$$k^2 - \frac{3}{5}k + \frac{9}{100} = \frac{2}{5} + \frac{9}{100}$$
$$\qquad\qquad\qquad \begin{array}{l}\textit{Complete the} \\ \textit{square}\end{array}$$
$$(k - \frac{3}{10})^2 = \frac{40}{100} + \frac{9}{100}$$
$$(k - \frac{3}{10})^2 = \frac{49}{100}$$

$$k - \frac{3}{10} = \sqrt{\frac{49}{100}} \quad \text{or} \quad k - \frac{3}{10} = -\sqrt{\frac{49}{100}}$$

$$k - \frac{3}{10} = \frac{7}{10} \qquad\qquad k - \frac{3}{10} = -\frac{7}{10}$$

$$k = \frac{10}{10} \qquad\qquad\qquad k = -\frac{4}{10}$$

$$k = 1 \qquad\qquad\qquad\qquad k = -\frac{2}{5}$$

17. $3k^2 + 2k + 3 = 0$ matches the general form, so use $a = 3$, $b = 2$, and $c = 3$ in the quadratic formula.

$$k = \frac{-2 \pm \sqrt{2^2 - 4(3)(3)}}{2(3)}$$

$$= \frac{-2 \pm \sqrt{4 - 36}}{6}$$

$$= \frac{-2 \pm \sqrt{-32}}{6}$$

Since $\sqrt{-32}$ is not a real number, there is no real number solution.

21.
$$\frac{c^2}{4} = 2 - \frac{3}{4}c$$

$$4\left(\frac{c^2}{4}\right) = 4\left(2 - \frac{3}{4}c\right) \quad \textit{Multiply by 4}$$

$$c^2 + 3c - 8 = 0 \quad \textit{Add (3c - 8)}$$

Use $a = 1$, $b = 3$, and $c = -8$ in the quadratic formula.

$$c = \frac{-3 \pm \sqrt{3^2 - 4(1)(-8)}}{2(1)}$$

$$= \frac{-3 \pm \sqrt{9 + 32}}{2}$$

$$= \frac{-3 \pm \sqrt{41}}{2}$$

The solutions are $\frac{-3 + \sqrt{41}}{2}$ and $\frac{-3 - \sqrt{41}}{2}$.

25. $(-1 + i) - (2 - i)$

$$= -1 + i - 2 + i$$

$$= -3 + (1 + 1)i$$

$$= -3 + 2i$$

29. $(5 + 2i)(5 - 2i)$

$$= 5 \cdot 5 + 5(-2i) + (2i)(5) - 4i^2$$

$$= 25 + 0 - 4(-1) \quad i^2 = -1$$

$$= 25 + 4$$

$$= 29$$

33. $\frac{2 - 4i}{3 + i}$

$$= \frac{(2 - 4i)}{(3 + i)} \cdot \frac{(3 - i)}{(3 - i)}$$
$\textit{Multiply numerator and denominator by 3 - i}$

$$= \frac{6 - 14i + 4i^2}{9 - i^2}$$

$$= \frac{6 - 14i + 4(-1)}{9 - (-1)}$$

$$= \frac{6 - 4 - 14i}{9 + 1}$$

$$= \frac{2 - 14i}{10}$$

$$= \frac{2}{10} - \frac{14}{10}i$$

$$= \frac{1}{5} - \frac{7}{5}i$$

37. $(3p - 2)^2 = -8$

$$3p - 2 = \sqrt{-8}$$

$$3p - 2 = \sqrt{4}\sqrt{-1}\sqrt{2}$$

$$3p - 2 = 2i\sqrt{2}$$

$$3p = 2 + 2i\sqrt{2}$$

$$p = \frac{2 + 2i\sqrt{2}}{3}$$

$$p = \frac{2}{3} + \frac{2\sqrt{2}}{3}i$$

or

$$3p - 2 = -\sqrt{-8}$$
$$3p - 2 = -\sqrt{4}\sqrt{-1}\sqrt{2}$$
$$3p - 2 = -2i\sqrt{2}$$
$$3p = 2 - 2i\sqrt{2}$$
$$p = \frac{2 - 2i\sqrt{2}}{3}$$
$$p = \frac{2}{3} - \frac{2\sqrt{2}}{3}i$$

41. $4q^2 + 2 = 3q$

$$4q^2 - 3q + 2 = 0$$
$$a = 4, \ b = -3, \ c = 2$$

$$q = \frac{-(-3) \pm \sqrt{(-3)^2 - 4(4)(2)}}{2 \cdot 4} \quad \textit{Quadratic formula}$$

$$= \frac{3 \pm \sqrt{9 - 32}}{8}$$

$$= \frac{3 \pm \sqrt{-23}}{8}$$

$$= \frac{3 \pm i\sqrt{23}}{8}$$

The solutions are $\frac{3}{8} + \frac{\sqrt{23}}{8}i$ and $\frac{3}{8} - \frac{\sqrt{23}}{8}i$.

For Exercises 45-57, see the answer graphs in your textbook.

45. $y = -x^2 + 3$

Let $x = 0$ in $y = -x^2 + 3$; then $y = 3$, so the y-intercept is 3. Let $y = 0$; then

$$0 = -x^2 + 3$$
$$x^2 = 3$$
$$x = \sqrt{3} \quad \text{or} \quad x = -\sqrt{3}.$$

These are the x-intercepts. Write the equation in the form

$$y = a(x - h)^2 + k.$$
$$y = -1(x - 0)^2 + 3$$

The vertex (h, k) is (0, 3). The parabola opens downward since a = -1.

49. $y = (x + 2)^2 - 3$

Let $x = 0$ in $y = (x + 2)^2 - 3$; then $y = 1$, so the y-intercept is (0, 1). Write the equation in the form

$$y = a(x - h)^2 + k.$$
$$y = 1[x - (-2)]^2 - 3$$

so we see that the vertex (h, k) is (-2, -3). The parabola opens upward since a = 1.

53. $y = x^2 - 10x + 24$

Let $x = 0$, then $y = 24$.   *y-intercept*
Let $y = 0$, then

$$0 = x^2 - 10x + 24.$$
$$0 = (x - 4)(x - 6)$$
$$x - 4 = 0 \quad \text{or} \quad x - 6 = 0$$
$$x = 4 \quad \text{or} \qquad x = 6$$
x-intercepts

Rewrite in the form

$$y = a(x - h)^2 + k.$$
$$y = 1 \cdot (x^2 - 10x \quad) + 24$$
$$y = 1 \cdot (x^2 - 10x + 25) + 24 - 25$$
$$y = 1 \cdot (x - 5)^2 - 1$$

So, the vertex is (5, -1) and the parabola opens upward since a = 1.

57.   The graph crosses the x-axis in two places, so the corresponding equation has two real solutions. Estimating from the graph, the solutions are -1 and 4.

61.
$$6t^2 + 7t - 3 = 0$$
$$(3t - 1)(2t + 3) = 0 \quad \textit{Factor}$$
$$3t - 1 = 0 \quad \text{or} \quad 2t + 3 = 0$$
$$3t = 1 \qquad\qquad 2t = -3$$
$$t = \frac{1}{3} \quad \text{or} \qquad t = -\frac{3}{2}$$

The solutions are 1/3 and -3/2.

65.
$$\frac{1}{2}r^2 = \frac{7}{2} - r$$
$$2\left(\frac{1}{2}r^2\right) = 2\left(\frac{7}{2} - r\right) \quad \textit{Multiply by 2}$$
$$r^2 = 7 - 2r$$
$$r^2 + 2r - 7 = 0 \quad \textit{General quadratic form}$$

The left side does not factor, so use the quadratic formula with $a = 1$, $b = 2$, and $c = -7$.

$$r = \frac{-2 \pm \sqrt{2^2 - 4(1)(-7)}}{2(1)}$$
$$= \frac{-2 \pm \sqrt{4 + 28}}{2}$$
$$= \frac{-2 \pm \sqrt{32}}{2} = \frac{-2 \pm 4\sqrt{2}}{2}$$
$$= \frac{2(-1 \pm 2\sqrt{2})}{6} = -1 \pm 2\sqrt{2}$$

The solutions are $-1 + 2\sqrt{2}$ and $-1 - 2\sqrt{2}$.

69.
$$7x^2 - 8 = 5x^2 + 16$$
$$7x^2 - 8 = 16$$
$$2x^2 = 24$$
$$x^2 = 12$$
$$x = \sqrt{12} \quad \text{or} \quad x = -\sqrt{12} \quad \textit{Square root property}$$
$$x = 2\sqrt{3} \quad \text{or} \quad x = -2\sqrt{3}$$

The solutions are $2\sqrt{3}$ and $-2\sqrt{3}$.

Chapter 9 Test (page 404)

1.
$$2z^2 - 5z = 0$$
$$z^2 - \frac{5}{2}z = 0 \quad \textit{Divide by 2}$$

Take half the coefficient of z and square it.

$$\left(\frac{1}{2}\right)\left(-\frac{5}{2}\right) = -\frac{5}{4}$$
$$\left(-\frac{5}{4}\right)^2 = \frac{25}{16}$$
$$z^2 - \frac{5}{2}z + \frac{25}{16} = \frac{25}{16} \quad \textit{Add 25/16}$$
$$\left(z - \frac{5}{4}\right)^2 = \frac{25}{16} \quad \textit{Factor}$$
$$z - \frac{5}{4} = \sqrt{\frac{25}{16}} \quad \text{or} \quad z - \frac{5}{4} = -\sqrt{\frac{25}{16}}$$
$$z - \frac{5}{4} = \frac{5}{4} \qquad\qquad z - \frac{5}{4} = -\frac{5}{4}$$
$$z = \frac{10}{4}$$
$$z = \frac{5}{2} \quad \text{or} \qquad z = 0$$

The solutions are 0 and 5/2.

2.
$$5x^2 = 2 - 9x$$
$$5x^2 + 9x = 2$$
$$x^2 + \frac{9}{5}x = \frac{2}{5} \quad \textit{Divide by 5}$$

Take $\left(\frac{1}{2}\right)\left(\frac{9}{5}\right) = \frac{9}{10}$.

Square 9/10: $\left(\frac{9}{10}\right)^2 = \frac{81}{100}$.

$$x^2 + \frac{9}{5}x + \frac{81}{100} = \frac{2}{5} + \frac{81}{100}$$
$$\left(x + \frac{9}{10}\right)^2 = \frac{40}{100} + \frac{81}{100} \quad \textit{Add 81/100}$$
$$\left(x + \frac{9}{10}\right)^2 = \frac{121}{100}$$

Use square root property.

$$x + \frac{9}{10} = \sqrt{\frac{121}{100}} \quad \text{or} \quad x + \frac{9}{10} = -\sqrt{\frac{121}{100}}$$
$$x + \frac{9}{10} = \frac{11}{10} \qquad\qquad x + \frac{9}{10} = -\frac{11}{10}$$
$$x = \frac{2}{10} \qquad\qquad x = -\frac{20}{10}$$
$$x = \frac{1}{5} \quad \text{or} \qquad x = -2$$

The solutions are 1/5 and -2.

3. $x^2 - 5 = 0$

    $x^2 = 5$

    $x = \sqrt{5}$ or $x = -\sqrt{5}$ *Square root property*

    The solutions are $\sqrt{5}$ and $-\sqrt{5}$.

4. $(k - 3)^2 = 49$

    $k - 3 = \sqrt{49}$ or $k - 3 = -\sqrt{49}$
    Square root property

    $k - 3 = 7 \qquad\qquad k - 3 = -7$

    $k = 10$ or $\qquad k = -4$

    The solutions are 10 and -4.

5. $(3r - 2)^2 = 35$

    $3r - 2 = \sqrt{35}$

    $3r = 2 + \sqrt{35}$

    $r = \dfrac{2 + \sqrt{35}}{3}$

    or

    $3r - 2 = -\sqrt{35}$

    $3r = 2 - \sqrt{35}$

    $r = \dfrac{2 - \sqrt{35}}{3}$

    The solutions are $\dfrac{2 + \sqrt{35}}{3}$ and $\dfrac{2 - \sqrt{35}}{3}$.

6. $m^2 = 3m + 10$

    $m^2 - 3m - 10 = 0$ *General quadratic form*

    $a = 1$, $b = -3$, and $c = -10$

    $m = \dfrac{-b \pm \sqrt{b^2 - 4ac}}{2a}$ *Quadratic formula*

    $m = \dfrac{-(-3) \pm \sqrt{(-3)^2 - 4(1)(-10)}}{2(1)}$

    $= \dfrac{3 \pm \sqrt{9 + 40}}{2}$

    $= \dfrac{3 \pm \sqrt{49}}{2}$

    $= \dfrac{3 \pm 7}{2}$

The solutions are $\dfrac{3 + 7}{2} = \dfrac{10}{2} = 5$
and $\dfrac{3 - 7}{2} = \dfrac{-4}{2} = -2$.

7. $3z^2 + 2 = 7z$

    $3z^2 - 7z + 2 = 0$

    $a = 3$, $b = -7$, and $c = 2$

    $z = \dfrac{-(-7) \pm \sqrt{(-7)^2 - 4(3)(2)}}{2(3)}$ *Quadratic formula*

    $= \dfrac{7 \pm \sqrt{49 - 24}}{6}$

    $= \dfrac{7 \pm \sqrt{25}}{6}$

    $= \dfrac{7 \pm 5}{6}$

    The solutions are $\dfrac{7 + 5}{6} = \dfrac{12}{6} = 2$
    and $\dfrac{7 - 5}{6} = \dfrac{2}{6} = \dfrac{1}{3}$.

8. $3(y^2 - \frac{5}{3}y + \frac{1}{3}) = 3(0)$

    $3y^2 - 5y + 1 = 0$ *Multiply by 3*
    $a = 3$, $b = -5$, and $c = 1$.

    $y = \dfrac{-(-5) \pm \sqrt{(-5)^2 - 4(3)(1)}}{2(3)}$ *Quadratic formula*

    $= \dfrac{5 \pm \sqrt{25 - 12}}{6}$

    $= \dfrac{5 \pm \sqrt{13}}{6}$

    The solutions are $\dfrac{5 + \sqrt{13}}{6}$ and $\dfrac{5 - \sqrt{13}}{6}$.

9. $m^2 - 2m = 1$

    $m^2 - 2m - 1 = 0$

    $a = 1$, $b = -2$, $c = -1$

$$m = \frac{-(-2) \pm \sqrt{(-2)^2 - 4(1)(-1)}}{2(1)} \quad \textit{Quadratic formula}$$

$$= \frac{2 \pm \sqrt{4 + 4}}{2}$$

$$= \frac{2 \pm \sqrt{8}}{2}$$

$$= \frac{2 \pm 2\sqrt{2}}{2}$$

$$= 1 \pm \sqrt{2}$$

The solutions are $1 + \sqrt{2}$ and $1 - \sqrt{2}$.

10. $(2x - 1)^2 = 18$

Use the square root property.

$$2x - 1 = \sqrt{18}$$
$$2x - 1 = 3\sqrt{2}$$
$$2x = 1 + 3\sqrt{2}$$
$$x = \frac{1 + 3\sqrt{2}}{2}$$

or

$$2x - 1 = -\sqrt{18}$$
$$2x - 1 = -3\sqrt{2}$$
$$2x = 1 - 3\sqrt{2}$$
$$x = \frac{1 - 3\sqrt{2}}{2}$$

11. $(x - 5)(3x + 2) = 0$

$x - 5 = 0$ or $3x + 2 = 0$

$x = 5$ or $3x = -2$

$x = -\frac{2}{3}$

The solutions are 5 and -2/3.

12. $(q - 5)(3q - 2) = 4$

$3q^2 - 17q + 10 = 4 \quad \textit{Multiply}$

$3q^2 - 17q + 6 = 0$

$a = 3, \ b = -17, \ c = 6$

$$q = \frac{-(-17) \pm \sqrt{(-17)^2 - 4(3)(6)}}{2 \cdot 3} \quad \textit{Quadratic formula}$$

$$= \frac{17 \pm \sqrt{289 - 72}}{6}$$

$$= \frac{17 \pm \sqrt{217}}{6}$$

The solutions are $\frac{17 + \sqrt{217}}{6}$ and $\frac{17 - \sqrt{217}}{6}$.

13. $(x - 5)(x - 5) = 8$

$(x - 5)^2 = 8$

$x - 5 = \sqrt{8}$ or $x - 5 = -\sqrt{8}$

$x - 5 = 2\sqrt{2}$ $x - 5 = -2\sqrt{2}$

$x = 5 + 2\sqrt{2}$ or $x = 5 - 2\sqrt{2}$

14. $y^2 = 6y - 2$

$y^2 - 6y + 2 = 0$

$a = 1, \ b = -6, \ c = 2$

$$y = \frac{-(-6) \pm \sqrt{(-6)^2 - 4(1)(2)}}{2 \cdot 1}$$

$$y = \frac{6 \pm \sqrt{36 - 8}}{2}$$

$$y = \frac{6 \pm \sqrt{28}}{2}$$

$$y = \frac{6 \pm 2\sqrt{7}}{2}$$

$$y = 3 \pm \sqrt{7}$$

Solutions are $3 + \sqrt{7}$ and $3 - \sqrt{7}$.

15. $p^2 = 5p - 7$

$p^2 - 5p + 7 = 0$

$a = 1, \ b = -5, \ c = 7$

$$p = \frac{-(-5) \pm \sqrt{(-5)^2 - 4(1)(7)}}{2 \cdot 1}$$

$$= \frac{5 \pm \sqrt{25 - 28}}{2}$$

$$= \frac{5 \pm \sqrt{-3}}{2} \qquad \sqrt{-3} = \sqrt{-1}\sqrt{3}$$

$$= \frac{5 \pm i\sqrt{3}}{2}$$

The solutions are $\frac{5}{2} + \frac{\sqrt{3}}{2}i$ and $\frac{5}{2} - \frac{\sqrt{3}}{2}i$.

16. $3m^2 + 1 = 2m$

$3m^2 - 2m + 1 = 0$

$a = 3$, $b = -2$, $c = 1$

$$m = \frac{-(-2) \pm \sqrt{(-2)^2 - 4(3)(1)}}{2 \cdot 3}$$

$$= \frac{2 \pm \sqrt{4 - 12}}{6}$$

$$= \frac{2 \pm \sqrt{-8}}{6} \qquad \begin{aligned} -8 &= \sqrt{4(-1)2} \\ &= 2i\sqrt{2} \end{aligned}$$

$$= \frac{2 \pm 2i\sqrt{2}}{6}$$

$$= \frac{1 \pm i\sqrt{2}}{3}$$

The solutions are $\frac{1}{3} + \frac{\sqrt{2}}{3}i$ and $\frac{1}{3} - \frac{\sqrt{2}}{3}i$.

17. $(3 + i) + (5 - 2i) - (1 + i)$

$= 3 + i + 5 - 2i - 1 - i$

$= (3 + 5 - 1) + (1 - 2 - 1)i$

$= 7 + (-2)i$

$= 7 - 2i$

18. $(4 - 3i)(6 + i)$

$= 4 \cdot 6 + 4 \cdot i + (-3i)(6) + (-3i)i$

$= 24 + 4i - 18i - 3i^2$

$= 24 + (4 - 18)i - 3(-1) \quad i^2 = -1$

$= 24 + 3 + (-14)i$

$= 27 - 14i$

19. $(2 + 5i)(2 - 5i)$

$= 2 \cdot 2 + 2(-5i) + (5i)(2) + (5i)(-5i)$

$= 4 - 10i + 10i - 25i^2$

$= 4 + 0 - 25(-1)$

$= 4 + 25$

$= 29$

20. $\dfrac{1 + 2i}{3 - i} = \dfrac{(1 + 2i)}{(3 - i)} \cdot \dfrac{(3 + i)}{(3 + i)}$

$$= \frac{3 + 7i + 2i^2}{9 - i^2}$$

$$= \frac{3 + 7i + 2(-1)}{9 - (-1)}$$

$$= \frac{3 + 7i - 2}{9 + 1}$$

$$= \frac{1 + 7i}{10}$$

$$= \frac{1}{10} + \frac{7}{10}i$$

See the answer graphs in your textbook for Problems 21-23.

21. $y = -(x + 3)^2$

Let $x = 0$, then $y = -9$, the y-intercept. Let $y = 0$, then

$0 = x + 3$ *x-intercept*

$-3 = x$.

Write the equation in the form

$y = a(x - h)^2 + k$

$y = -1(x - (-3))^2 + 0$.

The vertex is (-3, 0), and the parabola opens downward since $a = -1$.

22. $y = (x - 4)^2 + 1$

Let $x = 0$, then $y = 17$, the y-intercept. Let $y = 0$, then

$$(x - 4)^2 + 1 = 0$$
$$(x - 4)^2 = -1.$$

Since $(x - 4)^2$ cannot be negative, there are no real x-intercepts. The equation is in the form

$$y = a(x - h)^2 + k,$$

so the vertex (h, k) is (4, 1). The parabola opens upward since $a > 0$.

23. $y = x^2 + 6x + 7$

Let $x = 0$, then $y = 7$. *y-intercept*

Let $y = 0$, then

$$x^2 + 6x + 7 = 0$$

Use quadratic formula with $a = 1$, $b = 6$, $c = 7$.

$$x = \frac{-6 \pm \sqrt{6^2 - 4(1)(7)}}{2 \cdot 1}$$

$$= \frac{-6 \pm \sqrt{36 - 28}}{2}$$

$$= \frac{-6 \pm \sqrt{8}}{2}$$

$$= \frac{-6 \pm 2\sqrt{2}}{2}$$

$$= -3 \pm \sqrt{2} \quad \textit{x-intercepts}$$

Rewrite in the form

$$y = a(x - h)^2 + k$$
$$y = 1 \cdot (x^2 + 6x \quad) + 7$$
$$= 1 \cdot (x^2 + 6x + 9) + 7 - 9$$
$$= 1 \cdot (x + 3)^2 - 2$$
$$= 1 \cdot (x - (-3))^2 - 2$$

So, the vertex is (-3, -2) and it opens upward since $a > 0$.

24. There are two real number solutions in the previous problem since there are two x-intercepts

$$-3 + \sqrt{2} \text{ and } -3 - \sqrt{2}.$$

Appendix A   (page 407)

1.
```
    14.230    Line up decimal points
     9.810    and attach zeros
    74.630
 + 18.715
  -------
   117.385
```

5.
```
   219.00    Line up decimal points
  -68.51     and attach zeros
  -------
   150.49
```

9.
```
    8.600    Attach zeros
   -3.751
   ------
    4.849
```

13.
```
     42.1    1 decimal place
   × 3.9     1 decimal place
   -----
    3789      ↓
    1263
   ------
   164.19    2 decimal places in answer
```

17.
```
        4.14
   6) 24ˆ84
      24
      --
       8
       6
       --
       24
```

21.
```
          4800.
   .52) 2496.00    Move the decimal
        208         point in .52 two
        ---         places to the
        416         right and do the
        416         same in 2496
        ---
         00
         00
```

25. $129\% = 129 \cdot 1\% = 129 \cdot (.01) = 1.29$

29. $.9\% = .9 \cdot 1\% = .9 \cdot (.01) = .009$

33. $.007 = .7 \cdot (.01) = .7 \cdot 1\% = .7\%$

37. $.125 = 12.5 \cdot (.01) = 12.51\% = 12.5\%$

41.   22% of 1086 means $22\% \cdot 1086$ or
$.22 \cdot 1086 = 238.92.$

45.   To decide "what percent of 5820 is 6402," the part 6402 is of 5820 must be found by dividing

$$\frac{6402}{5820} = 1.1 \quad \text{In decimal form}$$

Then 1.1 must be converted to a percent.

$$1.1 = 110 \cdot (.01) = 110 \cdot 1\% = 110\%$$
$$\text{In percent form}$$

49.   118% of 125.8 means $118\% \cdot (125.8)$ Convert 118% to a decimal.

$$118\% = 118 \cdot 1\% = 118 \cdot (.01) = 1.18$$
$$1.18 \cdot (125.8) \approx 148.44$$
$$\text{(rounded to the nearest hundredth)}$$

53.   What percent of 198.72 is 1468 means

$$\frac{14.68}{198.72} \approx .0739 \quad \begin{array}{l}\text{Rounded to nearest}\\\text{ten-thousandth}\end{array}$$

Convert .0739 to percent

$$.0739 = 7.39 \cdot (.01) = 7.39 \cdot 1\% = 7.39\%$$
$$\text{(rounded to nearest hundredth)}$$

57.   Since 35% of the 2300 miles were by air, we have

$$35\% \cdot 2300 = 35 \cdot 1\% \cdot 2300$$
$$= 35 \cdot (.01) \cdot 2300$$
$$= .35 \cdot 2300$$
$$= 805.$$

805 miles were by air.

Since the family spends 90% of the $2000 each month, they must save 10% of the $2000.

$$10\% \text{ of } \$2000 = 10 \cdot 1\% \cdot 2000$$
$$= 10 \cdot (.01) \cdot 2000$$
$$= .10 \cdot 2000$$
$$= 200$$

Since there are 12 months in a year, the annual savings are

$$12 \times 200 = 2400,$$

or $2400.

61. Since the family spends 90% of the $2000 each month, they must save 10% of the $2000.

$$10\% \text{ of } \$2000 = 10 \cdot 1\% \cdot 2000$$
$$= 10 \cdot (.01) \cdot 2000$$
$$= .10 \cdot 2000$$
$$= \$200$$

Since there are 12 months in a year, the annual savings are

$$12 \times 200 = 2400,$$

or $2400.

65. The percent spent on advertising is $\dfrac{30755.20}{274600}$ changed to percent.

$$\frac{30755.20}{274600} = .112$$

$$.112 = 11 \cdot 2 \cdot (.01) = 11.2 \cdot 1\% = 11.2\%$$

The percent of income spent on advertising is 11.2%.

Appendix B (page 410)

1. "The set of all natural numbers less than 8" is {1, 2, 3, 4, 5, 6, 7}.
   (Remember: 8 is <u>not</u> less than 8.)

5. To date, there have been no women presidents, so this set is the empty set, written ∅.

9. 7 ∉ {2, 4, 6, 8} is true because 7 is not an element of the set {2, 4, 6, 8}.

13. D ⊂ B is false because all the elments of D are not elements of B.
    1 and 3 are elements of D, but they are not elements of B.

    {3, 1, 0} ∩ {0, 2, 4} = {0}

17. The symbol ∩ means the intersection of the two sets, which is the set of elements that are in both sets at the same time. Only 0 belongs to both sets, so the given statement is true.

21. A ∩ B
    The intersection of A and B is the set of all the elements belonging to A and B at the same time, or the set {a, c, e}, which equals B.

25. B ∪ D
    The union of B and D is the set of elements belonging to either B or D, or the set {a, c, d, e}.

SYMBOLS

+	Plus sign, addition
−	Minus sign, subtraction
×	Multiplication
a(b), (a)b, or (a)(b)	Multiplication
a•b	Multiplication
ab	Multiplication
÷	Division
a/b	Division
=	Equals
≠	Is not equal to
≈	Is approximately equal to
<	Is less than
≮	Is not less than
≤	Is less than or equal to
>	Is greater than
≯	Is not greater than
≥	Is greater than or equal to
$\|x\|$	Absolute value of x
{a, b, c}	The set containing the elements a, b, and c
{x|P}	The set of all x satisfying property P
∅	Empty set, or null set
(x, y)	Ordered pair
x^2	x squared; x•x
x^3	x cubed; x•x•x
x^n	x to the power n; x to the nth power
x^{-n}	x to the negative n; $x^{-n} = 1/x^n$
x^0	x to the power 0; $x^0 = 1$ if $x \neq 0$
P(x)	Polynomial having the variable x
$\sqrt{a}$	Positive square root of a; $\sqrt{a} \cdot \sqrt{a} = a$
$\sqrt[n]{a}$	nth root of a
i	$i = \sqrt{-1}$
a + bi	Complex number

FORMULAS

Rectangle

The length is L; the width is W.

    Perimeter $P = 2L + 2W$

    Area $A = LW$

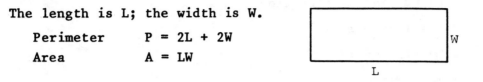

Square

Each side is s.

    Perimeter $P = 4s$

    Area $A = s^2$

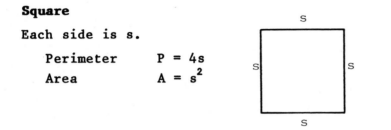

Trapezoid

The two parallel sides are b and B.
Altitude (height) is h.

    Area $A = \frac{1}{2}(b + B)h$

Rectangular solid

The height is H.

    Volume $V = LWH$

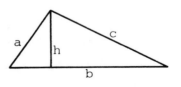

Triangle

The sides are a, b, c, where b is the base.
Altitude is h.

    Perimeter $P = a + b + c$

    Area $A = \frac{1}{2}bh$

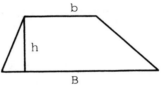

Distance   r is rate (or speed); t is time.

    $d = rt$

FORMULAS

Simple interest

p is the principal (amount of money);
r is the rate of interest (expressed as percent);
t is time (in years).

$$I = prt$$

Circle

The diameter is d; the radius is r.
Use the value $\pi = 3.14$

Diameter	$d = 2r$
Circumference	$C = 2\pi r$ or $C = \pi d$
Area	$A = \pi r^2$

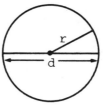

Right circular cylinder

The radius, r, is that of the top or bottom circle.
The height is h.

Surface area	$S = 2\pi r^2 + 2\pi rh$
Volume	$V = \pi r^2 h$

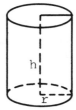

Right pyramid

The area of the base is B.
The height is h.

Volume $V = \frac{1}{3}Bh$

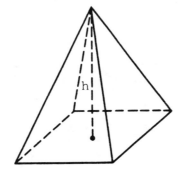

Temperature

C is the Celsius temperature.
F is the Fahrenheit temperature.

$$C = \frac{5}{9}(F - 32)$$

$$F = \frac{9}{5}C + 32$$